# F-111
## Success in Action

# F-111

## Success in Action

ANTHONY M. THORNBOROUGH AND PETER E. DAVIES

ARMS AND
ARMOUR

First published in Great Britain in 1989 by Arms & Armour Press Ltd.,
Artillery House, Artillery Row, London SW1P 1RT.

Distributed in the USA by Sterling Publishing Co. Inc., 387 Park
Avenue S., New York, NY 10016-8810.

Distributed in Australia by Capricorn Link (Australia) Pty. Ltd.,
P.O. Box 665, Lane Cove, New South Wales 2066.

British Library Cataloguing in Publication data:
Thornborough, Anthony M.
The F-111.
1. General Dynamics F-111 aeroplanes
I. Title   II. Davies, Peter E.
623.74'64

ISBN 0-85368-988-1

Edited and designed at Little Oak Studios.
Typeset by Typesetters (Birmingham) Ltd.

Reproduction by M&E Reproduction, North Fambridge, Essex.
Printed and bound in Great Britain by Courier International,
Tiptree, Essex.

Frontispiece: An F-111A negotiates the Vietnamese jungle and karst
terrain in 'Auto TF' mode, photographed by tail No. 154, 67-109,
which was fitted with recording cameras for this job. The camera ship
'109 was described as a 'dog'; it was later handed over to the Royal
Australian Air Force. (General Dynamics/USAF)

# CONTENTS

# FOREWORD

Having flown the F-111 since January 1972, I have seen a lot of controversy and success for this aircraft. It was designed as the do-it-all aircraft for the Navy and Air Force. The F-111 could never meet the Navy's weight requirements for carrier operations so they dropped it at the first opportunity. The Air Force ended up with an aircraft that could deliver bombs on target in virtually any weather at a great distance. I believe the capabilities and systems of the aircraft were not really understood

by the aircrews during 'Combat Lancer', the first F-111 combat operations, and this, coupled with a flight control problem, made for a relatively unsuccessful first employment. In September 1972 the F-111s were re-deployed to Takhli Air Base and well-trained aircrews allowed the F-111 to show its true colors. While other aircraft required pre- and post-strike tanker support to reach targets in North Vietnam, the F-111s flying from Takhli could reach *any* target in North Vietnam on internal fuel; the fuel, personnel and materiel costs required to support the other aircraft must have helped make this supposedly overpriced aircraft a much better deal. We received an avalanche of bad press, but the enemy respected us. We gave the POWs' morale a lift, and the aircrews and 'Brass' in Saigon believed in the aircraft. Many of the aircrew members had recent combat tours in other jets and they felt they had a better chance of surviving in the F-111 – our loss rate is proof of this belief.

The terrain-following radar, the variable-geometry wings and the aircraft's long-range capabilities set it apart from other tactical aircraft. The TFR system automatically follows the contours of the terrain to allow flight under enemy defenses. As a new system it performed well and has been improved over the years. The variable-geometry wings have been outstanding from the start and have caused no problems. The long range is a result of size (fuel capacity), VG wings and the afterburning turbofan engines. The size of the aircraft (high wing loading) accounts for its incredibly smooth low-level ride – the aircraft is very stable at even supersonic speeds. This stability makes it a 'fun' aircraft and takes a lot of the stress and work out of low-level flying.

That General Dynamics was able to successfully combine several new technologies into one aircraft was a tremendous engineering feat. It suffered undue amounts of bad press resulting more from political rivalries than from actual failings. It was, and has proved to be, a safe aircraft to fly. Its bad press was often a result of losses at night when no one was around to witness what happened. This was especially true of the combat losses. Most other aircraft were lost in formation so wingmen could relate why they were lost. The nature of the F-111's mission meant that losses occurred single-ship at night with no evidence of *why* they went down. These unexplained losses of a politically sensitive aircraft resulted in a negative press attitude towards the

**Left: Captain Brad Insley, a tiger among 'Tigers' and the senior statesman of the F-111 world. (Authors)**

aircraft. But *we* believed in the aircraft. *We* were the ones who risked our lives, and the F-111 brought us home with regularity. The Libya raids gave long overdue respectability to the F-111: no other land-based fighter had the capability to reach out and hit the terrorists where they live.

The F-111 does what no other fighter can do: attack the enemy low-level in his staging areas at night. I felt very good myself in North Vietnam when the enemy started firing because I knew I had beaten them: they were shooting at where I had been and not where I was going! The F-111 low-level-at-night gave me that edge. The F-111 will continue to serve into the next century as there is no long-term replacement planned. I have grown with the F-111 and have seen its bag-of-tricks grow to make it a more versatile weapons system. We have been hindered in the past with World War II-type weapons, but weapons development is now catching up with the tremendous leap in aircraft technology. New weapons are now entering service that can take advantage of the F-111's capabilities. With the upgrades planned and the new weaponry being developed, the F-111 will continue in useful service for a long time to come.

**Brad Insley**
**Captain, USAF**

**Authors' Note**

Capt. Brad Insley is a legend in the F-111 community. He started flying the F-111A in 1972 and went to Takhli RTAB, Thailand, later that year to fly over 75 combat missions against a well-defended North Vietnam; he has continued to fly the F-111 ever since. He is currently an instructor and combat-ready pilot with the 79th TFS 'Tigers' at Upper Heyford, Oxfordshire, England, and in August 1987 he clocked up his 4,000th hour in the aircraft – and four thousand hours 'down amidst the weeds' in, perhaps, zero visibility and moving at 900 feet per second is an experience which bears comparison to no other. His colleagues claim that 'he can tell which "tail" has a buzz here or there' and, having flown nearly every model of the 'One-Eleven', he has become the fount of 'Earthpig' wisdom.

# INTRODUCTION

Brad Insley says it all. The authors can only add a few points concerning the book itself, which they hope will be of interest.

First and foremost, unlike any other fighting aircraft, the F-111 has its own peculiar brand of 'magnetic appeal'. People stick with the machine; many have made a lifetime's career out of it! To those 'old heads' in the tightly knit 'One-Eleven' community we apologize for using the standard phonetic alphabet, 'Alpha', say, to denote the F-111A model, when many of the 'swing-wing jocks' have their own versions ('Ace', for example). To cater for all tastes the authors felt it important to standardize certain aspects of the vocabulary used, if for no other reason than to exclude some of the more lurid nicknames! Moreover, all the marks of F-111, and their differing avionics packages, have been discussed in their pre-Avionics Modernization Program (AMP) format; readers should note that AMP, which has been applied only to a portion of the inventory to date, is homogenizing the whole fleet into a common microchip 'Mk. III' systems configuration. The details of this effort are discussed together in 'TAB-V Pigs' (Part 3).

Secondly, previous works that have tackled this intricate subject have, in the main, divorced systems from operations, with the emphasis on the 'nuts and bolts' aspects of the aircraft. Highly skilled engineering is needed to fashion and integrate a modern combat aircraft's hundreds of thousands of subcomponents into a flyable, working machine but it is in the sphere of front-line flying – both in peacetime and under combat conditions – that the good and bad points of a sophisticated warplane become truly apparent. The aim of this book, therefore, is to address those issues and to give a fresh operational insight into the technology of the F-111 from the user's point of view, where it counts most. The other focal point of past F-111 works has been the hot-air politics that have beset this aircraft. The controversies were the result of many wranglings in Canberra, London and Washington, and not a few technical teething troubles as well, but the authors here have attempted to keep that side of the story to an absolute minimum and concentrate on the men and machines in action: what buttons and levers are pushed and pulled to set the aircraft in motion and get it to drop bombs, jam radars or fire missiles (the *raison d'être* of the F-111 'family') and what tactics and training doctrines – and remedies – have been employed over the years to maintain proficiency.

Another new element has been included by sheer luck. For a limited two-year period from 1986 'Project Warrior' permitted USAFE F-111 Wings, the 20th TFW in particular, to daub their hitherto drably coloured machines with elaborate artwork (SAC too have created a flurry of attractive markings), all of which have added a new dimension to the pictorial side of this volume.

To close, of the 562 test, pre-production and operational F-111s built – 573 if one includes four partially built, cancelled airframes and seven static fatigue examples – as of December 1988 no fewer than 416 were serving worldwide. Diplomats and arms negotiators speak of ICBMs, SLBMs, intermediate nuclear forces and bombers, but they *always* refer to the 'F-One-Eleven' by name – proof that, twenty-one years after the type first entered operational service, the well-loved 'Vark' still holds its place as the most potent tactical fighter-bomber in the world. It has truly come of age, and AMP will keep it at the forefront of tactical air power . . . for the next twenty-one years?

## Acknowledgements
Investigating the origins and habits of the 'Aardvark' has been a fascinating and complex task and the authors have been privileged to receive unstinted help and guidance from the following: CMSgt. Adams, Dennis Allen, Sandra D. Ahearn, Sgt. Deborah Aragon, Col. Rob Balph, Col. Thomas B. Barnes USAF ret., Lt. Col. Donald Black, Kearney S. Bothwell, Maj. Dick Brown, Joseph B. Brown Jr., Virnell A. Bruce, Lt. Col. Robert A. Brus, Vivienne Calderbank, 1Lt. Lester T. Carroll Jr., W. G. Chappell, Capt. Mike Conway, SSgt. James Colson, SSgt. Annette Crawford, Capt. George Cully, Wg. Cdr. Ray A. Debnam RAAF, Robert F. Dorr, SSgt. Dotson, MSgt. Farria, Sgt. Fox, Don Flamm, M. J. Francombe, Norma L. Gibson, Chip Glissom, Win Godwin, Capt. Alan C. Gregory, Ann Grizzel, Roger Holman, Dr. Haulman, Harold Heilsnis, Alan Howarth, A1C Jackson, Fg. Off. Norm R. Jones RAAF, Lt. Col. Jon Jordan, Helen A. Kavanaugh, Sharlane Kehlenbeck, Capt. George Kelman, Peter E. Kirkup, Ben Knowles, Don Laing, Tim Laming, Patricia A. Lesher, Col. Lewis, Lois Lovisolo, Capt. Greg Lowrimore, SSgt. David N. Malakoff, Col. Rick M. Matteis USAF ret., Capt. Mitchell, TSgt. Mitchell, David Moakes, Frank B. Mormillo, Pat Muldrow, Capt. Mary-Ann Neri, E. J. Olsen, R. F. Peters, MSgt. Stephen H. Pivnick, David Robinson, C. M. Reed, 1Lt. Lesley A. Rossillon, Ed Rossman, 1Lt. Chris Ross, Maj. Jim Rotramel, Lt. Col. Tom G. Runge, SSgt. Ismael Sarraga, Joe E. Sherrod, Lt. Col. Dave Skakal, Fran Slimmer, Lt. Col. Tony Sobol, Capt. Steven M. Solmonson, Maj. Joseph W. Steimer Jr., Maj. David Stringer, Sgt. Swanson, Mrs. Penny Telling,

Margaret M. Thornborough, Z. Joe Thornton, Vincent Vinci, Lt. Col. Joseph Wagovich, Robin A. Walker, Col. Robert Wendrock, John R. Whittenbury, James S. Wilson and Capt. Marie K. Yancey.

We also extend our sincere thanks to the production and layout teams, Roger Chesneau of Linewrights and David Gibbons of DAG Publications, to Mike Keep, for his work on the line drawings, and to the director of Arms & Armour Press, Rod Dymott, for helping to open many doors; and also to the Boeing Company, Bill Brookes (Squadron Supplies), Brunswick, Cincinnati Electronics, Ford Aerospace, General Dynamics Fort Worth Division, General Electric, the Grumman Corporation, the Grumman History Center, Hughes Missiles and Radars Divisions, McDonnell Douglas, the Norden and Pratt & Whitney Divisions of United Technologies, the Raytheon Company, Rockwell International, Texas Instruments and Westinghouse; and to the Air Force Historical Research Center, *Hughes News*, the Royal Australian Air Force, *Raven News*, Tactical Air Command, Strategic Air Command, United States Air Forces Europe, the Australian and United States Departments of Defence, the Retired Officers Association and *Air Force* Magazine.

**Anthony M. Thornborough**
**and Peter E. Davies**
**Bristol, England, January 1989**

# 1. PIONEERS

# McNamara's Baby

With hindsight the F-111 project can be seen as the climax of a period of unprecedented advancement in the design of US military aircraft. After 1945 the curves of performance, innovation and combat capability rose inexorably through the 'Century Series' fighters and through bombers like the General Dynamics B-58 Hustler. In 1958 the Mach 2.25 nuclear-capable Republic F-105 strike aircraft was entering the inventory, but the US Air Force was already contemplating its replacement. On 27 March that year initial specifications were published calling for a Mach 2 V/STOL design capable of delivering heavy weapons loads at long range and at low level. By 14 June 1960 those demanding specifications had hardened into Specific Operational Requirement (SOR) 183, later referred to as TFX, for Tactical Fighter Experimental.

SOR 183 deleted the V/STOL request but added an unrefuelled 3,300-mile ferry range and a short-field capability based on the new variable-geometry (VG) 'swing-wing' discoveries. One of the F-105 'Thud's main drawbacks was its appetite for runway and its pilots joked that if there were an airstrip which circled the Earth, Republic would build an aircraft which would use it all! The USAF wanted a fighter which had only half the take-off roll of the 'Thud' and a figure of 3,000ft was drafted. TFX was to offer a Mach 2.5 high-altitude dash, with Mach 1.2 at low level for the last 200 miles to target. These figures implied a large, complex two-seater, although just how large remained to be seen.

**Below: The first – and cleanest – F-111A prototype, 63-9766, at the roll-out ceremony at General Dynamics, Fort Worth Division, Texas. No. 1 made its maiden flight on 21 December 1964 with Dick Johnson at the controls. (General Dynamics)**

Coincidentally the US Navy was also sketching a replacement for its epoch-making F-4 Phantom, centred on the idea of a large but fairly slow missile platform for long-range fleet defence. From this emerged the proposed Douglas F6D Missileer. Congress cancelled this high-risk project, leaving a vacuum which provided the ideal opening for new Defense Secretary Robert S. McNamara. In 1961 he announced that SOR 183 would become the core of the joint-service design based on the apparently favourable economics of 'commonality', and thus was born the Navy's offshoot – TFX-N. McNamara envisaged saving truckloads of dollars by avoiding any duplication of development programmes for what he was convinced were overlapping objectives. It was an idea which had already met with resistance elsewhere, but TFX seemed like a good place to make a real splash of it. A figure of 85 per cent commonality between the US Navy and USAF fighters would enable TFX to both replace the Navy's and Marine Corps' F-4s and F-8s and take care of the Air Force's 'Century Series' fighters. With projected production runs of 3,000-plus, including exports, it seemed that unit costs would be attractively low and on 1 September 1961, despite their predicted objections, McNamara ordered the armed forces to refine a compromise design study.

On 1 October 1961 a Request For Proposals was issued to industry and on 6 December six sets of design studies were received from the major military aerospace suppliers. Those from Boeing and General Dynamics Fort Worth (GDFW) were thought worthy of further development, Boeing's being the favourite of the Systems Source Selection Board, a situation arrived at after three more rounds of proposals in which the company agreed to revert to the impressive Pratt & Whitney (P&W) JTF10 (TF30) turbofan engine and to adopt the 'crew capsule' contained in the GDFW submission. Finally McNamara surprised everybody by insisting on the GDFW model, largely because it seemed to offer greater 'commonality' than Boeing's 'two different airplanes'.

With Contract No. 8260 in their hands from 24 November 1962, GDFW and their TFX-N partner Grumman began to face the task of producing eighteen Research, Development, Test and Evaluation (RDT&E) F-111As and five RDT&E navalized F-111Bs, with the first scheduled to fly within 25 months. The F-111, as the Pentagon had designated TFX, introduced a whole range of innovations, any one of which was revolutionary in its own right. Satisfying SOR 183 meant the use of the variable-sweep wing, and the 'One-Eleven' became the first operational aircraft to employ it. The long-range parameters led to the use of the economical P&W TF30 turbofan engine with augmented thrust for supersonic flight. It thus became the first afterburning turbofan in service. Mach 1.2 flight at tree-top height

**Left: Three photographs showing the business end of the Pratt & Whitney TF30-P-3 (now known as the TF30-P-103) augmented turbofan showing its six ram-actuated, hinged nozzle segments, five-zone combustion system and three fuel spraybars. (Authors)**

Above: The uncluttered lines of the P&W TF30-P-3 duct-burning turbofan engine, the power source of the F-111A, F-111C, RF-111C and F-111E. (Pratt & Whitney Aircraft)

demanded reliable control systems, so the first automatic terrain-following radar was evolved for the F-111. To complete the suite of major innovations, a crew capsule replaced the conventional bucket ejection seats for the two-man crew. To no one's surprise all these radical novelties brought problems, but none more than the powerplants and their intakes.

## Triple Plow
P&W had originally built the two-shafted single-spool JTF10 for a Douglas airliner. Its military derivative, the TF30-P-1, pioneered both the afterburning turbofan and the first integral aerodynamically adjusted gas turbine nozzle qualified to go supersonic at sea level. However, most of the military operational requirements of the engine had only been explored in the wind tunnel or on test rigs. A major unrealized problem was the type of air intake needed for the design. General Dynamics spent thousands of hours in their wind tunnels creating their novel quarter-circle wing-root intakes. These worked very well at medium and low speeds, but problems soon emerged at high Mach numbers. Ed Rossman, working on the development of the engine from 1962, described it as 'One hell of a challenge'. This challenge manifested itself during the maiden flight of F-111A No. 1 (63-7966) on 21 December 1964. Dick Johnson, GDFW's chief of flight test operations, kept the landing gear down and the wing set at 26°; the flaps had locked in the take-off position and the flight was cut short to 22 minutes by a

compressor stall. On the second flight, on 6 January 1965, Johnson did manage to demonstrate the full range of wing-sweep settings but when he attempted supersonic flight both engines stalled and the jet never got beyond 460kts. It took until 5 March to pass Mach 1. The cause was an unequal distribution of air across the engine compressor face due to a distortion of the airflow in the intake. Pressure anomalies caused individual compressor blades to 'stall', disturbing the airflow through the compressor stages: the rather short intake duct did not provide the fast-flowing air time in which to achieve a homogeneous, smooth passage. Both P&W and GDFW, with a certain amount of mutual recrimination, addressed themselves to the problem with some urgency.

P&W performed their initial airborne engine trials using a pair of B-45 Tornados with the TF30s deployed from the bomb-bay on retractable 'banana' links. In 1966 F-111A No. 2 (63-9767) was delivered to P&W's East Hartford facility in Connecticut to investigate the problems which had persisted throughout 1965. After the first five test flights the engines were instrumented and the resulting data confirmed that the suspected engine/intake mismatch was indeed the root of the problem. P&W fitted their test engines with 'hundreds

Above: F-111A No. 2, 63-9767, in the bare metal scheme worn for some time by the second and fourth RDT&E jets. Used for engine development trials with Pratt & Whitney's East Hartford Plant, it flew from the local Bradley Field municipal airport because P&W's 6,000ft runway was not considered long enough at that stage of development. Later No. 2 became the test-bed for the Mk. I nav/attack system during Category I trials at Edwards AFFTC, California. (General Dynamics)

Below: A port Triple Plow II inlet under construction; note the vortex generators and the manner in which the duct is mounted some four inches away from the main fuselage body. The white interior is common to both Triple Plow I and II inlets. (General Dynamics)

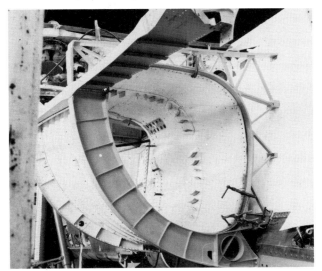

of pressure taps and temperature pick-ups' according to Ed Rossman, and although there were no failures in the air some test-cell engines 'exploded, big-time!' In 1965 P&W introduced trials models of the TF30-P-3 motor which featured modified compressor blades but this did not resolve all the stall problems. GDFW meanwhile experimented with revised intakes. Short inlets had the advantage of using the wing shock wave to aid precompression of the air and to reduce wetted area but the rapid change in inlet cross-section from the intake lips to the powerplant's compressor was contributing to the stalls. Their revised compromise Triple Plow I intake was fitted from F-111A No. 31 (66-013), introducing rows of vortex generators to mix intake flow and a series of extra 'lips' to split off or plough away boundary layer air, at the expense of only slightly greater fuel consumption.

P&W's test-bed F-111A continued its researches through 1966 carrying a heavy data pod called 'The Coffin' in its weapons bay — and some ingenious instruments. To provide a constant temperature base for data comparison an ice-filled thermos flask was installed with sensor probes inserted through its lid. Embarrassingly, on its first flight the F-111A was unable to muster enough power to lift off from P&W's test strip at Bradley Field because of compressor stalls. The company's pilots 'finally put their feet against the throttles' (the cables were binding) and got off — though they later had problems retarding the power!

Intake development continued and was not settled for several years — in fact not until the advent of the Triple Plow II intakes, designed to cope with the more powerful follow-on P-7, P-9, P-12 and P-100 series engines. These offered blow-in doors in place of the hydraulic translating cowl and added 14 square inches to the frontal area of the intake along with a greater separation from the fuselage for added 'plow'. They appeared on all production models from 1969. Yet the compressor stall problem has never really gone away. Air crews have simply learned to avoid it, or to cope with it: it is barely felt on the flight controls and a high-speed recovery can usually be made by cutting back power to the stalled engine. In other respects the TF30 has been a great success. It offers a five-stage 'soft light' afterburner fed by its own fuel system and air supplied through six blow-in doors in the ejector nozzle, to ignite without the customary 'kick in the back' associated with large afterburning turbojets. The definitive TF30-P-100 model uses an 18-section iris, an entirely new combustion system and a high-pressure turbine. At an all-up weight of 3,900lb it is even lighter than the P-3 yet it delivers an extra 6,500lb of maximum thrust. The TF30 has enjoyed a good reputation for reliability and long-serving 'One-Eleven' pilots continue to praise its dependability: in operational service there have only been occasional minor F-111 groundings due to engine difficulties. The TF30's problems in the similarly powered F-14 Tomcat result from the very different demands of the dogfighting mission in which the engine is cycled (spooled up and down) much more frequently, adding to wear and tear.

## 'Smooth as glass'

Of all the innovations introduced by the F-111 the 'swing wing' is the best known and most daring. Variable sweep dates back to Adolf Busemann's studies in Germany and the later Messerschmitt P.1101, on the verge of flight when the Second World War ended. Copied and incorporated into the American Bell X-5 in 1951, the concept called for a heavy, complex system of rollers and rails to change the wing's geometry. Bell's tests revealed many of the problems of transonic centre of lift changes and high trim drag and the need for simpler 'swing' mechanisms. Grumman's XF10F-1 variable-sweep Jaguar featured sliding wing roots but weight and complexity again precluded an operational application of the exciting technology. However there was obviously a promising future for the idea: it would offer high speeds combined with superior low-speed handling as well as long subsonic range and shorter runway rolls. Fortunately the Vickers research team in England had devised a system of fixed wing pivots placed at some distance from the centreline, enabling the centre of lift to remain constant irrespective of sweep, with a 'glove' area to house the wing when folded in the swept-back configuration. The data passed to NASA's Langley Research Center in Virginia and was refined by a team led by John Stack. He impressed Gen. Frank Everest, Tactical Air Command's boss, with the simplicity and versatility of the VG idea, giving rise to the wide-ranging specifications contained in SOR 183.

Combined with high-lift devices to enhance short-field performance, VG was irresistible. GDFW settled for a shoulder-mounted wing with a NACA 63 series section which could 'swing' between 16° and 72.5°: set at 16–25° the wings provide low-speed handling and

tremendous lift; at 26° an economical cruise setting; and from 54° a supersonic capability. The pivot points comprise a pair of 8½in steel journals, fitted to the sockets of a large, bolted-steel wing carry-through box (WCTB). It is a neat design, but the choice of Ladish D6AC metal has always caused some concern: this steel had often been used in the past for critical aircraft components, but British tests showed it to be susceptible to embrittlement by exposure to hydrogen.* Applied to the F-111, however, the installation was to cause troubles resulting from problems with quality control (as will be seen later), not hydrogen embrittlement. Sweep is activated hydraulically by a screwjack mechanism commanded by a 'trombone' control in the left-hand side of the cockpit just under the pilot's canopy rail. For harmonized stores carriage the four inboard wing pylons swivel in sympathy so that they are always aligned with the airflow.†

Full-span high-lift leading-edge slats and double-slotted trailing-edge Fowler flaps are fitted, able to operate at sweep angles of up to 26°, while the leading edge of the glove area pivots to straighten the airflow over the inboard slat section. A 'lock-out' at 26° is available for cruise and a weapons 'lock-out', to prevent the possibility of weapons coming into contact with the fuselage and to stop induced vibration, is at hand at 54°. With the wings swept back, sustained speeds in the upper range are limited only by skin temperature generated by friction; the crew are furnished with warning lights and a 300-second digital count-down during which time they must throttle back in order to avoid incurring structural damage.

Folded back, the wing is heavily laden and this contributes greatly to the steady low-level handling characteristics of the F-111. Its efficiency is unparalleled even today. Maj. Dick Brown, one of the senior pilots in the 'One-Eleven' community, gives an enthusiastic description of the aircraft's smooth ride: 'You can go from 300kt to 800kt and, with your eyes closed, you wouldn't know. There's no change, even in feel on the control stick.' To a great extent the glassy smoothness is the end product of the excellent stability augmentation (auto-trim) system. There are yaw, pitch and roll circuits, each with triple-redundant back-up. The system keeps the stick 'feel force feedback' response constant under all flight regimes, reducing sensitive control at high speeds and making light work of normally heavy or sluggish stick responses at slower speeds, while the computer-commanded system responds to turbulence with dampers. Without the stability augmentation the 'One-Eleven' becomes sensitive to rudder inputs (but still behaves). The only

---

*As a result of these studies D6AC steel was avoided in Concorde's critical structure.
†Fully operational pivot-pylons were introduced on RDT&E F-111A No. 4, 63-9769. The VG wing also has provision for four fixed outboard pylons which may be preset prior to take-off at angles between 16° and 26°. The longer-winged FB-111A and F-111C variants sometimes take off with the outboard pylons, carrying fuel tanks, skew-toed at 26° using a 16° wing setting – an odd sight! As a matter of interest, the wings take 24 seconds to sweep from 16° to 72.5° under normal conditions.

exception to 'feel' arises from a recent safety retrofit – the Stall Inhibitor System (SIS). Tested at McClellan AFB, California, in 1973 and installed from 1980, SIS prevents the pilot from exceeding the maximum recommended 18–20° angle of attack by increasing stick forces.

The augmentation system was one of the least publicized of the F-111's innovations but it was actually one of the most important and represented the first operational self-adaptive flight system of its kind. It also enables the F-111 to behave well 'on the boom'; the aircraft is one of very few high-performance jets to have been able to take on fuel from the propeller-driven KC-97 'gas truck' with consistent ease. The flight control system provides yaw control via the rudder and pitch control through the symmetrical deflection of the

horizontal stabilizers or 'tailerons', giving a quick firm response at high speed. VG rules out the use of ailerons so at lower speeds, with the wings set at less than 45°, spoilers pop up to augment roll control – what the pilots call 'spoilerated roll'. The only unresolved side effect of VG is base drag from the rear fuselage. This is partly a function of the mid-mounted position of the taileron and its location immediately aft of the fully swept wing. This area contributes up to 30 per cent of the total air drag, much more than anticipated. The resulting reduction in supersonic dash range and ferry distance became major sources of controversy in the late 1960s.

## Space-age capsule

The ejectable crew capsule, designed and produced by McDonnell Douglas, has been one of the F-111's least troubled innovations. Although the idea of blasting both crew and cockpit clear of a doomed aircraft never really caught on elsewhere, it has been demonstably successful in the 'One-Eleven'. The concept was very much in keeping with the space-shot era into which TFX was born and an unprecedented 24,300 pyrotechnic firings

**Below: The curious protrusion from the tail of RDT&E F-111A No. 4, 63-9769, is a spin-recovery parachute. This aircraft performed the lion's share of the early aerodynamic and stores compatibility trials and was the first to feature pivot-pylons synchronized with the VG wings. (General Dynamics)**

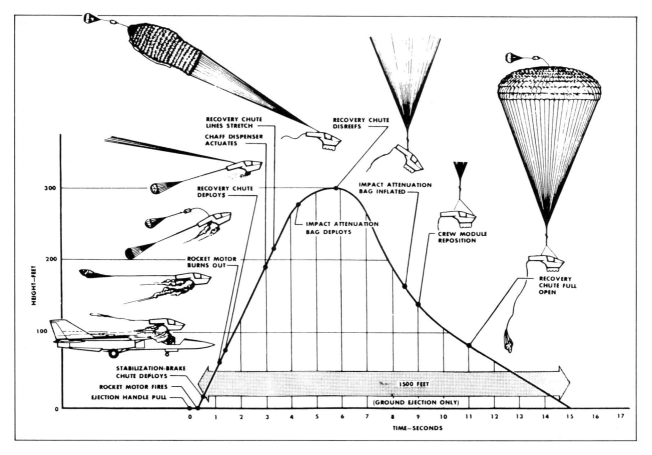

RECOVERY CHUTE LINES STRETCH

RECOVERY CHUTE DISREEFS

CHAFF DISPENSER ACTUATES

RECOVERY CHUTE DEPLOYS

IMPACT ATTENUATION BAG INFLATED

IMPACT ATTENUATION BAG DEPLOYS

CREW MODULE REPOSITION

ROCKET MOTOR BURNS OUT

RECOVERY CHUTE FULL OPEN

STABILIZATION-BRAKE CHUTE DEPLOYS

ROCKET MOTOR FIRES

EJECTION HANDLE PULL

HEIGHT—FEET

300

200

100

0

1500 FEET

(GROUND EJECTION ONLY)

0 1 2 3 4 5 6 7 8 9 10 11 12 13 14 15 16 17

TIME—SECONDS

**Above: F-111 crew module ejection sequence (typical low-speed ejection). (USAF)**

were accomplished to verify that the design would work; this it has done very many times, over land and sea and in peacetime and under combat conditions, in one instance remaining intact after tumbling down a mountainside in Nevada! The capsule, introduced in May 1966 on F-111A No. 12 (63-9777) and F-111B No. 4 (BuNo 151972), is designed to protect the crew during ejection at all speeds and altitudes, from 'zero–zero' to the upper part of the performance envelope where the risk of wind-blast injury and broken limbs is all too great. The crew sit in quite simple seats: flyers 'enter' the capsule-equipped 'One-Eleven'; previously, test crews faced with the Douglas Escapac 'bang seat' and its myriad leg and other restraints 'put the aircraft on'. GDFW described the cockpit as a 'shirtsleeve environment', with somewhat scant regard for USAF dress and safely regulations!

To eject, both crewmen have access to large yellow ejection levers located on the centre console. When these are tugged, dual initiators are fired which set off the Shielded Mild Detonating Cord (SMDC); simultaneously all electrical and control umbilicals are guillotined, to turn the pod into a self-contained 'survival vehicle' which feeds the crew with oxygen. A shaped charge releases the parachute cover and delivers the final *coup de grâce* to separate the assembly from the airframe. Depending on speed, altitude and attitude (all

automatically sensed), a pair of rocket motor nozzles then fire to ensure a balanced attitude at the correct trajectory. One interesting aspect of this is that the crewmen have to weigh within 65lb of one another so as not to upset the delicate balance of the system. Aerodynamic stability is aided by the small portion of wing root at the rear which contains the stabilization 'chute, fired 0.15 seconds after the SMDC, along with the flotation bags which guarantee that the capsule will emerge upright should it splash down in the sea; indeed, the capsule separation sequence may be initiated underwater, permitting ditching in favourable conditions. A neat feature is that the pilot's control stick becomes a bilge pump to tackle water ingress! Further minor SMDC detonations occur as the sequence progresses up to the deployment of the main parachute, which tugs on its bridles to ready the pod's posture for landing, the shock of which is largely absorbed by an inflatable ventral impact attenuation bag. An important extra is the emergency UHF radio, while a chaff dispenser is installed which can be activated to highlight the slow-moving capsule's position on search and rescue radar – something of dubious merit in this age of unchivalrous

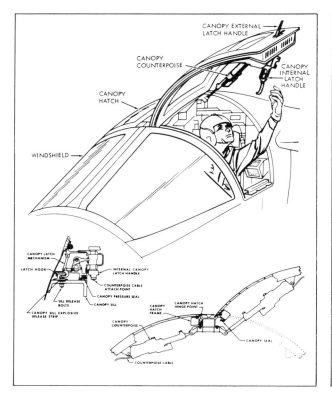

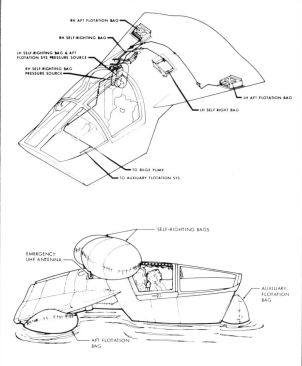

**Above: Canopy details, crew module. (USAF)**

**Above: Crew module flotation system. (USAF)**

air combat as the podded occupants might blossom into a radar-significant target!

These complex procedures take place 'in the wink of an eye'. The only recurrent problems to date have arisen from the necessarily lightweight windshield, which is susceptible to bird strikes, and the capsule's tendency to make hard landings, causing back injury to taller crewmen who have difficulty in setting the optimum seat pitch. The windshields are now on their third update. Lt. Col. Dave Skakal points out that 'They have tested it at 550kt for a 3lb or 5lb chicken – or was it a 350lb chicken at 5kt?!' Helmets have similarly evolved from heavy-duty 'domes' to a new, equally strong but lightweight grey plastic version. Visors are worn *always*, in tinted plastic for day flights and, optionally, in clear material for night-time operations. Continuing para-chute development aims to slow the capsule's rate of descent, but all pilots agree that upset vertebrae are better than making a smoky hole in the ground.*

### The TF-ing jet
The 'One-Eleven's revolutionary terrain-following radar (TFR) was just being perfected when the first aircraft flew and it completed its reliability assessment at Texas Instruments in Dallas a month later. Twenty-five million man-hours had already gone into F-111 development by this time – and the TFR was still to come! British research, coupled with work at Cornell Laboratories, had shown that a lightweight radar system could guide

an aircraft, via its autopilot, at constant altitude over uneven terrain, automatically. Using this work as a basis for their research, Texas Instruments came up with the AN/APQ-110 (and later -134 and -146) TFR, consisting of a set of black boxes and two 'bug-eye' antennae mounted behind the striker's long, pointed-duckbill radome.

The TFR scanners search 1,000ft ahead of the aircraft in a 'ski-toe' pattern, probing ahead like invisible searchlights, constantly on the look-out for terrain. Mountains, ridges and even gentle hillocks will all produce a noticeable return. With the 'Auto TF' mode selected, on receipt of such a return the system gener-ates commensurate pitch commands to the autopilot to pull the aircraft up, then down, over the topography in a 'hands-off' manner – though the term 'hands-off' must be qualified. Lt. Col. Dave Skakal reckons that it is 'not really a good word becaue you never take your hand off the stick when you're "Auto TF-ing" at low-level'. Capt. George Kelman agrees:

Your hand is *always* there. You trust the system implicitly but you don't let it go on its own because at any one time it may visually present something for you to diagnose and say, 'Yes, that's incorrect and I'm going to have to take

---

*Sandia Labs are testing a new triple parachute canopy arrangement designed to provide a softer, 25fs descent rate to compensate for the capsule's 450lb increase in weight since the module was first fielded.

action'. If your hand is over here doing something else it may not be quick enough.

Early 'One-Eleven' test crews described 'hands-off' as keeping their gloved digits gently wrapped around the stick, ready to exert pull-back at a moment's notice. The TFR checks itself constantly at 0.7-second intervals and if it detects a 'fail' it will switch over to the other antenna within 0.3 seconds. If the back-up antenna is 'on the blink' the system will initiate a no-notice 3g pull-up. Col. Rick Matteis, USAF Ret., with 2,050 hours in the 'One-Eleven' (his 2,000th back in 1975), explains how the system evolved from an initial 10° bank limitation:

In theory the TFRs originally worked OK up to 45° of bank; beyond that the aircraft would assume that something was wrong and would pull up. The TFR antenna would basically look straight ahead of the aircraft (except that it was corrected for wind drift, so that in a wind the antenna would look along the aircraft ground course). But in practice when you banked the aircraft the antenna would continue to look basically straight ahead. Thus it would be possible to slam into some terrain in the turn that the TFR could not see. For this reason we operationally restricted TFR turning flight to 10°. The TFR was later modified such that, when the aircraft is banked, the antenna is moved so that it looks into the turn. The 10° operational bank restriction was then relaxed to 30°.

This critical update took place in the late 1970s. The system keeps the aircraft at a more or less constant height above ground level (AGL), preset by a series of knobs on the cockpit centre console located between the crew. It offers five clearance heights ranging from 1,000ft AGL down to a 200ft minimum. In addition three 'ride' modes are available, 'soft', 'medium' and 'hard'. These determine how soon the aircraft pulls up or noses over in response to a terrain return: 'soft' is gentle, 'medium' draws a sharper sine wave through the air and 'hard' is literally hard on one's rear-end! Rick Matteis explains that

The maximum pull-up authority for *all* ride selections is 2.0g. That is on top of the 1g that the aircraft and aircrew experience due to the pull of the Earth and, therefore, equates to 3g on the G-meter. The maximum pushover that the TFR can exert is dependent on the ride selected.

He also explains that 'hard' ride is very disorientating and uncomfortable when trying to fly or navigate the aircraft because on the pitch-over, at zero g, anything

**Below: RDT&E F-111A No. 5, 63-9770, was used to test the General Electric M61A1 20mm gun installation at Eglin ADTC, Florida, and was later used to perfect the self-protect RHAWS and ECM electronics. In its retirement it became a GF-111A instructional airframe at Sheppard TTC, Texas. Note the two other RDT&E F-111As lurking in the cool Carswell hangars. By 30 November 1965 eight 'One-Eleven' test-beds had amassed some 282 sorties or 397 flight-hours. (General Dynamics)**

| TFR PUSH-OVER FORCES | | |
| --- | --- | --- |
| Ride selection | Max. push-over | G-meter reads |
| Level flight | – | 1 |
| Soft ride | .25 | .75 |
| Medium ride | .50 | .50 |
| Hard ride | 1 | 0 |

not battened down starts flying around the cockpit. Capt. Greg Lowrimore comments that 'It's a chance to knock all the dust loose. All the stuff flies up – a little house cleaning!'

The TFRs work in harmony with an extremely accurate and reliable Honeywell AN/APN-167 Low Altitude Radar Altimeter (LARA), which serves as a fail-safe system during automatic descent and 'Auto TF' operations – especially over water or smooth ground such as desert salt lakes where there are no terrain returns for the TFR to digest. The system works at altitudes of up to 5,000ft AGL, 20° of pitch plus 45° of bank, and was programmed for 75 per cent (that is, if the TFR were selected for 1,000ft AGL clearance and the aircraft came within 750ft of the ground, LARA would automatically command an immediate 3g pull-up). This was later changed to 68 per cent (at 3.8 incremental g) and has now been standardized at Strategic Air Command's 83 per cent level, to cope with heavier aircraft loads and airframe stresses and to introduce extra safety and fleet-wide commonality. The whole package, fleetwide, is on about its fifth upgrade.

The evolution of the auto terrain-hugging systems takes us ahead in the story a little, yet it is interesting to see how rapidly the F-111's crews adapted to this totally new and, at first, disconcerting method of flying the mission. Don Laing, a right-hand seat radar operator (or 'fightergator' as he prefers to be known) describes what was involved in a routine TFR sortie in the early days:

We would normally launch and climb to a reasonable cruise altitude in order to check out the systems, specifically the TFR, prior to entering the low-level routes onto the ranges. At TFR let-down we would closely monitor the initial pitch-down and descend through the 5,000ft AGL point where the TFR would 'sense' the radar altimeter lock and increase the descent pitch another two degrees. One of the important jobs of the 'Fightergator' at that point was to ensure that he was aware of the ground elevation near the proposed level-off point and make sure that the aircraft was beginning to level off at the predetermined altitude – in most cases 500ft AGL. Peacetime limitations for night TFR were 500ft minimum and down to 200ft in daytime. Normal low-level cruise speeds were 480kt. The low-level routes were a test and challenge for both crew members due to the close proximity of the ground and the very high airspeed. The right-hand seater was responsible for low-level navigation and had to monitor closely route and centreline by radar and pilotage, ETAs [estimated times of arrival] at turn points, and TOTs [times on targets].

The TFR let-down to which Don refers is fully automatic; the 'Auto TF descent' takes the aircraft into a terrifying 'hands-off' 10,000ft/min dive, with pull-out at the preselected 'Auto TF' height. To the newly

initiated this can be a worrying experience, particularly at night, and demands constant attention in the cockpit just in case a systems failure goes undetected. To fly safely in this hair-raising manner the pilot keeps a watchful eye on the proceedings by gluing his vision on four relevant dashboard displays: the radar altimeter needle; the attitude director indicator (ADI), a black and white 'floating ball' and a standard aircraft instrument which moves smoothly within its fixture to denote whether the aircraft is banking, diving or climbing; the coaming-mounted General Electric (GE) AN/ASG-23 Lead-Computing Optical Sight (LCOS, also known as the Optical Display Sight or ODS), which flashes up a collimated image on a combining glass and which is used for heads-up weapons delivery and steering; and, most important of all, the TFR scope, a large electric-green TV display situated smack in the middle of the top of the dashboard between the pilot and navigator. The TFR scope is tied to the TFRs to present an E-scan, comprising two distinct lines, the upper denoting the aircraft 'command line' and the lower the 'terrain line' or 'video'. This is the primary cue, supplemented by the ADI and ODS which each incorporate a 'command bar' or pitch steering cue which, while not tied directly to the TFRs, nevertheless serves as a useful indicator.

Rick Matteis explains how the pilot uses these instruments to ensure safe flight 'down in the weeds':

The primary pitch steering cue is the one on the ADI, but this is repeated on the LCOS and you can use either one. The normal use of this cue during 'Auto TF' is that if the pitch steering bar moves, the aircraft should pitch in the same direction. If not, the pilot should find out why and perhaps take some action to correct the apparent malfunction. It is also possible to hand-fly the aircraft by turning off 'Auto TF' and using the pitch bar. When it goes up the pilot should pull the aircraft up etc. My experience was that the pitch bar was sloppy and had a definite lag in it. Manual TF, which we almost never did, could be accomplished better by using the command line on the E-scope. If there was a gap between the ground video and the command line you should push the aircraft over. If the video started penetrating the command line you should pull the aircraft up. I used to think of it as if the command line was the control stick. If the video penetrated the command line I would pull it away from the video. If the gap between the command line and video got too great I would push the command line (control stick) towards the video.

Although this technology was substantially assimilated within a couple of years from the F-111's maiden hop, a considerable amount of intensive testing preceded the service shake-down of the new type.

Category I (prime contractor's) tests continued into 1967 at Carswell AFB, Texas, adjacent to the voluminous Fort Worth assembly factory, and at Edwards Air Force Flight Test Center (AFFTC) in California, during which time weights had risen steadily from the original F-111A estimate of 45,000lb gross to a massive 70,000lb. While this problem was death to the F-111B (as will be seen later) it was good news to the Air Force, whose demand for sustained Mach 1.2 at low-level necessitated a beefy, heavy airframe which led the designers on the spiral of extra fuel, leading to extra weight, and so

**Above:** RDT&E F-111A No. 7, 63-9772, in the process of punching off sixteen BLU-27 napalm-type tanks from its four pivot and four fixed pylons. Note the pointed 'speed bumps' and early tail configuration, and the Douglas triple ejector racks, later replaced by more streamlined Douglas Bomb Release Units (BRUs) which use closer-fitting square lug bomb attachments instead of big D-rings. (General Dynamics)

**Below:** The collimated lead-computing optical display sight imagery (LCOS or ODS) presented to the pilot in all F-111s except the B and D. The ring sight provides lead and drift compensation for manual and automatic CCIP visual attacks and incorporates a 'pull-up' command bar and roll indices. The airspeed and altitude differential can be preset on the sides, as added heads-up cues.

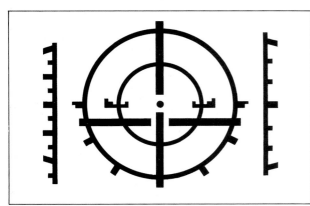

on. The final outcome was an aircraft far removed from the short-field, highly manoeuvrable fighter concept. Air Force thinking readily adapted itself to the idea of a rather different aircraft, but TFX failed to meet a number of their original requirements: for example, ferry range came out initially at around 2,500 miles as opposed to the promised 4,180, and Mach 1.2 low-level dash endurance totalled only 40 miles in a 920-mile tactical radius – 170 miles short – while altitude at military (non-afterburning) power with a full load 'even on a good day' was not much over 18,000ft. To the press, eager for a quick-buck bad-news story, TFX became synonymous with 'Terrible F****** Experience!' In all fairness, many of the figures improved dramatically by the time the jet reached operational service, while it took several painful years to realize that these early statistics were less important than the fact that, for the first time in aviation history, here was an aircraft with the ability to make 'blind' first-pass attacks with substantial warloads using automatic terrain-following.

Throughout 1966 and 1967 the force of RDT&E F-111As forged ahead with proving the concept. On 25 March 1966 a simulated low-level penetration mission flight of 1,203 miles was accomplished, using TFR for half that distance and averaging 400kts at 1,000ft AGL. The belly gun, fitted largely as a result of pressure from TAC crews, was tested in the fifth machine (63-9770) in January 1967, while other 'One-Elevens', including Nos. 7, 12 and 17, undertook a massive programme of weapons testing. The first pre-production F-111A (No.

19, 65-5701) made its maiden flight on 12 February 1967 and was handed over to the Air Force in April. By September two dozen aircraft were involved in working out the diverse aspects of the F-111's systems, four of these, Nos. 3, 8, 9 and 22, being assigned to Category II Air Force Systems Development trials at Edwards. There were many encouraging signs. In April and May the Edwards test force flew a string of sorties code-named 'Combat Bullseye' demonstrating that the F-111A could accurately strike targets in all weather conditions, even though the particular aircraft em-ployed were handicapped with the basic TF30-P-1 engine and troublesome intakes; and on 22 May 1967 Col. Tom Wheeler flew from Loring AFB, Maine, to the Paris Air Show – without external fuel tanks or in-flight refuelling support. While Category II tests proceeded with vigour at Edwards, Category III trials, the operational phase, were brought forward with some haste and began with the 4480th Tactical Fighter Wing (TFW) at Nellis AFB, Nevada, next door to the gambling capital Las Vegas.

# Combat Lancer

On 17 July 1967 Colonel 'Ike' Dethman collected a brand new pre-production F-111A from Fort Worth and flew it to Nellis AFB to mark the opening of a new era. He had been given command of Detachment 1, 4481st Tactical Fighter Squadron (TFS), 4480th TFW, a special unit that was to introduce the jet into operational service and then to combat in troubled South-East Asia (SEA). An initial Stateside work-up code-named 'Combat Trident' was to be followed by the real thing, designated 'Combat Lancer'. Col. Rick Matteis, USAF Ret., then a captain, was in the initial batch of twenty pilots selected to join Col. Dethman's pioneering party that July, and a pair of Navy pilots, Spade Cooley and Bruce Ashley, were also included, to show them how the Air Force did things. Rick Matteis was flight-lead-qualified on F-4 Phantoms with the 33rd TFW at Eglin AFB, Florida, at the time. His initial impressions of the 'One-Eleven' were not ones of delight:

I was not pleased to be selected to go to the F-111 for two reasons. The first was that nine of us who were fully checked out and combat-ready in the F-4 front seat were selected from the same base, Eglin, to occupy the right seat of the F-111. The Air Force wanted nothing but pilots in the early crew force so that either crew member could fly the aircraft and bring it back for landing in case of emergency. We flew as what we referred to as Integrated Crews, composed of an Aircraft Commander [AC] and pilot-navigator. The thought was that the individuals would get used to each other and be able to anticipate how each other would think and react. I was crewed with Tom Germschied. On rare occasions, such as when the Det commander flew, we did break up the Integrated Crews, and we right-seaters even got an occasional left-side ride! However, we perceived ourselves as having been down-graded from ACs in the F-4 to 'pilots' in the F-111. We had been trained to take full responsibility for the safety and accomplishment of an aircraft and its mission and now we were being required to take orders from someone else during flight operations. All nine of us asked the Air Force to allow us to resign rather than take this assignment. Our request was denied. The second reason for being disap-pointed with our assignment to the F-111 was the fact that we were trained as *fighter* pilots and enjoyed the prestige that goes along with flying a fighter.

The F-111A is capable of leaving the ground at an all-up weight (AUW) of 91,300lb, clearly placing it in the 'bomber' category, though its crews prefer the term 'attack aircraft'; even Robert McNamara eventually conceded that 'A-111' would have been more appro-priate. Rick Matteis continued:

Only experienced fighter pilots were initially assigned to the F-111 for 'Combat Lancer'. The reason was that the Air

Force wanted us to train as quickly as possible and take the aircraft into combat. It was our belief that the Air Force was embarrassed by the Navy's capability to fly and fight at night in their A-6 and wanted that kind of capability in place in the war zone in the shortest time possible.*

**Harvest Reaper**

The team wasted no time and kicked off its training effort using anything with swing wings – initially the pre-production airframes (Nos. 19–30) assigned to Nellis's 4480th TFW, followed by the full production standard F-111As (No. 31+) featuring the Triple Plow I inlets and TF30-P-3s, deliveries of which had started in earnest by November. These were followed by six machines specially dedicated for the 'Combat Lancer' deployment and known as the 'Harvest Reaper' jets, all ready for service by January 1968. The 'Reaper' mach-ines had some special extras not fitted to the 'vanilla' models (dealt with later) and could be readily distin-guished by their revised decor of dark olive green undersides, designed to cloak their presence in the night sky. Pre-deployment training was largely self-structured. As Rick Matteis explains:

We went initially to Cannon AFB in Clovis, New Mexico, for our ground training in F-111 systems. This lasted three weeks. At Nellis we were trained for a very short time by a small group of pilots that came from the F-111 Flight Test Force at Edwards AFB. This training concentrated just on takeoffs and landings. After that we planned and accom-plished our own training.

Charlie Coker handled ground training in Nevada:

Basically we flew at low level with the TFR in control of the aircraft. These initial nav flights were flown in the daytime to allow us to understand how the aircraft worked. We were surprised at how close the systems would take the aircraft to a mountain before it would command the pull-up to fly over the terrain – we all would have pulled up sooner if we had been hand-flying it. These day flights developed in us the confidence that we needed in the aircraft and its systems. We then started flying *only* at night. We quickly determined that it did little good to look out of the windows. Terrain obstacles always appeared closer at night than they really were. In addition the TFRs required close attention if we were to be able to detect any malfunction before they could kill us. We therefore treated night flight

---

*The F-105F 'Thud'-equipped 'Ryan's Raiders' were flying from Korat RTAB, Thailand, in the night interdiction role but lacked the true all-weather capability of the Navy/Grumman A-6 Intruder and USAF/General Dynamics F-111. Consideration had been given to deploying GD B-58A Hustlers to fulfill the task, but these plans were later dropped.

as an instrument flight situation: we concentrated on the flight instruments and the TFR and attack radar and only occasionally looked out to avoid other aircraft. Looking out was really a waste of time because *no one else* would possibly be a fool enough to fly that close to the ground at night!

The object, of course, was to get to grips with the flight controls and nav/attack systems – later known as the Bomb-Navigation System, or BNS – 'down in the weeds'. A discussion of the switchology involved best explains what went on in the cockpit. The Mk. I suite was composed – as it is today – of a number of integrated systems: the TFRs and radar altimeter, a Litton AN/AJQ-20A navigation computer unit and inertial navigation set (NCU/INS), a GE AN/APQ-113 attack radar set (ARS) and, unique to the 'Harvest Reaper' models at that time, a ballistics computer unit (BCU); additional equipment comprised a LADD timer and a GE AN/ASG-23 gunsight.

Prior to take-off the INS is aligned with present latitude/longitude position, fed in using a pair of knobs and counters or 'windows': 'We were given the coordinates of our parking spots and we aligned in the parking spot. It took at least six minutes, but it could take as much as sixteen minutes on a cold day.' Runway markers could be used, in theory, but 'it would not be prudent to tie up a taxiway for this period of time'. The NCU/INS subsequently senses any movement via its gyros and accelerometers, processes the information and then constantly informs the crew of their geographical position by means of the same large spinning digital counters, not dissimilar to those found on a car's

milometer. Flight planning involves a careful study of maps and charts and jotting down a list of co-ordinates, one for each leg of the sortie. Following take-off these 'destinations' are then fed into the NCU/INS via another set of lat/long 'windows' on the dashboard, one set at a time, as the crew fly 'hands off' along their intended track, progressing from point to point. The aircraft possesses a limited '3 destinations' storage capability, which can be called up by pressing the three 'Dest' buttons on the nav panel. It enables the crew to fly a completely 'hands-off' three-legged navigation manoeuvre but the inevitable drift that creeps in after take-off makes it of limited use; it has always proved to be just as easy to set the next co-ordinates in as they are required. In this manner, as the crew pass each way-point, the navigator reaches down to the dashboard once more and enters the next destination, which commands an automatic change of heading to the auto-pilot while the TFR takes care of the terrain-hugging pitch commands. The system is akin to flying-by-buttons, with the option always at hand of decoupling the autopilot from the NCU/INS and/or TFR and using stick and rudder in the normal manner to take advant-age of radar-masking terrain slightly off the planned track or to take charge in the event of a systems failure of some kind. As explained earlier, 'hands off' means letting the systems fly the aircraft while maintaining a strict vigil with hands ready to come to the rescue in microseconds!

The ARS is the 'big eye', the sensor which permits the navigator to survey the terrain ahead, check on way-points, track the target, update the inertial platform and even assist with independent landing approach. Imagery is quite good and a navigator is normally able to identify factories, runways, buildings and even picket fences. At low level he will keep his brow on the large rubber radarscope hood and confirm that the TFRs are not missing anything he can see. The ARS offers three

**Below: The 'Reaper' F-111As parked at Nellis. The special blue and yellow insignia on the fin and dark olive green undersides were their decorative trademarks. Seen here are No. 38, 60020; No. 40, 60022 (lost on 28 March); No. 36, 60018 ('Ike' Dethman's jet); and No. 42, 60024 (the 'tail loss' of 22 April). (Via Rick Matteis)**

display modes, all plan position indicator (PPI), radar ground-map sector scans: 'Ground Auto' and 'Ground Manual', the former with wind correction and the latter as back-up, both wide scans used for general navigation; and 'Ground Velocity Stabilized' (known simply as 'Ground Vel'), which is an expanded display used during the attack sequence. Crosshairs, comprising a straight azimuth and a circular segment range cursor, driven by the NCU/INS, appear on the display.

With the target looming ahead and its co-ordinates spun into the relevant 'window' on the dashboard, the navigator presses the 'target' button and the crosshairs should fall right in place, automatically. Position is dependent on INS accuracy and if the system is 'slightly out of whack' so are the crosshairs. (When all the cogs, gears and pulleys were new the INS would drift a mere 0.5nm an hour on average but the figure is much higher nowadays.) To correct their position the navigator grasps his tracking handle, a pistol grip-like device located under the canopy sill, and squeezes the 'enable bar'. By moving the tracking handle in the appropriate direction the crosshairs are slewed gently into the desired place. A fold-down armrest assists with this 'lite stuff'. If the target is non-radar-significant, as was often the case in the jungles of SEA, the navigator will have already spun-in the range and bearing of an 'offset aiming point' (OAP). The 'offset' is a prominent, radar-significant feature at a known range and bearing to the target which can be readily identified on the sweep. Rick Matteis explains the general procedures used:

> If the target was a radar-significant one we would carry an offset only as back-up. More often than not the target was not radar-significant and we were required to carry an offset. We would try to select a point that would be clearly predictable on the radar and which was *beyond* the target. Once this was done you could move the radar crosshairs from the offset point to the target with only one button depression for each change [by pressing the 'target' or 'offset' buttons on the dashboard]. It was typical to select

the offset and once that was found the crosshairs would be moved to place them directly on that point on the radar. Then the operator would switch from the offset to the target and back. If the target ever broke out on the radar the operator would stay on the target until bomb release.

Offset crosshair position is refined using the tracking handle as before. With crosshairs in place the system is generating steering cues and radar slant-range, the INS is realigned and the nav panel furnishes distance and time to target.

Other important manual elements which need to be performed by the navigator are the requirements to preselect bomb stations, release mode, fuses, 'ballistics' and 'interval'. Selecting bombs is straightforward: large knobs on the right-hand console's weapons control panel (WCP) are used to choose stations, bomb fuses (nose or tail or both) and release in singles, pairs or salvo. Salvo means the whole lot coming off in one go; singles alternate between each wing; and pairs come off each wing simultaneously. All these modes ensure an even weight distribution for an accurate, wings-level bomb-run lest the impact pattern culminate in a crazy-S! 'Ballistics' involves cranking in the type of bomb (e.g. Mk. 82 Snakeye) into the panel behind the right-hand stick, to inform the BCU as to what weapons are to be used – a process usually conducted before take-off when the navigator can cross-refer to the ironware strapped to the BRUs (Bomb Release Units, low-drag versions of the Douglas multiple ejection racks, or MERs, used exclusively by the F-111 and introduced to service on the 'Reaper' jets). 'Interval' is set by turning yet another knob, located on the WCP, to set milli-seconds spacing for bomb release in singles or pairs. At 480kts nose-level and with a setting of .075, for example, the bombs hit the ground some 60ft apart. Weapons release can thus be programmed to straddle the target to ensure its destruction.

With the switches set up in this manner the pilot needs only press the 'pickle' (bomb release) button on the stick to commit the BCU to 'blind' radar attack. All the same, 'visual bombs' remains an important option, catered for by the GE AN/ASG-23 ODS, which provides a Continuously Computed Impact Point (CCIP) mode. With CCIP selected plus radar and other switches set up as before 'to refine the equation', the pilot rolls in on the target, lines it up on the ODS 'pipper' (aiming dot) and presses the bomb release button when the desired aimpoint passes through the eerie electric ring sight. It is as simple as that. Even in a full systems, low-level 'radar bombs' attack the pilot is not merely there for the ride: the radar steering may put the F-111 slightly off the mark so if the target has been hit before and is burning, or there are streetlights or flares in the area, or even a full moon out, the pilot can make appropriate heading corrections. Attack sequences are flown 'hands on' and the BCU offers 'uncanned' attack profiles so that the pilot is free to play with the flight controls provided he maintains target heading and does not exceed any limits imposed by the ordnance. The net result is the same: with the switches set for 'visual bombs' or 'radar bombs' and the 'pickle' button pressed,

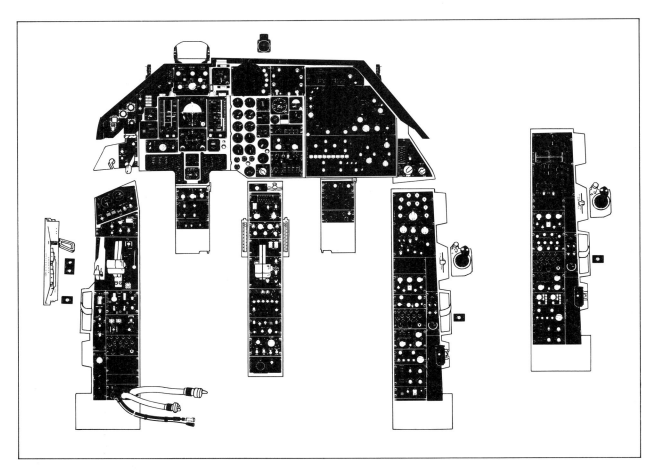

Above: The F-111A cockpit incorporating the Mk. I avionics formed the basis of the virtually identical F-111C and very similar F-111E; the primary difference between the 'Alpha' and 'Echo' lies with the revised push-button right-hand WCP console, and both types are illustrated for comparison. (General Dynamics)

Below: A wind-corrected 'Ground Auto' radarscope mode is displayed in the first RSP shot as the 'One-Eleven' heads west into Moreton Bay. Note the distinctive demarcation between land and sea. 'Ground Vel', the expanded display, centres the crosshairs in the narrow 'pie slice', in this case over Brisbane Airfield. The navigator can adjust range and tilt and is presented with these sweeping PPI sector-scan radar images as he peers into the rubber radarscope hood. (Authors' collection)

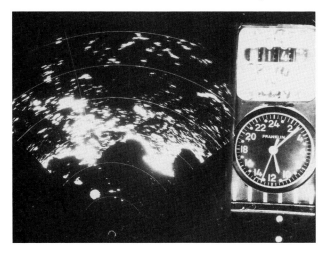

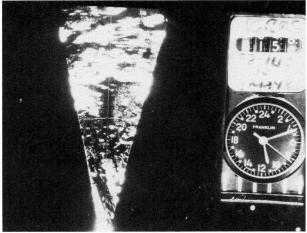

the BCU will constantly compute the release parameters and will trigger ordnance release at the right moment automatically, to put high explosives or cluster munitions on target.

Redundancy is an important feature of the 'One-Eleven', and this is where the crew's expertise really comes into play: should the computers start 'going down' the ODS can be set for a manual, 'canned' visual bomb run, using set airspeed, delivery angles and release heights; in instrument weather conditions the ARS can similarly be used for a 'manual range line', 'blind' attack with 'manual trail' bomb release. These options are used if the NCU/INS or BCU fails. Manual bombing procedures are practised frequently and formed a big part of the early training effort.

All these techniques, very familiar to 'One-Eleven' crews today, were very new to 'Ike' Dethman's detachment and an inordinate amount of time was spent perfecting them. In all, the unit flew no fewer than 500 attack training sorties by winter's end to ensure that they were 100 per cent combat-ready. Crews flew as much as 40 hours a month, the aircraft a demanding 59 hours apiece. Ground crews became masters of their new charges by necessity.

## Mark One Stealth

An additional element of the pre-deployment work-up was a week-long session at Eglin AFB to check out the newly installed self-protect systems. Flying at night over simulated threats, Rick Matteis remembers that 'We were not impressed'. The main problems revolved around the automatic nature of the packages. Located at the top of the fin was a device known as the Countermeasures Receiving Set (CMRS), the pre-production Cincinnati Electronics AN/ALR-23, which could be tied to the spring-loaded AN/ALE-28 Countermeasures Dispenser Set (CMDS) built into the 'speed bumps' to command automatic release of chaff and flare decoys on receipt of a threat indication:

> It was supposed to warn us of an aircraft behind us or a missile being shot at us. This system was so unreliable and gave so many false alarms that we never turned it on. It was possible to eject both chaff and flares simultaneously via the four rectangular dispenser channels but, because of the false alarms, we only used these devices manually, which is to say never. If you dropped a flare at low altitude it would signal the ground gunners to 'shoot there'.

Similar sentiments were felt about the otherwise superb Sanders AN/ALQ-94 multi-band electronic countermeasures (ECM) deception jammer, designed to fox 'Fan Song' SA-2 surface-to-air missile (SAM) and 'Fire Can' anti-aircraft artillery (AAA) tracking radars. This system could detect and respond to those threats automatically when switched on. In addition the internal AN/ALQ-94 was supplemented by a pair of optional GE AN/ALQ-87 noise-jamming pods which could be bolted on mini-pylons located under the weapons bay and between the strakes. These pods provided a 'Beacon' jamming mode not available to the Sanders equipment, but

Above: Col. 'Ike' Dethman's 'One-Elevens' roar over Nellis in their six-ship formation before turning en route to Andersen AFB, Guam, on 15 March 1968. (Via Rick Matteis)

> Our concept was to fly low, fast and with everything that could announce our position turned *off*. You might say it was our version of 'stealth'. We were concerned that ECM could be triggered by a ground threat that was not looking at us and that that could give us away.

Passive radar homing and warning systems (RHAWS) initially comprised the Bendix AN/APS-107, and Loral AN/ALR-31 'See Sam' launch warning lights, which by today's standards

> . . . were primitive. We would get a strobe to indicate angle to a threat and the length of the strobe was supposed to be indicative of the range of the threat. We also got an audio signal that could be used to identify the type. That is all great for a large bomber crew or an aircraft that flies at high altitude and is therefore vulnerable. We had a high crew workload and trusted that our low altitude would save us so we pretty much ignored the RHAWS.

Suitably convinced that survival rested on a surprise approach to target and the effective use of the TFR, the 'Combat Lancer' crews 'psyched themselves up' for the impending deployment to Ban Takhli RTAB, Thailand, situated some 90 miles north of Bangkok. On 20 January 1968 Col. Chester L. Van Etten had taken charge of the newly organized 474th TFW, which absorbed the Det 1 4481st TFS, 4480th TFW 'Harvest Reaper' aircraft and crews. The Nellis 'boss' was Gen. Taylor, and less than two months later he confirmed that the 'Combat Lancer' assignment had received the 'green light'; Lt. Col. Ed Palmgren was Ops Officer for the deployment. Det 1 CO 'Ike' Dethman briefed the crews on 14 March with the judicious use of a chalkboard and pointer: two cells of three aircraft flying in echelon, he leading in pin-striped 60018, would fly non-stop to Guam. A further flight would take them on to Takhli, to arrive in formation on 17 March. Rick Matteis again:

After eight months' total training we went to war. I think we knew about six weeks in advance that we were definitely going. A fairly large contingent of ground troops left about a week early to be in place at Takhli to receive the aircraft. We also sent a group of ground troops to Guam to receive us and turn us around [known as En-Route Support Teams, or ESTs]. I really don't recall much about the events leading up to it but the night before we left with the aircraft we were not allowed to sleep at home. The thinking was that there would be too much emotional stress. Maybe that is right – I don't know – but we didn't like being away from our families. On the day of the deployment, the 15th, we saw our families for a short time then got into our aircraft and

took off. We were all ex-fighter pilots and always wanting to show off, so we joined up in a neat six-ship formation and roared over Nellis before turning en route to Guam.

The aircraft flew all the way on their inertial platform, and received occasional top-ups from KC-135 Strato-tankers:

Three refuelings and 13¼ hours later we arrived at Guam without incident. Funny things that happened en route included the fact that the commander, Col. Dethman, had a problem talking on the radio. He would key the mike and wait for five or more seconds before transmitting. Pretty soon we all adopted this ridiculous method of radio operation. Also, Roger Nunnamaker would come on the radio every hour and announce 'Only seven easy hours to go!' We were beat when we got to Guam. We actually had to be helped out of the cockpits, because our legs were so numb. Guam was very hot and humid. We ate and went right to sleep. Eighteen hours after arrival at Guam we took off again. Charlie Tosten could not get his slats to come up, but he never told anybody and flew all the way to Takhli with them down.

The crews had crossed by way of northern South Vietnam: 'We saw some aircraft on our radars and got really worried about it'. Col. Dethman ordered them to 'green' (select and arm) the belly-mounted 20mm Gatling guns but the 'bogeys' turned out to be USAF tankers.

**Below: A tail view of five of the 'Reaper' jets, with the glass optical peephole of the fincap-mounted AN/ALR-23 receiver in clear view. It tended to generate many 'false alarms' in the early days and was replaced by the production standard Cincinatti Electronics AN/AAR-34 from late 1968. (Via Rick Matteis)**

It took 6½ hours and one refueling to get from Guam to Takhli. We formed up into our show formation on arrival and had a really great reception. The whole base turned out to meet us and then threw a big party for us. We tried to sleep that night but after crossing thirteen time zones in two days it was not possible.

The next few days were spent making familiarization flights, getting to know the local terrain and laying down plans for the combat missions which would commence a week later. Settling in presented few problems as the 355th TFW, the parent unit of the 'Combat Lancer' Detachment while at Takhli, had been there for several years and had gone to a lot of trouble to spruce up their habitat with American-style 'mod cons':

Facilities for fighting a war were very good. No one ever shot at us while we slept, such as you might expect if you lived within the combat zone. We had good barracks-type living accommodation with two men to a room. The buildings were air-conditioned with a marginal but acceptable system for the extreme high temperatures in Thailand. We had a nice Officers' Club and a movie theater and Armed Forces Thailand Network (AFTN) broadcast music and news in English. Since we flew exclusively at night we blacked out our windows and slept during the day. The only discomfort was that our barracks building was close to one end of the runway. F-105s were also stationed at Takhli and they frequently started their takeoff roll from *our* end of the runway. The F-105 has an extremely 'hard light' when they select afterburner, which makes a very loud noise that can be disturbing to people trying to sleep nearby! We drank a lot and frequently went into Takhli town for dinner or other activities. The Thai people were basically friendly but we never went into town alone'.

Combat operations began on Monday 25 March. These pioneers still had little in the way of the great entourage of prediction artists and mission support personnel enjoyed by today's crews. Radar prediction, a sketch based on maps which is drawn to look like the actual radar picture anticipated at specific waypoints, forms an integral part of mission-planning.

We were required to make our own radar predictions. This is primarily what we used. We did maintain a library of our own radar film and whenever it overlaid the flight path or target on a subsequent mission we would use it.

The F-111's ARS features a camera which can take

**Above: Capt. Rick Matteis and Col. 'Ike' Dethman exchange the customary handshake on return from the first ever F-111 combat mission on Monday 25 March 1968. (Via Rick Matteis)**

radarscope photography (RSP) for future reference on subsequent sorties to assist with navigation and target recognition, just like the predictions. Mission loads and routes were also in the lap of the crews, to their relief:

Only the target was specified in our frag orders. The air crew were permitted to select the type of ordnance and the method of attack (headings, altitudes etc.). I can only remember using 500lb and 1,000lb bombs. All targets were area-type targets, such as bomb storage areas, truck parks, personnel areas.

Typically the aircraft carried a dozen Mk. 82 500lb Snakeye or M117-RE 750lb retarded weapons. Mission planning would also involve a careful analysis of terrain contours so that a route could be plotted which would offer maximum terrain-masking against known 'hotspots' of anti-air activity. Times, bearings and coordinates would thus be jotted down, along with the assigned call-signs and mission numbers, for subsequent cranking-in on the dashboard and relay over the radio to the Airborne Command and Control Center (ABCCC).

The very first mission was assigned to Col. Dethman; Rick Matteis flew as his radar operator. Maps and other paraphernalia in hand, they settled in the cockpit and ran through the pre-flight checks, confirming that all the equipment was working to order: 'We had to have both channels of the TFR, and the attack radar, to feel safe in combat. Beyond that, it was pretty much up to the individual crew.' With the INS aligned they thundered off into the black and stormy night. Rick Matteis plays the major event down:

Not much to tell. The target was a bomb dump on a small island just off the coast of southern NVN [Hon Co, otherwise known as Tiger Island]. We planned the mission to approach from the west so that we would be heading out to sea as our bombs went off. We typically flew at high altitude from Takhli to the Laos border, then descended to 1,000ft over Laos.

Laos is full of very treacherous terrain, tertiary stage

limestone karst which features huge vertical cliffs and collapsed gorges, covered in a layer of tropical rain forest. It challenged the TFRs:

At 1,000ft the terrain would not make the flying uncomfortable. In rough terrain at lower altitudes the aircraft would fly up abruptly to pull over hills and would nose over a little less abruptly to descend down the other side. After we got used to it the crew hardly noticed the effect of the pull-ups and nose-overs. [Medium ride was always used.] We found that hard ride was unusable because on the pitch-over after coming over the top of a hill the aircraft would go to zero g and your books and everything else in the aircraft would come flying up in your face. Needless to say, this made it difficult to operate the aircraft!

Out of Laos, the crews would drop down.

We then descended to 300–500 feet over NVN; again the altitude was dependent upon the severity of the terrain. After bomb release we continued out to sea, then climbed to altitude and returned to Takhli over SVN.

A follow-on sortie struck bivouac areas north of Dong Hoi, 35 miles north of the DMZ, in North Vietnam.

All missions were single-ship. The idea was to operate undetected as much as possible. I believe that we were successful in remaining undetected because no one ever shot at us until after the bombs went off. And then, they just shot straight up in the air hoping for a lucky shot.

Bomb release profiles were conservative:

All of the modes in use today were available but we did not train in nor use most of them. We would attack our targets using a level delivery if we were delivering retarded weapons, or in a 10° climb with 'slick' bombs. There was a danger in the level delivery in that the bombs could go off very close to the aircraft and probably damage it if the retarding devices did not open.

The routine settled down quickly but just three days later, on 28 March, 60022 and her crew disappeared. They were assigned to attack a truck convoy near the DMZ and were carrying a full load of four Mk. 82 'six-packs':

The first of our losses involved Ed Palmgren, our Operations Officer, and Spade Cooley, one of the Navy pilots. We never knew for certain what happened to this crew, but we all knew that they felt that they could hand fly the aircraft at a lower altitude than the automatic TFR would permit and we surmised that they probably flew their aircraft into the ground. Based on my experience that we never got shot at until after our bombs went off, I felt fairly sure they were not shot down, unless it was a lucky shot.

The next air crew loss involved Hank McCann and Dennis Graham in 60017, a mere two days later. The strict rules of engagement and procedures fobbed on US airmen may have played a part in this loss.

We had a rule that we could not enter Vietnam until we had

**Below: Standard equipment for all 'Combat Lancer' F-111As included a GE M61A1 20mm 'Gat-pack' and AN/ALQ-87 'Beacon' mode, noise-jamming pods. Ballistic canvas shields the fuel tank above the weapons bay. (Frank B. Mormillo)**

contacted the airborne command post. As it turned out, we were advised that a ground radar operator at Nakhon Phanom (NKP), Thailand, was watching the flight of this aircraft. He saw them cross from Thailand to Laos and fly up to the Vietnam border and then enter a racetrack holding pattern. This is definitely not a good thing to do so close to the combat area but they were having some trouble contacting the command post. After a while they were seen on radar returning from the holding point to NKP, but slower than they went in. I must believe that they were shot at while in the holding pattern and that the slower speed was the result of their losing an engine. In any case they crossed NKP and turned south-west to Thailand. From that point the aircraft and aircrew were never heard from again.

Jarred a little by the second loss, the team nevertheless continued unabated. These missions continued to concentrate on the southernmost sectors of the North Vietnamese panhandle in Route Pack 1.* The battle for Khe Sanh earlier in 1968 had left some residual but lucrative enemy targets scattered around the DMZ and in RP1, 'but all generally nondescript and unimpressive', Rick remembers. Most were merely co-ordinates in the thick of the jungle where RF-4C Photo-Phantoms, ground-based sensors and other intelligence had located enemy supply caches such as POLs, ammunition and truck dumps.

Gatling guns were carried on all missions. Supplied by GE, the M61A1 'Gat-pack' consists of six rotating barrels of 20mm calibre fed by an impressive 2,084-round drum. The starboard weapons bay doors are removed and the entire gunpack assembly is bolted in and wired up. It is a visual weapon for air-to-air or air-to-ground use. The same company's ASG-23 ODS was tailor-made to work with the gun and provides pitch corrections to help the pilot put the shells, fired in short bursts at a rate of 83rds/sec, smack on target.

> We carried a loaded gun on *every* mission but no one ever used it in combat. In our night-time low-altitude role the gun could never be a primary weapon. It was a self-defense item, but the F-111 is not a fighter and no enemy aircraft ever maneuvered itself into our 12 o'clock position so that we could shoot at it!

MiGs were never encountered. The F-111A was much too fast and elusive. The low-drag BRUs assisted in the high-speed egresses but did have their fair share of 'hung bombs' (ordnance which fails to release):

> We were permitted to jettison our bombs and/or bomb racks into the Mu Gia Pass if they would come off, or we could just land with the armed bombs. While this is not a desirable thing to do, Tom Gerschied and I landed with bombs on board with no incident.

Mu Gia made a good dumping ground. It was a bottleneck in the Ho Chi Minh Trail on the border between Laos and Vietnam. Much of the enemy's supplies going to the guerrillas in the South trickled through there and the crews might cause some damage with a lucky jettison.

Things eased up and settled into a 'frag' rate of about 0.2 (1–2 sorties per night). Although two aircraft and crews had vanished, the 'Lancer' men felt that their loss

was due to mistakes which could be avoided in the future. Things seemed to be going very smoothly otherwise, given the inevitable learning curve one associates with pioneering such a 'sh**-hot' attack jet in combat. Replacement 'tails' and crews – two 'Alphas' plus new pilots Fred Dejong and Ben Murph among them – had joined by 5 April. Then, on the 22nd of the month, Sandy Marquardt and Joe Hodges had a very unpleasant shock while flying 60024. Rick Matteis remembers the events:

> The third loss occurred prior to crossing from Thailand into Laos. This crew experienced a break in the weld joining the horizontal stabilizer to its actuator and the tail went hard over and caused the aircraft to go uncontrollable. The aircrew bailed out safely and landed in Thailand. Shortly after they landed the aircraft crashed. They both believed that they were in Laos. The aircraft fire caused the gun ammo to cook off, and these guys thought they were being shot at. They worked as hard as they could in the jungle to get away from their landing area and thought that they had covered several miles. When they made contact with a rescue helicopter and were picked up they were embarrassed to find that they were in friendly territory and that they had not made even one mile from the aircraft! The break in the tail occurred at a relatively high altitude and the aircraft was completely destroyed. Shortly thereafter a similar break occurred on an F-111 flying low-level in the States. There was enough left of this aircraft for the investigation board to determine that the cause was the deficient electron beam weld.

The Nellis loss occurred on 8 May and the crew, who had successfully parted company from their stricken machine, told the same story as Sandy Marquardt and Joe Hodges. The third Takhli loss effectively put a halt to the 'Combat Lancer' programme while GDFW worked on a fix for the defective control-valve rods:

> We were made to stop flying combat. We flew only training missions within Thailand until the Presidential Election in November and then we were brought home. I can't remember any operational restrictions being placed on us.

The crews were waiting for another 'go' signal but it never arrived. Instead they hitched combat rides in the resident 355th TFW EB-66 Destroyer barrage-jammer aircraft, feeling a little disillusioned.

> We were saddened by the loss of the aircrews and aircraft but I don't believe it demoralized us until the Air Force made us stop flying F-111 combat sorties. That probably was the right decision, but we were there to fly and fight.

Spirits were kept up by a few 'in-jokes'.

> The F-111 and the ill-fated Ford Edsel were both products of Robert McNamara. Both projects fell short of Mr. McNamara's goals: the Edsel didn't sell and the F-111 was found to be unable to satisfy all of the Air Force and Navy requirements. In the pre-deployment days at Nellis, Dennis Graham found an Edsel which was in a poor state of repair

---

*The US Department of Defense divided North Vietnam up into Route Packs, numbered 1 to 6. RP6 was further divided into 6A and 6B. In March 1968 the Johnson Administration halted all 'Rolling Thunder' bombing north of the panhandle, effectively confining attacks to RPs 1 and 2.

**474th TFW (12th AF, TAC) 1970**

**Nellis AFB, Nevada**

| Squadron | Colour | Nickname | Code | Aircraft |
|----------|--------|----------|------|----------|
| 428th TFS | Blue | Buccaneers | NA | |
| 429th TFS | Gold | Black Falcons | NB | F-111A |
| 430th TFS | Red | Tigers | NC | |
| 442nd TFTS | Green | | ND | |

The 442nd TFTS was known as the 4527th CCTS prior to October 1969. All 474th TFW tail-codes were changed to 'NA' during the course of 1972. Also based at Nellis at this time was the F-111A/E-equipped 422nd FWS, 57th FWW, known as the 4539th FWS, 4525th FWW prior to October 1969. The Fighter Weapons Squadron carried the tail-code 'WF', changed to 'WA' in 1972.

and bought it just to get the distinctive grill from it. We hung the grill in the squadron lounge at Nellis and all had a big laugh every time we saw it. Just prior to the deployment we received word that a major TV network news team was to visit us (which turned out to be incorrect). Col. Dethman directed us to get rid of the grill. Instead Dennis Graham had it packed up and sent along to Takhli.

The Thais are big on making nice wood carvings from teak wood. We purchased a 3ft-long set of wooden pilot's wings, mounted the grill in the center and mounted the

combination in the pilot's lounge at Takhli. Seeing that helped to relieve the frustrations and tensions of our situation!

All five surviving jets, and indeed the three losses before they went down, showed not the slightest scratch or dent attributable to enemy fire. The programme had been a qualified success: 60 per cent of the 55 combat missions completed through late April were flown in poor weather, proving the ability of the 'swing-winger' to fly at night, below the thunderclouds, and put its bomb load on target. Moreover the crews themselves felt proud to be members of the F-111 team. The old jokes about the 'fat bomber with the tires from a B-47 and the nose of a B-58' had ceased long beforehand.

**Below: Crew line-up at Takhli in October 1968 (from left to right, starting with the back row): Paul Fierman, Sandy Marquardt, Joe Keene, Norm Rice, Fred Dejong, Tom Germschied, Ken Powell, Rick Matteis, Charlie Arnet, Joe Hodges, Bill Coltman, Mac Armstrong, Bill Sealy; and Charlie Tosten, Les Holland, Ben Murph (the new Det commander), Dean Salimeir and Roger Nunnamaker. (USAF, via Rick Matteis)**

The 'Combat Lancer' team returned to Nellis by 22 November, with Ben Murph as Det Commander.

The US Air Force put the lid on 'Combat Lancer' but the crews' debriefs were studied in great depth. The BCU and BRU racks were subsequently retrofitted to the remainder of the F-111A fleet over the next three years and, along with a new KB-18 strike camera (never retrofitted to the 'Alphas'), became production-line features on the next two analogue models, the F-111C and F-111E. Late 1968 also saw a major self-protection revamp, following several Engineering Change Proposals (ECPs) and Technical Orders (TOs): the Dalmo-Victor AN/APS-109 RHAWS and updated Loral AN/ALR-39 See-Sam replaced the old equipment while the troublesome AN/ALR-23 CMRS was cured of most of its 'glitches'. The RHAWS remained primitive by modern standards, still utilizing the strobe and warning lights, but did offer 'prioritization' of the threats and a more complex interface with the rest of the self-protection equipment. More important was the new Cincinnati Electronics AN/AAR-34 CMRS, the fully-fledged production version of the AN/ALR-23 sensor, which remained tied to the AN/ALE-28 CMDS. Cooled by a refrigeration process to temperatures of 77K (−196°C), it was now much more reliable at detecting SAMs or fighters attempting interception, its false alarm rate having been reduced by a new multiple-wavelength discriminator so that it was no longer apt to light up the dashboard like a pin-ball machine and pop chaff and flares every time it saw the moon or a spooled-up blast of turbofan exhaust.

## Structural saga

By early 1969 there were some seventy F-111As parked on the ramp at Nellis, a dozen working with the newly established F-111 Fighter Weapons Squadron and the remainder divided between the rapidly expanding components of the 474th TFW: the 4527th Combat Crew Training Squadron (CCTS); the 429th TFS 'Black Falcons', which had started to equip in August 1968; the 428th TFS 'Buccaneers', which received its 'own' aircraft concurrent with the return of Detachment 1; and, starting in March, the 430th TFS 'Tigers'. For the first time inbound crews were coming straight from undergraduate pilot or navigator training, while instructors came mostly from the 'Combat Lancer' team and the fast growing pool of veterans with F-105 'Thud' experience. The twin Integrated Pilot Crew concept was also being abandoned. Instead aircraft commanders and 'pilots' would follow two separate professions as pilots (still called 'ACs') and Weapons Systems Officers (WSOs, or 'Wizzos') respectively.

The 4527th CCTS programme dominated Nellis. In addition to padding out the operational squadrons the unit was responsible for initial training for the new overseas 'Aardvark' customer, the Royal Australian Air Force (RAAF), and, alongside the 27th TFW at Cannon, was soon to provide flyers for USAFE's F-111Es. The basic course included up to thirteen sorties or 45 hours' flying time which would be followed up with a further equal work-up training period with the operational unit.

Rick Matteis, who remained at Nellis as an instructor, explained how novices would have to overcome the shock of 'TF-ing' so close to the mountainous terrain around Nevada but emphasized how quickly they became confident in the system. 'The main lesson that I would try to pass on was that the aircraft's systems worked very well. It was therefore possible for the crew to get *lazy*: if you did that, a failure in a system could go undetected and kill you.' Crews had to be weaned off pure stick-and-rudder principles and become re-moulded as 'systems managers'.

As pride in the community grew, so the hitherto drably camouflaged jets, now sporting matt black bellies, were redecorated with huge banded chevron markings on their vertical tails, in their appropriate squadron colour – blue, yellow, red or green. One hundred and twenty-nine fully fledged production F-111As had been accepted by August 1969 and follow-on F-111C/E production was well under way with 24 'Charlies' and 20 'Echoes' delivered by November. Oddly enough the F-111 had still not yet received an 'official' name, so Instructor Pilot Al Mateczun introduced a nickname – 'Aardvark'. 'If you stand in front of it and slightly off to one side or the other, the F-111 has a long sloping nose that might remind one of an aardvark'. The dictionaries say that 'aardvark' is Afrikaans for 'earthpig'; that nickname also entered the F-111 lexicography. The 474th TFW, too, adopted the unofficial name the 'Roadrunners', based on their mountain-zooming antics, and a large 'Looney Tunes' bird was painted on the roof of a Nellis hangar. Things seem to go like a dream – until December, when things suddenly went horribly wrong.

Only a year beforehand a wing carry-through box cracked around several bolt-holes during routine static fatigue testing of Article A4 at Fort Worth.* GD introduced what they considered to be an adequate fix, in the form of two 3in × 8in steel gussets which were retrofitted to the WCTBs to relieve local stress. Aircraft were limited to 3.5g manoeuvres pending retrofit but everyone felt happy with the aircraft. Then on 22 December 1969 a gusset-reinforced 'Aardvark' shed an entire wing. Rick Matteis recalls the incident:

> The aircraft was performing a pull-out after a dive-bomb run on the Nellis ranges. The aircraft, of course, went into a violent roll. The aircrew was able to actuate the ejection system but, since the aircraft was diving at the ground, the ejection system was not within its design envelope and both crewmembers were killed. The investigation revealed a defect – a carbon deposit – in the wing pivot structure that was thought to be a one-of-a-kind situation.

The entire fleet was grounded and the RAAF trainees returned to Australia while the United States embarked on a massive structural inspection programme to prove it was not a design flaw. Four test chambers were constructed, one at Sacramento Logistics Center

---

*Article A4 failed at 50 per cent of the aircraft's design life. Construction of the WCTB was subcontracted to Selb Manufacturing who were eventually subject to litigation and an investigation by the FBI which exonerated GDFW.

Above: Wing-box inspections and other due maintenance in progress at Fort Worth in 1970. Closest to the camera are five 429th TFS 'Black Falcons' birds, with a 430th TFS example at the rear, while under final assembly in the background are F-111Es, FB-111As and F-111Ds (which bore the mark numbers A1, FB or B1, and A6, respectively, on their tails; the shop number for the RAAF F-111Cs was D1, that of the aborted British F-111K E1 and that of the definitive F-111F E2). (General Dynamics)

(SMALC), two at Fort Worth and another at Waco, Texas, in which each and every aircraft was frozen at temperatures of –40°C and then subjected to rams which flexed the aircraft's wings and tails, to simulate forces equal to those encountered during 7.33g and –2.4g aerial manoeuvres.* This process continues to this day on a Time Compliance Technical Order (TCTO) basis and, although expensive, has proved to be extremely worthwhile. The root of the problem extends to the whole aviation community because fatigue-testing of critical structural components or large portions of airframes, although a time-honoured technique, is rarely adequate: despite stringent quality control during manufacture, each and every complex flying machine, made from hundreds of thousands of parts, inevitably has its own unique flaws, known to engineers as 'rogue flaws'.

The F-111 integrity effort has been very successful, with three failures of WCTBs or tails taking place within the safety of the proof chamber deep freezes. All such examples have been restored to flying condition, suitably repaired or modified and 'rescued' before a potentially fatal crash occurred, and the USAF is now considering the application of similar techniques to all its most hard-flown jets, under a major Durability and Damage Tolerance Assessment effort.

The cataclysmic in-flight failure of the F-111's WCTB, however, generated massive shockwaves which badly concussed the whole programme and which still contributes towards the unfounded stigma attached to the 'One-Eleven' to this day. As a consequence of the prolonged grounding order, lifted eventually on 31 July 1970, attack profiles remained conservative and 'mobility' status was not achieved by the 474th TFW until 1971; but that date proved more than adequate for the needs at hand. In the Eastern 'Year of the Rat', 1972, the F-111As would once more deploy to Takhli, this time in significant numbers.

*An additional chamber has been constructed at BAe Filton, Bristol, England – see 'TAB-V Pigs' (Part 3) for a full description of the proof chamber procedures. F-111A 66-057 was the first aircraft to complete the tests, on 30 April 1970.

# Whisperin' Death*

To the frightful town of Hanoi, came a stranger one dark
  night
To Phuc Yen, Kep and Haiphong, came this stranger to the
  fight.
She flew low, she moved fast, two hundred feet TF,
To the Delta came this stranger known as Whisperin'
  Death,
Known as Whisperin' Death.

The war trudged on for many years, then one day she got
  her chance
To fly and fight for freedom, and the cause to help enhance.
Col. Nelson obliged, he headed way out West.
He gathered up his fighters and said 'We'll do our best'.
He said 'We'll do our best'.

She remained a stranger not for long, her victories were
  soon acclaimed:
She'd cut the Northeast Railroad, and SAM sites she had
  maimed.
She hit hard, she hit true, her deeds you won't forget,
Nor the stress and strain of combat, and of goin' out feet
  wet,
Goin' out feet wet.

## Constant Guard V

On 14 August 1972 TAC issued a deployment 'frag'
order sending 48 of the 474th TFW's F-111As back to
SEA as part of the augmentation of USAF strength. In
the four years after 'Combat Lancer', bombing of North
Vietnam had been severely restricted, enabling the
population to rebuild and enlarge its defences on a
massive scale. Some 200 MiGs and a vast network of
AAA and SAM sites were in place by the spring of 1972.
Supply trails along the Ho Chi Minh network were
developed, creating 2,000 miles of routes to the South.
Expansion into Laos and Cambodia was rapid, eased by
the reduction in US air power. Responding with a series
of 'Commando Hunt' 'Trails' operations, the Americans
brought ever more sophisticated airborne technology to
the theatre but by April 1972 the North Vietnamese
were still in a position to launch a massive invasion of
the South, overrunning a considerable area. President
Nixon resumed the air war against the North. 'Defeat,'
he said, 'is simply not an option. I want the military to
get off its backside. We have the power to destroy the
enemy war-making capacity.' From 8 May to 23 October
1972 'Linebacker I' missions were authorized to blast
the enemy transportation systems. This time the F-111A
was a major weapon in backing Nixon's new-found
determination.

    The 'Roadrunners' second deployment, 'Constant
Guard V', opened on 27 September 1972 when twelve
aircraft under the charge of Col. William R. Nelson, the
new CO, departed from Nellis, arriving at Takhli RTAB
with a single four-hour stop-over at Guam. First in was
67-086. Twelve more, all 430th TFS aircraft under Lt.
Col. Eugene Martin, followed on 1 October and the
'Black Falcons' (429th TFS) deployed in toto between
29 September and 3 October with 24-hour rests at
Hickam and Clark AFBs. All 48 aircraft deployed within
six days, along with 1,487 support personnel and 40
transport aircraft loads of cargo. Transit was not
without problems: co-ordination with tankers was poor
and several crews arrived at Clark 'hurting for gas',
luckily in VFR conditions. At Takhli the situation was
not exactly relaxing either. For 36 hours the base was
crowded out with two of the 49th TFW's F-4D squadrons, delayed in redeploying Stateside by tropical storm
'Kathy'.

    Reopened only six months previously, Takhli had no
air-conditioned crew quarters. All copper wiring and
plumbing had been 'salvaged' by the Thais, the Officers'
Club had been trashed and worst of all there were kraits
and cobras in the showers. For the air crews the vital
thing was that they had a mission to perform –
straightaway. Their first strike was scheduled against
targets in RP5, 55 miles north-west of Hanoi, within
four hours of arrival at Takhli. Crews had been pre-
positioned, rested for 24 hours and given 8 hours of
theatre indoctrination and target study. When the
'Tigers' initial aircraft landed, six were turned around
and bombed up immediately. Many now question the
wisdom of such a rapid combat induction. Maj. Jon
Jordan, ex-'Constant Guard V', felt there may have been
an underlying attempt to beat a SAC record for bombs-
on-target-after-deployment. At any rate the 28 September mission did not go well. Aircraft No. 1 was
delayed for 50 minutes when no bolts of the correct
length could be found to screw on its AN/ALQ-87 ECM
pods. No. 2 launched, but all contact was lost after 36
minutes, causing Nos. 5 and 6 to be called off. Only the
third and fourth F-111As flew the strikes, but one had
to go for his secondary target.

    To the 'Roadrunners' it was bitterly disappointing.
Some may well have felt that the 'Combat Lancer' jinx
still lurked out there in the jungle. Ironically Bill
Coltman, pilot in the missing F-111A 67-078, was ex-
'Lancer'. Apart from the presence of five veterans of the
1968 deployment there was actually very little training
feedback from it. It seemed that the Air Force wanted

---

*The verses opening and closing this section are from 'Whisperin'
Death' by Gary R. Rundle, revised and edited by Jim Tanzola. Song via
Col. Tony Sobol.

to sweep a publicly perceived failure under the carpet even though reactions at squadron level had been positive on the 'Lancers' return. Lt. Col. Jordan was not sure that very much was learned in any case. Sixteen years on, Bill Coltman's former colleagues all have their own theories about his loss, and these illustrate some of the initial hazards facing the troops. WSO Bill Wilson, himself shot down on 22 December in 67-068 with Capt. Bob Sponeybarger, felt that they may have suffered disorientation going 'hard ride' in the precipitous karst landscape. Other 430th TFS veterans confirmed to the authors that Coltman and Brett went in using the potentially bone-jarring 'hard' TFR setting at 200ft. Lt. Col. Jordan thought they may have been 'inordinately concerned about MiGs', possibly suffering distraction at low level as a result. Capt. Brad Insley, who flew 75 combat missions with the 474th, attributes some of their losses to weather. 'Combat Lancer' began in the worst of the monsoon and it was discovered that the TFR could not cope with heavy rain. Screens on both TFR and ARS just blanked out with raindrop attenuation which absorbed the radar energy without giving a fail-safe fly-up. The TFR assumed that the terrain had become 'no show' like sea, so it would fly the F-111 straight and level off the radar altimeter. Often

that rain would be hiding solid karst rock faces so a manual pull-up was vital. This problem had not been encountered in the F-111A's testing and it took several years to sharpen radar discrimination.

To the others who flew the early missions the problems were rooted in a lack of experience. Col. Robert F. Wendrock, the 20th TFW's Deputy Commander for Operations in 1988, remembers his first combat sortie over the North. Flying to the Thai Nugyen area, north of Hanoi, he was with his right-seater for the first time, his regular WSO having broken an arm: 'I had never been lower than 1,000ft at night and I had never been in instrument conditions on TFR because neither was allowed in training. That was why a guy could end up hitting the ground at 200–300ft.' Col. Wendrock compared training at Nellis then with the situation today, where pilots have to be IMC and night-capable at 400ft in order to be basically mission-ready: 'The first time some of us went up in combat it was pretty goddam exciting'. Other crews reckon that, by today's standards, Nellis was a 'flying club' with perpetual good weather.

That first loss meant a five-day suspension of combat while all aircraft received a thorough maintenance shake-down and tactics were reviewed. On 1 October a training programme, including a local sortie by day plus a night flight, was introduced and on the 5th the first medium-altitude strikes were flown in Laos and RP1. Combat flying in the North was resumed as crews completed in-theatre training and by 13 October the

**Below: Echoes of pre-'Combat Lancer', three years on: a neat line-up of 429th TFS tails at Nellis AFB a year prior to the 'Constant Guard V' deployment to Takhli, Thailand. (Don Laing)**

Above: Lt. Col. Robert D. Anderson, CO of the 429th TFS 'Black Falcons', with his 'Wizzo' and F-111A No. 103, 67-058, in April 1971. The two MiG kills belong to Lt. Col. Anderson, not the 'Aardvark', and were scored early on in the Vietnam War; they include a MiG-21, shot down on 23 April 1967 in F-4C 64-776. (Don Laing)

planned 0.5 combat sortie rate was achieved. Thirty-three sorties a day were being flown by 6 November – a 0.7 sortie rate. There was also time to catch up on the logistics. No one had allowed for the fact that 80 per cent of F-111 maintenance has to be done with wings extended. Takhli's 34 revetments were too narrow to permit this so 46 new ones had to be constructed. Large areas of the runway's north end were in bad shape and the patch-up job which was satisfactory for the Phantoms did not help a heavy FOD (foreign object damage) eater like the the F-111A which hoovered up all manner of concrete debris.

Medium-altitude drops in Laos became common. Singly, or occasionally in pairs, aircraft attacked targets along the trails in the 'Steel Tiger' or Plain of Jars (PDJ) areas of Laos. Fixed ground-based radar beacons gave steering commands and targets were either pre-planned or allocated by forward air controllers (FACs). Col. Tony Sobol, flying with the 430th TFS, recollects:

Over in the Steel Tiger and Mu Gia pass area we dropped a lot of ordnance; I think we changed the magnetic anomaly of the Earth there! In RP1 we were looking mostly at road targets, suspected troop parks and bridges. In the PDJ we went after troops and storage areas. There was a pretty good war going on down there and we'd drop off CBU-58s, the primary ordnance, or 500 and 2,000lb bombs.

Although the F-111s were officially assigned ARREC (armed reconnaissance) in this area they never went against targets of opportunity. In Laos there were five beacon sites which gave offset and bearing on radar, used in conjunction with the FAC's directions. Changes of target would be notified via ABCCC. (At one stage the title FAC was changed to FAG – Forward Air Guide – but the understandable protests elicited a rapid re-think!)

F-111 crews were frequently required to offer 'buddy bombing' facilities for less capable aircraft too. Bad weather over much of SEA often prevented Phantoms and A-7 Corsairs from delivering ordnance visually so they would formate with an F-111A and use its attack radar to make their drop for them. After releasing their own ordnance the 474th crews would ask their 'Cricket' or 'Moonbeam' control centres whether there were other tactical aircraft in need of assistance. They could go to a tanker and extend their mission to take in several 'buddy' aircraft. In the F-111's document cases were the weapons ballistics – rack delays, systems data etc. – for the F-4 and A-7 among others, and they could of course assist other F-111s with 'down' systems.

'Linebacker I' kept the 'Constant Guardsmen' flying round the clock in Laos and Cambodia. Initially crews were on call at any time but they were soon limited to either day or night shifts to ease body-clock adjustment. It was over the PDJ that the F-111 earned its 'Whisperin' Death' *nom de guerre*. According to Tony Sobol, 'The reason was we came in at medium altitude and the first time they heard us was when the bombs went off'. Gen. Vang Pao of the Royal Laotian Army had heard his troops use the term to describe the F-111 and he used it in a letter of commendation to the 474th TFW. Although the 'trails' areas were officially 'low-threat' compared with the industrial North there was plenty of ground fire to contend with, though aircraft were very seldom hit. Some of the damage was self-inflicted. On a two-ship pathfinding mission over the PDJ Dick Skeels and Price McConnell suffered a mid-air collision with another F-111A flown by Glen Perry and Ken 'Alley Cat' Alley. The lead aircraft had a radar problem and asked the other crew to pathfind for them. Brad Insley takes up the story:

> As they departed the target IP [initial point] they passed the lead over to No. 2 (Perry and Alley). An unclear exchange of radio messages took place leaving both aircraft commanders with the impression that they were leading the flight.

No. 2 lost several feet off its wing and had to make for the emergency strip at Udorn, Thailand.

> He landed at about 240kt, necessary to maintain a proper descent rate with reduced wing area. Lowering the tailhook after passing the approach-end BAK-12 arresting barrier, he didn't realize there was also a BAK-9 barrier at mid-field. He took out the BAK-9 and carried it all the way down to the departure end BAK-12, which he caught successfully.

Perry's F-111A was repaired and in 1988 was still flying at Mountain Home AFB, Idaho, but 'with the nickname "Arnold" because it does not fly straight'. Several other aircraft have this problem too.

Lt. Col. Jon Jordan reckons he flew a third of his 75 missions over North Vietnam, half of these at low level, and half of those against the massively defended targets of the Hanoi/Haiphong area: 'Those were the very exciting ones'. On their arrival at Takhli the 474th were lectured on the practical meaning of 'high-threat environment' by Navy A-6 pilots who had been flying a similar mission (though more slowly) since 1965. Like those Intruder crews, the F-111 men gradually evolved their own solutions to the MiGs, SAMs and AAA. The main defence was to ensure that the F-111's unique TFR and attack systems could be employed to the full. This meant painstaking mission preparation and route planning, for which crews had the main responsibility. They were given 'frag' targets and TOTs (times over targets), received by the Wing the previous day and split between the squadrons, to be assigned to crews by the Commander or Operations Officer. 'Intel' people provided situation reports on defences and target data and radar strike people would suggest offsets. The F-111A's single offset capability at the time made choices crucial. Initially there was a shortage of target analysts and no data bank of useful offsets so they had to be acquired by trial and error and occasionally by sending a 'sacrificial lamb' to test a new possibility. In the early days crews would spend up to eight hours planning a sortie, studying contour maps ('bumpies') and sketches predicting how targets and offsets would appear on radar. Although these became quite good in time many WSOs followed Jon Jordan's advice – 'Just sit down with an experienced navigator and a chart'. Eventually a good library of radar film was assembled covering the comparatively small area that the 'Aardvarks' were working and the good offsets – bridges, large industrial buildings and conspicuous terrain features – soon became apparent.

Operations staff would then study routes and timings to avoid clashes. Capt. Insley mentioned one night when eight crews had picked the same crossing point within a five-minute period. Some 'de-confliction' of times was necessary to avoid a 'Red Arrows cross-over'. Target approaches were largely a matter of choice. Brad Insley preferred to come in over the Delta from the coast, approaching targets in the North at TFR altitude and ingressing to the west – and home. Others favoured the time-honoured terrain-masked approach along the back of 'Thud Ridge', the range of small mountains stretching north-west from Hanoi. By 1972 there were radars on all the high ground in Vietnam so the chances of an undetected approach were minimal whatever route was chosen. One 4,000ft mountain to the west of Hanoi was particularly favoured for shelter. Robert Wendrock made use of it often, including during his mission on 22 December, but by that time the F-111s needed all the tricks they could muster as 'Linebacker II' was in force.

## Linebacker II

President Nixon's frustration with the North Vietnamese policy of buying time by refusing to negotiate a peace settlement led to a JCS directive of 17 December 1972 demanding a 'maximum effort of B-52 and TACAIR strikes against targets in the Hanoi/Haiphong area. The object is maximum destruction.' For the first time virtually all suitable targets which involved minimal collateral risk to civilians were made available, including airfields, SAM sites and military installations which had previously been considered sensitive or urban. During the resultant eleven-day war (18–29 December, excluding the 25th) 700 B-52 sorties were flown against the country's transport and war-making capacity. Many of these targets also received attention from the 613 TACAIR sorties which were flown too. Essentially the B-52s took the railheads, military storage areas and some airfields and the F-111s marshalling yards, barracks, airfields and, later, SAM sites. Paveway laser-guided bomb (LGB) equipped F-4s were tasked against powerplants, bridges and pinpoint targets in civilian areas. Among these was a target of great psychological significance – Radio Hanoi, the insidious and insistent propaganda voice of the North. In fact Brad Insley was sent to remove that particular thorn but had to retreat to base with double TFR and ARS failure. Phantoms took out the station with LGBs a couple of days later.

Col. Wendrock's 22 December sortie demonstrates

some of the less obvious hazards of low-level attacks. Using that 4,000ft mountain for cover, he was aiming for Hanoi docks:

It was the same target that Sponeybarger was on [Bill Wilson and Bob Sponeybarger in 'Jackal 33']. When we got in our jet the NCU wouldn't align so they had to put in a new unit so we were a bit late. We got a TOT 'slip' and launched. As we were coming in we knew Sponey was down. It was almost full moonlight, about 1,000ft overcast. We were a black aircraft against a white background. ['Hardly the ideal F-111 weather,' as Bill Wilson observed.] We were about a minute or so out and a gun opened up on us. I thought the airplane was hit and I told Lt. Col. Larry Crowley in the right seat, 'Larry, we're hit!' He was an 'old head' so he just said 'Rog, press on'. As we started rolling out he realized that when we had changed the NCU he had failed to set his offset data and the one we had was way off. So he was trying to crank the data in. At the same time the aircraft started climbing. They had laid chaff corridors for the B-52s [due in immediately after the F-111s] so maybe that's what was doing it. There was nothing on the TFR scope but the pitch steering bar was up and the aircraft was climbing. So I hand-flew it.

Above: 'Linebacker II' pushed the Takhli-based F-111As into an intense series of night attacks over North Vietnam. Here F-111A No. 110, 67-065, flies with ease with an impressive payload comprising a 20mm gun, a pair of AN/ALQ-87 noise-jammers (one of them camouflaged) and no fewer than sixteen CBU-58 cluster bombs. Each CBU packed 800 1lb bomblets, which proved especially effective against SAM sites. (USAF, via Robert F. Dorr)

Col. Wendrock asked his WSO for manual delivery as he could see the target in the moonlight but a 'discussion' ensued and the target passed unscathed.

Most guys coming off the target had turned west, back to the mountains. I decided that was what they were expecting so I turned east, but every gun in the Delta was opening up on us, very close. They were just tracking us visually. In my headset I heard a voice over there saying 'Don't hit the ground!' I looked at the altimeter and we were at 75ft and decreasing. I had no clue we were that low and could still see the reflection in the rice paddies. Doing all that maneuvering, with me looking outside, we were descending

**Above: A 429th TFS 'Black Falcons' F-111A demonstrates the customary level delivery technique employed with CBU-58s, in this instance from medium altitude. As the bombs near the ground the casing splits from nose to tail to dispense 800 submunitions. (USAF photo by Sgt Richard Sullivan)**

all the time. My right-seater, who had screwed-up on the bomb run, saved my butt.

Col. Wendrock suspects that several of the six losses may have happened in similar circumstances. In the memorable words of 474th TFW WSO Lt. Steve Glass, 'At 500mph you are only a quarter of a second from hitting the ground [at minimum TFR]'.

There was also the nasty problem of insidious, uncommanded decrease in TFR altitude. Col. Rob Balph, 55th TFS CO in 1988, remembered an incident in which another pilot, Jerry Fedder, was just riding along at 200ft on TFR and was getting no indication that he was losing height until he suddenly realized and caught the F-111 at about 70ft. The TFR was supposed to activate a 68 per cent fly-up.* It is likely that Ops Officer Dick Ward's aircraft 67-099 was lost in this way on the first day of 'Linebacker II'. The indications are

that, after going 'feet wet' over the coast, the F-111 flew into the sea at a shallow angle. Stafford and Cafferelli, who always liked to exit over the sea with 200ft altitude and 72° wing angle, may also have suffered a creeping TFR height loss. After an attack in RP1 they went 'feet wet' and vanished. Pieces of the aircraft were washed up at Da Nang and it was possible to establish that the wing sweep was at 72°, that impact had been at a shallow angle and that there had been no attempted ejection.

Evidence of this kind after crashes was rare for the simple reason that each F-111A was on a solo mission and in radio silence, so making the location of crash sites extremely difficult. After the second loss, of Hackridge and Graham on 16 October in 67-060, the Air Force decided that steps should be taken to track the free-ranging F-111As in case of trouble. Although Radio Hanoi announced that '060 was 'blasted to pieces' over Vinh Phu province the wreck was never located. It was attacking Phuc Yen airfield with four 2,000lb Mk. 84 bombs. As there was no retarded-drop version of that weapon at the time, a climb to at least

---

*See 'The TF-ing Jet' in 'McNamara's Baby' (Part 1).

1,700ft was necessary before release to prevent blast damage to the aircraft. 'Slick' weapons tended to pursue the aircraft as they were released. It seems that '060 was hit, possibly by a SAM, as it climbed to that uncharacteristically high altitude. 'After that we never saw a Mk. 84 the rest of the time we were there,' Rob Balph recalled.

The Air Force's response to the untraced crashes was to require crews to file a flight plan before each mission. Tony Sobol:

As we stepped out of the command post building to go to the airplane we'd hand in a copy of our flight plan and when we came back they'd just throw it away. We felt a little sensitive that we didn't want to give it to them any earlier because people would know our route.

They were aware that there were plenty of highly attuned eyes and ears among the indigenous workers on the base. As an additional precaution crews were obliged to check in by HF radio with 'Moonbeam' or 'Roadrunner' (Takhli) at each turnpoint en route so that there would be a record of their last known heading. Even those monosyllabic calls were a nuisance at a busy moment in the cockpit. Knowing that he did not have to report in at or after the IP to the target, Brad Insley sometimes contrived to make that his one and only turnpoint. Other crews just ignored the calls.

In the press, memories of 'Combat Lancer' were revived and the F-111 once again got a hard time after the second loss. In truth the attrition rate was the lowest for any SEA combat type. In all, 48 F-111s flew 4,000 sorties between October 1972 and March 1973, losing six aircraft in battle – a 0.15 per cent loss rate. (There were also two operational losses, one of which, 67-072, crashed on the runway, cooking off its 24 bombs.) Comparisons are difficult and it is perhaps no more than interesting to note that seven F-102As, five F-5Cs and six EB-66s were also combat losses, all types which appeared in minor roles and tiny numbers. On the other hand the F-105, which performed the Air Force's strike mission for the first four years of the war, suffered 334 casualties. When one considers the nature of the F-111's task these figures are all the more remarkable. In discussing those missions with the men who flew them the authors were repeatedly impressed by the confidence which the aircrews felt in their machine and its advanced systems. When everything was working well they knew they had the plane to beat the threats.

MiGs were rarely seen and caused no damage. Brad Insley had one of a pair of MiG-21s turn in on him on his 27 December mission near Hanoi. Having escaped heavy AAA over the Delta and target he pulled up to 10,000ft but heard a 'Blue Bandits' call on 'guard' frequency. Looking up he saw two aircraft, one of which turned to pursue his F-111. Brad made a rapid 'auto-TF descent' to an altitude where the MiG chose not to join him and kept to it for quite a distance. Robert Wendrock had a MiG shot down directly above him as he egressed north-west of 'Thud Ridge' after a B-52 support strike. As they flew over a suspected SA-2 site a missile appeared to arc up and descend on two aircraft above, exploding one of them. Back home the F-111 crew were asked to confirm a MiG kill by the F-4 unit. It was the Phantom's missile they had seen, not a SAM. Col. Wendrock also noticed that both MiGs carried white lights on their undersides, presumably as protection from ground gunners.

'Constant Guard' F-111s still carried the M61A1 'Gatpack', de-rated some years previously from 6,000 to 5,000 rounds a minute maximum after an aircraft was lost at Edwards: its gun, still revolving after a burst of fire, continued to load live rounds and ejected them directly into the spent shell box where the heat exploded them. Like their predecessors in 1968, the 'Constant Guardsmen' never fired the gun – and rarely loaded it.

Speed was their main defence against MiGs. With the capability of Mach 0.9 in military power the 'Aardvark' could outrun low-level pursuers without having to resort to missile-magnet afterburners. With four Mk. 84s and full afterburner the A model will still do over 640kts on the deck. Low altitude and speed were the best solution to SAMs also. Tony Sobol asserts that the SA-2 was not a threat to an F-111 below 500ft: 'I had a couple shot at me – it wasn't a big deal. Our biggest threat was hitting the ground, and then came AAA'. He also feels that the internal ECM was particularly effective against the new ZSU Quad 23 gunlaying radars but 'Generally we didn't give a sh** about ECM. Going low level was good enough'. As in the previous deployment AN/ALQ-87 pods were carried fore and aft but seldom turned on to avoid betraying the F-111 to hostile radars. Even so the 474th TFW had plenty of flak shot at them, though most of it was aimed at the sound of their jets and thus fell behind them. North Vietnam's 'bush telegraph' signalled the predicted attack routes to all AAA sites in their path. Brad Insley:

It was like they were shooting a fire-hose in the air. The ones you worried about were the tracers that looked initially as if they were going in front of you and ended up staying in one spot in the canopy – they would come very close.

Most of the 1,000-plus SAMs fired during 'Linebacker II' were aimed at the waves of B-52s which assaulted their 'downtown' Hanoi/Haiphong targets each night. F-111A strikes were usually scheduled in just before the first wave. Initially they went against MiG airfields to prevent the interceptors reaching the B-52s and 'pacing' them to report back speed and altitudes to the SAM operators whose radars were 'freaked out' by ECM. It seems that runway damage limited the MiG pilots to around 30 sorties a day. Five were shot down, two by B-52 tail-gunners as part-recompense for the loss of fifteen of their own numbers to SAMs. Anti-airfield strikes were generally effective. Like all F-111 operations in 'Linebacker II' they were single-ship, first-pass, low-level TFR attacks – over 25 per night on some occasions. Just one of these put Hoa Lac runway out of action for the whole period, but there were eighteen other airfields too. The job would have been easier with a better anti-runway weapon. Unretarded Mk. 84s could

not be dropped at low altitude or 'tossed' with sufficient accuracy. Lt. Col. Jordan preferred the CBU-58 as its 800 time-delay bomblets kept heads down. For the most part 500lb 'slicks' and Snakeyes were used but to limited effect on runways. With their instantaneous fuses they merely 'FOD-ed the runway' according to Brad Insley. Snakeye delivery meant slowing the aircraft to less than 500kts for the drop to prevent the bombs' extending fins being damaged. Tony Sobol used to cut throttles to idle and ride silently on kinetic energy as the target approached. Otherwise fin failure could cause the bombs

**Below: The 347th TFW took over the Thai-based 'Aardvarks' on 30 July 1973 and the birds' tail-codes subsequently changed to 'HG'. The 428th and 429th TFSs rejoined the 474th TFW in Nevada in June 1975. Here F-111A No. 138, 67-093, undergoes flight-line inspection beneath a threatening sky. (Don Logan)**

to 'Go "slick" and go off underneath you – and that was kind of a depressing thing to have happen'.

Usually, little was seen of the targets, though both ex-F-105 pilot Jackie Crouch and Robert Wendrock were amazed to have the runway lights turned on at two airfields – Phu Tho and Phuc Yen respectively – that they were about to attack. Col. Wendrock responded to this bonus by asking his WSO for 'manual' and 'We just did a visual drop right down the runway'. Unexpected illumination of a different sort greeted him on his first mission, against Thai Nguyen barracks. His TFR had blown a fuse at the sight of karst scenery which dropped from an indicated 200ft altitude to 4,000ft in a second. Pulling the recommended 20° climb to reach minimum in-route altitude and get his TFR to see reason, Col. Wendrock saw his RHAWS light up as he headed back towards the target. Just as he neared 'Thud Ridge' the sky suddenly lit up like daylight as a series of parachute

flares were fired ahead of him. This was a signal to all the gunners in the area, including those at the oft-bombed Thai Nguyen steel mill. 'Fortunately that was not our target and we went by all that stuff.'

Another nasty trick from the opposition was to fire chaff rockets ahead of the F-111 to make its TFR command a fly-up, thus setting the aircraft up at a convenient altitude for the gunners. One crew experienced this coming down 'Thud Ridge' and got a 20° pitch-up. At that angle the radar altimeter gives up and the fly-up continues until manually corrected.

So they ended up at 10,000ft running out of airspeed and ideas. They lit the 'burners right over Hanoi, so scared that they didn't drop their bombs. They were in full afterburner at 10,000ft over the defences and no one shot at them. They learned about the fly-up phenomenon!

Another crew had an even riskier ride over Hanoi. Crewed by ex-'Lancer' Les Holland, and WSO Pepper, an F-111 homed in on its target using the Paul Doumer bridge as the offset. 'The old bridge must have exerted some kind of bomb-magnetism because they dropped their load right on it instead of their target.' To cries of 'Oh sh**, I bombed the offset!', the panic-stricken crew hauled their bird around and went back for a second (bombless) run, just to get the correct radar imagery on film, complete with a simulated release marker. By convincing their superiors that they had realized their error prior to release and returned for a second shot they hoped they might escape trouble over the 'collateral damage' embargo.

Above: F-111A No. 158, 67-113, heads out on the last combat mission of the Vietnam War on 15 August 1973 armed with a dozen Mk. 82 'slick' bombs, a 20mm 'Gat' and a pair of 'Beacon' noise-jamming pods. At this stage the 428th TFS was commanded by Lt. Col. Guy A. Hummon III and the 429th TFS by Lt. Col. Clarence J. Beaudoin Jr. (USAF, via Robert F. Dorr)

There were also the psychological pressures of coping with aborts, though at under 1 per cent these were the lowest in the war. Moisture caused numerous problems with the avionics and crews were required initially to have all systems operating at 100 per cent for each mission. A problem with TFR, NCU or other systems meant an abort. However the stigma attached to consecutive aborts meant that crews tended to ignore the problems if they were not too serious and fly rather than risk the censure of their fellows. It was usually possible to revert to manual operation with all but the TFR. On one flight Brad Insley's crew lost everything but their standby instruments over North Vietnam. They returned to Takhli, picked up another F-111 and still made it to the target fractionally ahead of the B-52s' first TOT.

Aircraft also tended to shred BRUs. After releasing bombs the circuit carrying the release pulses was still slightly overcharged. The MAU-12 rack built into the pivot-pylon consequently 'assumed' that the BRU was another bomb and pickled it off too. Col. Nelson offered his munitions maintenance people a case of whisky if they could go a week without dropping a BRU. He did not have to pay up. Moisture also caused some of the aircraft's honeycomb panels to debond when it froze or was heated by friction after seeping into the structure; on one occasion Brad Insley returned with almost all of his rudder missing.

As 'Linebacker II' developed, the F-111As were sent against SAM sites too. Unlike the hunter-killer 'Wild Weasels' they made single-pass, low-level attacks using CBU-58s. Data from SAC SR-71 and U-2R reconnaissance flights pinpointed the assembly and storage sites for the SAMs as well and these were bombed after 26 December. In the last few days of the offensive the defences were out of ammunition and the B-52s brought about the ceasefire virtually unscathed. The F-111 had proved its value in an entirely convincing manner. One tribute to the 'Aardvark' accuracy came when Lt. Col. Jordan found himself targeted against an ammunition storage area 20ft × 20ft: 'A bit extreme for an aircraft dropping bombs 100ft apart!' Another came from a POW in the 'Hanoi Hilton' who noticed that the usual procedure of locking up prisoners, air raid sirens etc. was reversed when the F-111s struck: 'The bombs

**Below: One of CO Col. Thomas E. Wolters' 'Aardvarks': F-111A No. 112, 67-067, roars down the strip at Nellis AFB in March 1976 in a haze of sunshine and hot engine exhaust. Col. Maurice E. Seaver Jr. took over the force on 24 May 1976 but by 6 August 1977 the 'Roadrunners' had transferred all their F-111As to the 366th TFW 'Gunfighters' at Mountain Home AFB, Idaho, under Operation 'Ready Switch', bringing to a sad end Nellis's intense affair with the 'One-Eleven'. (Frank B. Mormillo)**

would go off, *then* the warning sirens would sound, searchlights came on and the cells would be locked, long after the F-111 crew had set course for Takhli. The Vietnamese did not like the F-111.'

After the January 1973 peace agreement the F-111As remained in Thailand, with the 428th TFS 'Buccaneers' and 430th TFS 'Tigers' trading places while the 429th TFS 'Black Falcons' remained on station. They then moved to Korat with the A-7Ds, F-4Ds and AC-130Hs of the 347th TFW. Carrying 'HG' codes, they flew against Cambodian targets until Congress stopped all air action in SEA on 15 August 1973. The last combat mission of the war was flown on that day by F-111A 67-113. Takhli closed in October 1974 and thirty F-111As left Korat for Nellis in September 1975. Before they departed there was one last shot – the *Mayaguez* incident in May 1975, in which a USN vessel was seized by the Cambodians. Two F-111As on a training sortie helped shadow the vessel and sank or damaged several Cambodian gunboats near Koh Tang Island where the *Mayaguez* crew were thought to be prisoners. Heavier F-111 action might have been called up had the crew not been released.

When the F-111As returned to Nellis there were a few modifications made to them. ECM was updated and the target offset 'box' added.* The main impact, though, was on training. As Brad Insley sees it, 'In Vietnam the Air Force learned how to use the F-111'. It took 4,000 sorties to build the knowledge which is the basis of all F-111 operations and training to this day.

*See 'New Dynamics and Ironmongery' in 'Work Smarter, Not Harder' (Part 3).

Now the Aardvark's not a pretty name, but here it earned respect,
And we're sure there are BUFF drivers who'll swear they saved their necks.
We held our heads high, knowing of prestige she was to claim,
That sleek and silent fighter with the strange and amusing name,
Strange and amusing name.

But the struggle wasn't easy, and the price we paid too high.
Many friends were lost for freedom, but still our hopes were high

That someday soon we'd see the end and know the war would cease.
We'd be proud of Whisperin' Death and how she helped to being the peace,
Helped to bring the peace.

Now my story has no moral, for you see it has no end:
What the 'Vark has done for Liberty she's prepared to do again.
We pray she'll not be needed, but if conflicts do arise
We'll be proud to fly her, through dark and perilous skies,
Dark and perilous skies.

# 2. SPECIALS

# Seapigs

On 11 December 1962 the Navy made it official, endorsing Robert McNamara's public announcement of 24 November: as primary subcontractors to GDFW, the Grumman Corporation on Long Island, New York, headed by project manager Al Lemlein, was authorized to fabricate the TFX-N – or, as it was known by then, the F-111B.* Mock-up approval of the new model was given in August 1963 and, under contract 8260, Grumman set about producing five RDT&E 'Bravos' for Fleet trials.

The first to be rolled out was Bureau of Aeronautics Number (BuNo) 151970, on 11 May 1965. Apart from its 70ft span wings, blunter, 6.75ft shorter nose with an upward- instead of sideways-folding radome, much

tougher tailhook, and higher-pressure, 5in narrower main gear wheels (all designed for carrier compatibility), the new model did show a remarkable similarity to the F-111A. In his ceremonial speech at the unveiling of the new Grumman product Secretary of the Navy Paul H. Nitze said the type 'will forge yet another link in the carrier weapon system's chain armor, capable of accompanying carrier attack aircraft out to their maximum range; capable of long-range fighter interception; and capable of conducting individual strike missions themselves.'† A week later, and timed for lunchtime on 18 May when everyone was free to witness the event, a pristine BuNo 151970 took to the blue skies over Peconic River, Calverton, with project pilot Ralph

Donnell and co-pilot Ernie Von Der Heyden at the helm, pushed by a pair of TF30-P-1 engines. During the 1hr 19min sortie functional checks were completed successfully and the wings swept through their adjustable positions by the 100hp hydraulic motor. Navy F-111B project manager Rear Admiral William E. Sweeney was well pleased with the preliminary results but suspected that the 'Bravo' was far too heavy to be seen spotting the decks of carriers in the envisaged clusters of two dozen per capital ship: grossing around 77,000lb, the F-111B was several tons heavier than the North American Vigilante and Douglas Skywarrior, neither of which were ever embarked on board ship in numbers greater than a handful at a time; in a related programme commencing in 1966 the Navy quietly started to modify its carrier elevators so that they could cope with 45-ton aircraft! At Grumman members of NAVPRO, there to oversee construction, shook their heads and winced at the sight of the enormous beast. Not surprisingly its large well-built airframe later lent the F-111B the unofficial nickname 'Seapig'.

The second F-111B, Bu No 151971, flew from Calverton on 24 October 1965, by which time No. 1 had already logged a total of 45 flights and 64.9 hours, including nine supersonic runs, one of them sustained for 37 minutes. The F-111B certainly held out high hopes. Eighteen months later five aircraft were engaged in full-time contractor and Navy Preliminary Evaluation (NPE) tests at Calverton, Culver City and Lakehurst and at the missile test centre at Point Mugu in California, forging ahead with preparing the textbook for the projected production run of 231 aircraft. There were some moans and groans, but such was to be expected in a complex development programme.

## Phoenix

The greatest achievement of all, and one which confronted remarkably few hiccups, was the F-111B's advanced fire control system and related cockpit displays. The RDT&E prototypes rolling out of Grumman's Plant 6 were, essentially, fully functional flying testbeds, with a bare minimum of cockpit instrumentation and devoid of mission equipment, which were ferried by flight-test crews to Hughes at Culver City in California

**Left: April 1966: F-111B No. 3, BuNo 151972, undergoes pre-flight checks with Grumman test pilot Ralph Donnell in the left seat and Hughes Aircraft Co. flight-tester C. A. McDaniel nearest the camera. Note the Douglas Escapac ejection seats, used by the first trio of F-111Bs and eleven F-111As. (Grumman Corporation)**

**Overleaf: F-111B BuNo 151970, the Navy's first example, made its maiden flight on 18 May 1965 at Peconic River, exactly one week after its roll-out from Grumman's Plant 6 at Calverton, New York. Test pilots were Ralph 'Dixie' Donnell (seen turning towards the camera) and Ernie Von Der Heyden. Note the 'barbershop pole' pitot and short-nose configuration. Early F-111B test aircraft were outfitted with P&W's revolutionary TF30-P-1 afterburning turbofan, replaced by the improved P-12 from No. 6 onwards. (Grumman Corporation)**

with mere ballast on board. The Hughes team, headed by Meade Livesay, would discard the deadweight and add the raw essentials, to convert the baseline machines to systems-capable aircraft. In this reworked configuration the F-111Bs carried a Litton INS and extensive data-link equipment, a left-seat vertical display indicator/head-up-display (VDI/HUD or V/HUD), a CP-741/A secondary armament computer and, central to the new 'Seapig', a Hughes AN/AWG-9 planar pulse-doppler radar antenna, an allied infra-red search and track sensor (IRSTS), computer processors, and related right-seat tactical information display (TID) and detail data display (DDD) tubes. These novel instruments replaced the conventional bank of old-fashioned needles and dials such as the ADI, the compass-like horizontal situation indicator and the crude, direct-view radarscope presentation with a set of video displays: the pilot's V/HUD and Mission Control Officer's (MCO's) DDD and TID provided everything in processed graphics, flashed up on the three tubes and circular combining glass in easy-to-follow synthetic form, enabling the crew to fly to the target and conduct a stand-off attack in 'blind', 'popeye', zero-visibility conditions. The package was far in advance of anything then in service and was designed with one goal in mind – to guide the F-111B's armoury of six 1,000lb, 100nm-range Hughes XAAM-N-11 Model 92 AIM-54 Phoenix air-to-air missiles on a terminal collision intercept against multiple enemy airborne targets.‡ An imaginary mission conducted from the cockpit of the F-111B and of the type performed during No. 5's (BuNo 151974's) sea trials on board the USS *Coral Sea* in the spring of 1968, with a little artistic elaboration to embrace the use of live missiles, provides an opportunity to delve into the systems a little further.§

Hauled off a deck elevator and tractor-towed to its holding position, a 'Seapig', already fuelled with JP-5 kerosene and toting a full load of Phoenix missiles (one on each pivot-pylon and a pair in the adapted weapons

---

*The Grumman project engineer was Paul Anbro and the flight test manager Sam Fletcher. As major subcontractors to GDFW, Grumman produced the aft fuselage, horizontal stabilizers and landing gear for all F-111s built. Grumman later perfected the welded titanium VG wingbox now fielded in the Grumman VXF/F-14 Tomcat and European MRCA/Tornado. The Hughes development team was led by Meade Livesay with Jim Ferrero as assistant programme manager – the latter was a key figure who helped to obtain the TFX-N contract to begin with, alongside Allen Lange, both of whom toured Navy offices to stir up interest prior to Robert McNamara's pronouncement of November 1962. Walt Maguire later took over as TFX-N programme manager at Hughes.
†The Navy had recently commenced fleet operations with the Grumman A-6A Intruder all-weather bomber, E-2A Hawkeye airborne early warning aircraft and the latter's cargo-hauling derivative the C-2A Greyhound. Whole Carrier Wings of exclusively Grumman products were envisaged, a feat which has been realized in the case of some of today's embarked Wings flying Hawkeyes, Intruders and Tomcats.
‡USAF RDT&E F-111A No. 4 (63-9769) performed initial aerodynamic captive-carry trials with dummy Phoenix missiles. The first live launch was made on 27 April 1966 from an A-3 Skywarrior trials aircraft flying from Point Mugu; the first intercept of a drone target was achieved by the same aircraft on 12 May that year.
§The carrier trials performed from May 1968 included nine catapult launches and ten arrested landings.

**Above: BuNo 151972's cockpit, refitted at Culver City, California, shows off all the novel technology pioneered by the F-111B RDT&E aircraft: the MCO's DDD and TID cathode ray tubes at right, used to display target velocity, bearing and missile assignment, and the pilot's V/HUD at left. Behind the stick, just in front of the Escapac bucket seat, is the stores select and manual 'ballistics' panels. (Hughes)**

bay) is prepared for a combat air patrol (CAP) mission. Green-coloured 'shirts' remove the plastic covers which protect the capsule and IRSTS from the corrosive influences of the sea between missions, and red 'jackets' pull the weapons pins from the AIM-54s. The Plane Captain is at hand as the pilot and MCO strap into the cockpit, awaiting the low-profile air starter trolley which will put the engines in motion at the casual flick of a switch. Once turning, the engines will provide electrical power to light up the cathode ray tube displays, permitting the crew to perform pre-flight built-in test (BIT) checks of their electronics and displays. The F-111B features only one set of stick and pedals, freeing the right-seater to concentrate on his job as

navigator and missile controller; the pilot is concerned purely with flying the aircraft properly.

As the INS is aligned using the SIS (Ship's Inertial System) the canopies are clanked shut and the Plane Captain and his entourage provide hand signals for turbofan spool-up and taxi to the catapult position. In common with other Grumman products of the era there is no need for a criss-cross of thick steel bridles to be hooked to the airframe; instead a simple drop-down nosewheel tow bar lowers itself to engage the catapult shuttle. With the launch weight confirmed and the water-cooled blast-deflector shield raised behind the two screaming TF30s, now in fifth-stage afterburner, the F-111B crew brace themselves against the headrests in anticipation of possible whiplash, and provide the 'ready' salute; the Flight Deck Officer touches the deck and within three seconds the jet is vaulted off the nose of the carrier, into wind, in a haze of 200 gallons of superheated steam and burnt kerosene vapour. Pulling a few degrees away from the bow at 250ft and 170kts, lest both engines malfunction, forcing the crew to ditch in the path of the gargantuan ship, the MCO recomposes himself and checks the INS: the violent 'cat' can sometimes 'tumble' the INS and cause it to dump its memory, necessitating in-flight realignment. Co-ordinates will then be set for the CAP point.

On climb-out, still with 'Takeoff' mode selected on the left console for the V/HUD, the pilot switches to INS to get his steering cues. True airspeed and radar altitude are furnished by little spinning digital counters in two 'windows' located immediately above the VDI tube, yet everything else is presented in graphics on the V/HUD: the dividing line between the background pale and dark shades of green denotes the horizon, with vertical and horizontal reference lines, spaced at set increments, to provide more exact bank and climb/dive indications; the heading indicator is displayed as an inverted 'T' on both the TV tube and combining glass, which moves left and right to guide the pilot to the CAP destination. Throttles are toyed with to bring the left-hand V/HUD markers back to the datum line – above the marker, more power is called for, and vice versa – while the right-hand markers furnish similar 'up' and 'down' cues to take the crew to the CAP 'command altitude', again preset. There is no need to watch the back-up conventional instruments or to look out of the windshield, and if the INS is coupled to the autopilot the crew can even sit back and let the controls take them to their destination automatically.

Arriving on station the two crewmen monitor their displays and take peeks out of the cockpit, with radar and IRSTS switched on and trawling the sky with active and passive nets in a set scan pattern, attempting to catch enemy air activity. The V/HUD is now working in the 'Normal' mode as a pure raster-scan ADI-display while the MCO's DDD is blank and his TID radarscope tube is showing a large clutter-free 'V' sector-scan shape, at present devoid of targets; its 'pie slice' covers only a portion of airspace so the pilot is continually manoeuvring in a figure-of-eight holding pattern around the CAP hub co-ordinates, to give pseudo 360° radar coverage at ranges of up to 200 miles.

In automatic Track-While-Scan acquisition mode the AN/AWG-9 will lock on up to 24 targets should they come within its view; range and gain (receive power) are tinkered with by the MCO to assist this process. More likely than not the 'eyes and ears' of the Fleet – an E-2A Hawkeye airborne early warning (AEW) scout, whose massive 24ft GE AN/APS-96 'Screwtop' radar antenna can acquire potential 'hostiles' on the basis of much weaker returns – will pick up the 'bogeys' first, so the F-111B crew keep all data-link channels open for a possible vector on to inbound targets. The Grumman AEW is a vital extension of the F-111B – what Grumman describe as their 'clean air act' team. On receipt of one or more imminent, perhaps unidentified threats, target information is relayed directly to the F-111B's AN/AWG-9 computer and back to ship, where the final decisions are made. Floating on the sea in his steel monster 20,000ft below, the captain, using the electronic and verbal reports coming in, decides whether or not he should ignore the UFO, perhaps an

Below: F-111B V/HUD symbology. A. The 'Normal' mode is shown at left, with peripheral indicators on the VDI faceplate around the tube. The detail data display (DDD) is shown upper right; the lower scale related to heading and the vertical one to relative target velocity. The tactical information display (TID) at lower right provides a radar and computer-generated graphic 'god's eye view' of events, showing target heading, range and classification and, later in the attack sequence, missile assignment and launch parameters. B. Typical VDI sequence during a Phoenix missile attack. C. 'Simultaneous' mode, with horizon line and steering symbol superimposed; airspeed and altitude error can also be displayed, as here. In this example the steering symbol directs the pilot to turn to port and intercept the targets. (Grumman Corporation)

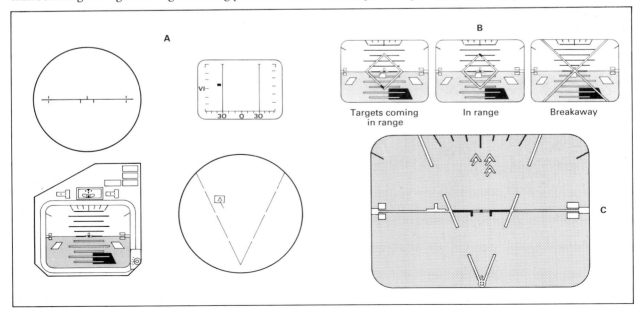

Targets coming in range    In range    Breakaway

airliner, or order the 'Seapig' to close in and make a visual identification; a third option at his disposal is to instruct the fighter to terminate the existence of the 'bogeys' with missiles. The decision is conveyed by the secure airborne (E-2A) or naval (ship) tactical data-link system, ATDS or NTDS; with the target update buttons depressed on the F-111B's dashboard the crew are provided with a correct heading for the target on the V/HUD, permitting the pilot to manoeuvre the jet to place the enemy within the AN/AWG-9's forward-looking scan. The MCO has a right console-mounted slew handle to move the TID's 'pie slice' 'V' about, to compensate for the pilot's yanking and banking, and, once within range, the target symbols should appear on the 10in TID, their relative range and bearing denoted by their position in the large 'V'. Additional information is presented on the small 5in DDD above, which will provide a 'blip' to display relative target velocity.

Below: Described by Hughes Missiles as 'an aerial haymaker', the Phoenix missile system was flight-tested on F-111Bs by Hughes and the US Navy at Point Mugu Pacific Missile Range, California, starting in 1968. Seen here on F-111B BuNo 151972 is a prototype XAIM-54A Phoenix test round: up to six missiles could be carried, one on each pivot-pylon and two in the internal weapons bay. The missiles were kicked free of the aircraft's slipstream before their rocket motors ignited. (Hughes)

Below right: Looking forward towards the nosegear, this photograph shows an F-111B weapons bay under assembly. Two AIM-54s could sit side by side, though the bay was often used for air-crew baggage, secured with wire. (Grumman Corporation)

The AN/AWG-9 features sophisticated identification friend or foe (IFF) interrogators but it is customary for target classification to be furnished by data link: an inverted 'U' symbol in the TID scan will denote that the target remains unidentified; a little inverted 'V', also with a 'tadpole' tail to indicate its heading, will confirm it as hostile. On receipt of one or more inverted 'V' the MCO selects and arms the Phoenix missiles, leaving the AN/AWG-9 computer to 'prioritize' the threats automatically and assign a specific weapon to each target – in effect, the potentially most dangerous half-dozen. Should the enemy start disruptive jamming activity, overwhelming the radar's extensive built-in electronic counter-countermeasures (ECCM) burn-through capability, IRSTS may be used to acquire the targets and slave radar to those points by picking up the targets' heat signatures; in the event of a computer malfunction, thumbwheel cursor controls at the MCO's fingertips near the DDD and TID permit him to lock the sensors on in a manual fashion and assign a missile to each target one at a time.

Maintaining a mean heading towards the targets with the AN/AWG-9 firmly locked on, the crew await the moment when the quarry comes within missile launch parameters while the computers continue to feed target information into the missiles to prepare them for independent flight. At this juncture the pilot may choose to select 'Simultaneous' mode on the V/HUD, which displays a simplified version of the MCO's TID sector-scan combined with a horizon reference line and airspeed, altitude and steering indicators. 'Normal' or 'Simultaneous' modes can be used to provide cues to hold the aircraft within the desired pre-launch para-

meters; 'Simultaneous' has the advantage that it gives the pilot a 'god's-eye-view' of events but at the expense of a less comprehensive flight director display. As the Phoenix missiles warm up for launch a diamond 'time' symbol will appear on the VID along with a similar but octagonal design on the HUD, featuring a marker (VID) or gap (HUD) that moves counter-clockwise around the symbol; at 12 o'clock, time = zero ! A bright red 'in range' lamp will flash and, in true Navy tradition, a dashboard mounted 'launch' button of submarine fire control proportions illuminates and is pressed to unleash the Phoenix missiles. Taking their initial target headings and heights from the AN/AWG-9, the weapons are ready to tackle anything from 50ft to 100,000ft, dropping, igniting and zooming to target all by themselves: each missile's active antenna and DSQ-26 processor will lock on to the assigned target in an autonomous, launch-and-leave manner. The F-111B is now free to 'knock it off': a large 'Breakaway X' flashes up on the TV displays, signalling the crew to make an about-turn, while the missiles dart at Mach 3.8 until their proximity sensors, fused to pick up the opposition at close quarters, detonate the impressive 132lb fragmentation warheads, capable of felling either cruise missiles or bombers.

Mission completed, and with the fuel indicator reaching the critical 'bingo' point, the MCO sets a heading for the carrier into the INS to provide steering back to ship – either 'hands off' with the autopilot engaged or manually, with left and right instructions on the V/HUD, with the pilot in complete authority of the throttles and stick.*

Back in the carrier landing circuit, heading down-wind, the pilot flips the tailhook deploy toggle, sweeps the wings forward, lowers his flaps and slats and dumps any excess fuel in order to bring the aircraft within its 'max trap' limit, careful not to dump too much in case he is required to bolter and make another circuit. Banking and lining up on the stern of the colossal (though seemingly tiny) ship at a range of some two miles, with landing gear locked down, he places the V/HUD in the 'Landing' mode. With the automatic carrier landing (ACL) system in operation the HUD combining glass provides all the required glidescope information – airspeed, angle of attack and radar altitude – in the pilot's line of sight to deck as he brings airspeed down to 125kts. The ACL can be coupled to the autopilot and approach power compensator for a 'hands-off' 'trap' on deck, or the pilot may elect to take charge of his heavy machine and follow the pointers on the HUD. The comparatively slow cyclic response rate of the turbofans demands forward thinking and intense concentration. The MCO is passive but anxious as the machine crosses the wake of the carrier in line for a 'lucky third wire' hook-up on deck. If the pilot is off the glidescope, too fast or at too low a sink rate the 'Breakaway X' will appear and flash abruptly at two cycles per second to command a 'wave off', full throttle climb and another attempt at approach. All going well, and with the ship's mirror-light 'meatball' and Landing Signals Officer providing added cues from around a half mile astern,

*The F-111B had no TFR capability but did possess a terrain clearance display mode on the V/HUD. For extended range it incorporated a probe-and-drogue refuelling provision via a rectractable arm to back up its capacious internal fuel. Drop tanks were not tested.

Left: The TF30-P-1, standard propulsion for the RDT&E
and pre-production 'Alphas', and 'Bravos' Nos. 1–5
inclusive. (Pratt & Whitney)

the 'Bravo' comes in and flumps down on the steel deck
to catch one of the four pendants (wires), to be
anchored to a halt in 150ft. Engines are spooled down
to idle and the hook and wire will untangle. On signal
the F-111B and its crew are then free to throttle up and
be guided slowly to a parking spot on deck, pilot and
MCO both eager to discard their heavyweight sea-
survival flight gear while the Plane Captain and his aides
oversee the refuelling and rearming of the 25-ton jet
ready for another CAP launch.

The off-the-deck, all-weather multiple-missile kill
capability of the F-111B was never demonstrated to its
full, but it serves to provide an interesting perspective
on a mark which has always, and somewhat unjustly,
been considered a complete lemon. Its air-to-ground
capability was not ignored either, and a modest package
was put together to enable the 'Bravo' to drop iron
bombs, trigger rockets and even launch conventionally
armed or nuclear-tipped AGM-12 Bullpup missiles with
some degree of accuracy. The CP-741/A secondary
computer calculated range which was in turn presented
by the moving gap in the octagonal HUD display. With
'ballistics' cranked into the weapons panel located
behind the pilot's stick and the 'master arm' activated,
the pilot had then only to set the correct HUD 'lead
elevation angle' prior to his bomb or rocket pass. This
last setting was accomplished by twisting the 'MILS'
knob on the left console, to input a thousandths-of-an-
inch numerical value corresponding to the chosen dive
angle to be used, which depressed the aiming reticle –
a dashed cross symbol in the pilot's line of sight – so
that he had the aircraft properly pitched up at the
moment of weapons release, conducted at a predetermined slant range to (height above) target, to compensate for ordnance ballistics. For missile attack, the range
pointer (gap) in the HUD 'moved in discreet steps to
indicate successive stages in the delivery sequence'. As
a secondary function the air-to-ground capability was
not taken too seriously at Fleet level but it did make the
F-111B a contender for possible USMC use. In July
1966, to a chorus of 'you should be so lucky', the
Commandant of the Marines wryly stated that they 'do
not expect to adopt the F-111B'. The 'Seapig' had no
identifiable niche in that service's requirements, even if
funding made allowances for extra 'Bravos'. It was not
bad news for commonality; the Navy's exit from the
whole TFX programme not long afterwards, however,
was a major blow.

## The New York diet
From an air-to-air 'systems' point of view the F-111B
was unparalleled in capability; from the Navy flyers'
vantage point however the aircraft was seriously flawed.
For a start, the AN/AWG-9 did not 'keep the faith', as
the expression of the day went: there was no gun, and
no provision for short-range AIM-9 Sidewinder heat-
seeking missiles. The mission of the 'Seapig' was strictly

stand-off air-to-air and there would be no epic tales of
hard-fought dogfights to recite on return to ship.*
Worse, the machine was grossly underpowered for the
fighter role. Other niggles were confronted. In March
1967, a year before carrier qualification trials began, a
new ejectable crew module was authorized. The revised
design would compensate for the F-111B's more pro-
nounced nose-up attitude on approach, to improve the
pilot's visibility for safe deck landings, but it reduced
commonality in a key area of technology. Other major
changes were deemed necessary. The wings required a
different flap and slat arrangement for improved handling in the carrier circuit, while the narrow 10ft track of
the main gears presented further headaches and plans
were formulated to shift them aft to counterbalance the
F-111B's tail-heavy characteristics. The advanced displays were not all joy either: rumour has it that during
the last leg of a ferry flight from California to NAS
Lakehurst, New Jersey, test crew John Norris and Ted
Tate experienced a massive failure of all electronics and
following a rather impromptu recovery on a very soggy
standby field John Norris was so huffed that he wore his
still soaked and stained flight suit *and* crash helmet on
the commercial airline flight back to Texas!

More grave problems were highlighted during the
second batch of NPE trials in 1967, in particular during
Grumman's Glidescope Controllability Program at
Calverton – when seven test pilots (five Navy, one
Grumman and one from GDFW) made 216 passes and
touch-and-goes on a piece of runway laid out to
simulate a carrier deck complete with a mirror-landing
'meatball' – and during carrier trials on board the *Coral
Sea* the following year. Deck hands described the
aircraft as 'terrifying': it had a tendency to wallow and
dip its wings after touch-down on a pitching deck and
would cause mischief in all but the most skilled hands.
Of all those issues however none was more serious than
weight. The cry for commonality had produced an
excessively heavy aircraft and everyone was sure that
sooner or later the 'Seapig' would 'trap' so hard that it
would plummet down straight into the maintenance
and galley quarters below! In a major redesign effort
Grumman incorporated its Super Weight Improvement
Program (SWIP) measures from No. 4 (BuNo 151973)
and then undertook a series of Colossal Weight Improvement Programs (CWIPs I-III) to reduce the aircraft's gross weight to more manageable proportions. A
long, complex, almost painful string of structural diets
followed, none of which produced a satisfactory result.
What was essentially an engineering dilemma rooted in
ill-advised 'commonality' – in the words of a Grumman
spokesman, 'an involved issue' – soon became a

---

*The F-111A by contrast could accommodate up to six GAR-8/AIM-
9B Sidewinders on the pivot-pylons (one on each inner pylon, on
stations 4 and 5, and two on each outer, shoulder-mounted on stations
3A, 3B, 6A and 6B), plus a further two on the special 'Trapeze' which
could be fitted to the weapons bay as a pre-flight option. All F-111As
had the capability to carry the 'Trapeze' but it was prohibited from use
by the time the F-111A achieved combat-ready service in 1968.
'Trapeze' tests were performed at Edwards AFFTC by RDT&E F-111A
No. 7 (63-9772).

| No. | BuNo | Notes |
|---|---|---|
| 1 | 151970 | Scrapped Dec. 1969 after flight-test programme completed. |
| 2 | 151971 | Crashed into Pacific Ocean off Californian coast 11 Sept. 1968. |
| 3 | 151972 | Scrapped Dec. 1971 after completion of AWG-9 programme. |
| 4 | 151973 | First SWIP model, first with crew module. Crashed at Calverton, New York, 21 Apr. 1967. |
| 5 | 151974 | Crash-landed at Point Magu, California, 11 Oct. 1968; scrapped. |
| 6 | 152714 | First with TF30-P-12 engines. Now inactive at SMALC, McClellan AFB, California; stricken from inventory May 1971. |
| 7 | 152715 | Now inactive at China Lake, California; stricken from inventory May 1971. |
| 8 | 152716 | Partly-built; never accepted. |
| 9 | 152717 | Partly-built; never accepted. |

**F-111B MANUFACTURE**

political football. Several thick volumes on the subject appeared during the Fiscal Year (FY) 1968 and 1969 House and Senate Armed Services Hearings, highlighting the inadequacies of the design for naval operations. To summarize, by July 1967 the take-off weight had risen to 79,000lb and the planned CWIP III would hack a mere 4,000lb of flab off the beast. Moreover commonality fell from the 83.7 per cent specified in the original GDFW/Grumman proposals to a nominal 29 per cent! An untimely crash further complicated the manufacturers' work: No. 4 was lost on 21 April 1967 when both engines flamed out on what was otherwise a normal take-off from Calverton, killing both crewmen. Quite apart from the tragic loss of life, the crash resulted in a six-month programme slippage. The US Senate eliminated funding for the F-111B a year later, the US House similarly vetoed funds in July and on the 9th of that month the contractors were given formal notification of cancellation. A stop-work order came into effect the next morning.

All was not lost. Flight-tests continued for another two and a half years so that the highly-prized AN/AWG-9 and Phoenix missile system could be fine-tuned in good time for the follow-on VFX, dedicated Navy Fighter Experimental programme. To fulfil the development work F-111Bs No. 6 (BuNo 152714) and 7 (152715) were given a reprieve and completed. Accepted on 17 June 1968 and 28 February 1969 respectively, they joined two other F-111Bs already with Hughes and the Navy's nearby Point Mugu missile test facility. As well as minor improvements to the avionics No. 6 introduced the TF30-P-12 engine, rated at 20,250lb thrust in afterburner and offering the extra power so badly needed by the type; No. 7 incorporated the revised 'superplow' intakes, an interim version of the Triple Plow II with double blow-in doors.

Phoenix survived the blow and was perfected, but not before another two harrowing crashes claimed more lives: on 11 September 1968 'Bravo' No. 2 (151971) plunged into the Pacific 20 miles north-west of San Miguel island off the California coast during missile tests, taking Hughes Aircraft test pilot Barton Warren and radar operator Anthony A. Byland down with it; a heavy landing the following month claimed 'Bravo' No. 5 (151974), damaging it beyond economic repair and injuring radar operator Bill Bush. Its pilot, George Marrett, at least walked away unhurt, though dazed. Despite these sad losses, in March 1969 a Hughes F-111B, with its colourful Phoenix emblem dominating its fin, successfully engaged two BQM-34 drones to open up a series of highly successful intercepts. This aspect of the TFX-N project remained sound and, true to the legend of the Phoenix, the AIM-54 and AN/AWG-9, with the very familiar V/HUD, DDD and TID cockpit displays rearranged in tandem positions, found a new home in VFX – Grumman's follow-on feline VG, TF30-powered F-14 Tomcat.* Today, only relics of the once-proud F-111B remain intact. Never suited to naval operations, the 'Seapig' did a fine job in perfecting what must be considered as the most outstanding intercept avionics suite of the day.

*The normal take-off weight of the F-14 Tomcat is about 58,000lb. The AN/AWG-9 remained in production for the Tomcat from February 1970 until August 1988 when it was replaced by Hughes' follow-on AN/APG-71 system. Repackaged in the F-14 the AN/AWG-9 offers both short- and long-range intercept modes with various dogfight and stand-off acquisition capabilities and a lead V/HUD for a built-in 20mm Gatling gun; it also has an AIM-9 Sidewinder and AIM-7 Sparrow missile capability. The 'core' avionics of the F-111B and F-14A were virtually identical at the cross-over point from TFX-N to VFX in 1968–71.

# Warsaw Pact Central Heating

As the F-111B faded into history another variant of the 'Aardvark', at the other end of the performance spectrum, was about to write a new chapter – the FB-111A. In his tireless pursuit of commonality, on 10 December 1965 Robert McNamara made the official announcement that Strategic Air Command also would receive the 'all-singing, all-dancing' Texan VG bomber, which would oust the aged B-52s and still shiny, comparatively new B-58s from the inventory.* RDT&E F-111A No. 18 (63-9763) would be modified on the production line to validate the concept, and SAC could expect to receive 210 production examples – 263 including 'pipeline' attrition replacements and training aircraft. In strict cigar-chewing, Curtis E. LeMay tradition SAC viewed any flying machine which grossed in at less than 50 tons with considerable disdain. On the quest for bigger and heavier bombers LeMay himself had commented of the General Dynamics B-58A, 'It didn't fit my a**!' Gen. John D. Ryan, CinC SAC in 1965, was keen to welcome new technology into the Command but insisted on a bigger, longer-range version of the 'One-Eleven', with emphasis on the new 'B' in the type's prefix. To General Dynamics it was clear that 'commonality' was being stretched to its limit: whereas the Navy were seeking a lighter machine the USAF were now insisting on an even heavier one!

RDT&E 'Alpha' No. 18 took to the skies for an initial 45-minute work-out on 31 July 1967 with GDFW's test pilot V. Prahl at the controls. To everyone's amazement it slid through Mach 2 with ease despite the test-bed's troubled inlets and TF30-P-1 engines. A year later, on 13 July, the first production FB-111A, 67-159, became airborne with more powerful TF30-P-7 (now P-107) engines, rated at an impressive 20,350lb each, to clinch the deal.† The production FB-111A featured provisions to carry six drop tanks safely. The typical maximum capacity would call for four tanks, providing a total of 7,438 US gallons of fuel – enough for about 4,150nm of flight with two nuclear weapons snuggled together in the weapons bay (later reduced to 6,238 gallons and four nuclear weapons, with a commensurate reduction in range). The FB-111A certainly appeared to meet the 'intercontinental' requirement if supported by tankers, albeit possibly on a one-way mission with recovery in Iceland or Turkey.

To accommodate the extra equipment, fuel tankage and heavy nuclear weapons – which pushed the all-up weight (AUW) over SAC's psychological 50-ton barrier – GDFW introduced a much-modified, strengthened landing gear to cope with the extra strains and stresses. In theory the FB-111A is designed to cope with an overload on take-off of 119,243lb, give or take a few pounds, and a maximum of 57 tons for normal operations; a gross landing weight of 109,000lb, or 54½ tons, at a sink rate of up to 8ft/sec was also met. These features, combined with expanded weapons requirements and a brand new avionics fit, dealt with presently, required a rigorous development effort. RDT&E F-111A No. 18 was joined by pre-production FB-111As Nos. 1 and 2, together with four production aircraft for Category II trials, while in the mile-long Fort Worth plant GDFW fabricated three part-built static test-beds, none of which bore tail numbers or were intended to fly, purely to verify the soundness of the beefed-up structure: Article B4 served as the airframe fatigue test-bed and B6 as a landing gear fatigue example, while B5 was subjected to destructive landing gear drop tests.‡ The FB-111A performed ably, as predicted.

On 29 September 1969 Col. Winston E. Moore, commander of the newly formed 340th Bomb Group at Carswell AFB, Texas, picked up the first production aircraft to enter operational service, 67-7193.§ During the official acceptance ceremony on 8 October SAC CinC Gen. Bruce K. Holloway was there to review the new hardware and talk to his people. In his speech he proudly announced that the FB-111A 'will play a substantial role in contributing to the SAC mission of deterrence through the 1975 time period'. He was, of course, already thinking of what would emerge as the Advanced Manned Strategic Aircraft (AMSA) or Rockwell B-1A, a super-sized VG bomber which would gross in at 200 tons and be able to fly 6,000nm with a battery of nuclear weapons, the funding for which had already commenced. Seeing the FB-111A as an 'interim bomber' pending the AMSA, new Secretary of Defense Laird

---

*Two days earlier, on 8 December, McNamara had announced plans to retire all GD B/TB-58As and Boeing B-52C/D/E/Fs by June 1971. All but the B-52Ds, given a reprieve by the war in SEA and later refurbished under Project 'Pacer Plank', were duly retired by that date.
†No. 1, 67-159, featured Triple Plow I translating cowl inlets with the distinctive splitter plates. No. 2, 67-160, was the first USAF machine to feature the blow-in door inlets and represented the pre-production example. Only aircraft No. 3 and subsequent machines were deployed to operational units. No. 1 is still active at SMALC.
‡Additional static examples included A3 for F-111A fatigue tests, A4 for F-111A/B fatigue trials and A9 which performed wing-loading tests. Of the production FB-111As engaged in Category testing at Edwards, Nos. 3 and 6 performed avionics and systems development work, No. 4 acted as a stability, control and performance test-bed and No. 5 was used as a weapons separation and launch platform. Unit costs for the FB-111A averaged $33.7 million in late 1960s dollars – the most expensive version procured.
§The 340th BG was organized at Carswell AFB on 2 July 1968 with the specific job of training combat-ready FB-111A air and ground crews.

slashed FB-111A orders to 112 and then, on 19 March 1969, to a mere 76. It was made official on 11 April 1969 and GDFW diverted three dozen partly built airframes to the production of another variant – another example of a continuing knock-on irritation the Corporation had to face throughout the TFX production drama. In fact the B-1A was cancelled in 1977, with the result that the FB-111A held the fort as SAC's only viable, fully operational penetrating bomber for some eighteen years!

Training at Carswell got into rapid motion in the summer of 1970 when the fleet-wide grounding order was lifted. The 340th BG weaned a generation of already experienced pilots, navigators and defensive systems operators – some of them with as much as a staggering 5,000 hours in the Command – off the 'hot' B-58 Hustler and heavy B-52 Stratofortress and introduced them to the new 'Bullet Bomber', this time in comparatively tiny crews of two, under an intensive seven-month conversion course. The 340th BG was to enjoy a challenging but ephemeral existence which faded out on 9 September 1971 after the unit had notched up 3,179 sorties and 13,312 flying hours preparing crews for the combat-ready Wings.

The FB-111A's modest range dictated semi-forward basing and New England was chosen as the ideal site. First to re-form, receiving its initial aircraft on 17 December 1970, was the 509th 'Enola Gay' Bombardment Wing (Medium) at Pease AFB, New Hampshire, forty miles north of Boston. Since November 1966 the Wing had been on temporary duty (TDY) rotation in SEA, flying 'Arc Light' B-52D raids as 'Big Belly' close air support ships; flying the petite FB-111A in the nuclear standby role was a completely different affair. New facilities were constructed at Pease and the two-mile 300ft-wide runway was refurbished as the 509th undertook the arduous task of performing Category III user trials while working up to alert status, which it achieved with two aircraft in October 1971. By the time full operational capability had been achieved in 1973 two Bombardment (Medium) Squadrons had formed – the 393rd BMS 'Tigers' and the 715th BMS 'Eagles'. The next unit to re-equip, in overlap fashion, was the 380th BW(M), then a Strategic Aerospace Wing, at Plattsburgh AFB in upstate New York, one of whose three squadrons of 'swing-wingers', the 4007th CCTS, took over the RTU function from Carswell three months after the final FB-111A delivery had taken place on 30 June 1971. Of the final production tally, one had been written off before delivery and SAC went into business with an Authorized Unit Establishment of 66 aircraft.*

## Digital Aardvarks

Today Plattsburgh flies a force of 36 of SAC's 61 surviving active 'Bullet Bombers' and performs three functions: it maintains an element of eight aircraft from its two operational squadrons on rotational standby as a key element in America's 'triad' strategic arsenal; it provides ground-crew training under the auspices of the tenant Field Training Detachment 210(S); and it provides air-crew conversion under the aegis of the recently redesignated 530th CCTS.†

Plattsburgh's CCTS insists on the best. Pilot candidates are accepted from a long list of applicants and assignees with a previous tour on B-52 bombers, KC-135 or KC-10 tankers or the tactical F-111; as for the navigators, a previous tour is not a prerequisite but those straight out of Undergraduate Navigator Training at Mather AFB in California must have excelled academically, ranking among the top 10 per cent of the students. This quality is deemed essential as SAC still draws on the bulk of its Mach 3+ SR-71 'Habu' crews from 'One-Eleven' circles, so whether or not they stay in the 'FB Program' or move on to even more sophisticated aircraft – and the minimum tenure is usually three years – their standards are maintained. In the early days, getting an assignment on the FB-111A meant 1,500 hours of flying in other 'appropriate' types, although as the resurrected B-1B VG superbomber steals the limelight from the FB-111A in the late 1980s so the requirements have been relaxed a little. The details of the conversion course itself remain classified, but on completion the new flyers will be checked as 'mission ready' by the commander and then assigned to an alert unit in New York or New Hampshire, 'pulling' week-long alert duties on a TDY basis and undergoing constant review by the Standardization and Evaluation (Stan/Eval) crews who perform a type of 'air-crew quality control' function at every USAF base. From 'Ready' they may progress on to 'Senior' and ultimately 'Select' status as they log further hours, eventually perhaps managing the induction process themselves. Status determines how many hours a flyer will receive: the 'Ready' juniors can expect a minimum of some thirteen sorties each quarter, 'Select' crews with staff functions a maximum of a dozen. Much time is taken

---

*Official deliveries comprised the two prototype and pre-production machines in August and October 1968, a further seven between June and December 1969 and a final 67 between August 1970 and June 1971. The four Category trials aircraft rejoined the force after tests were completed.
†An average of eight aircraft, from both BW(M)s are in for depot-level overhauls at SMALC at any one time.

Above: In a delightful decor of gloss white and red, FB-111A No. 1, 67-159, serves with the SMALC Engineering Flight Test force at McClellan AFB, California. The aircraft features Triple Plow I inlets with the distinctive splitter plates. The black dot near the radome is the AN/ASQ-119 astrocompass. (General Dynamics)

up in the three-axis-motion Singer-Link simulators, modified in 1977 with 'out of the window' vision, in which emergencies and procedure functions are practised.* The standard requirement is a minimum of eighteen 'sim rides' each year but there is no substitute for the real thing.

Just like its tactical sisters, the FB-111A can 'Auto TFR' down to 200ft AGL, relying on its Honeywell AN/APN-167 LARA and Texas Instruments AN/APQ-134 TFRs to skim over the tops of hills, ridges and mountains, and most pilots who have transitioned from all but the 'Delta' mark of the TAC-AIR 'One-Eleven' variants feel very much at home in the cockpit. The instruments and flight controls are all to be found within familiar reach, and even the TFR video, ADI and GE AN/ASG-25 ODS sight are visually identical,

providing the same reassuring 'E-scan', altimeter needle and 'command lines'. Subtle differences include the TF30-P-107 engines, which are noticeably more powerful than the P-3s that were a regular feature of other marks at the FB-111A's début, and the 70ft-span extended wings, which provide a superior turning performance. These are all welcomed changes. Should the pilot imagine that he is flying an analogue F-111 however he need only take a quick glance at the right-hand side of the cockpit to jar him back into the world of the FB-111A and its completely different digital technology: the most prominent feature introduced by the 'Bullet Bomber' is its extensively revised dashboard navigation display unit (NDU) filled with bright digital numerics; the old spinning counters were discarded in favour of a series of LED-type displays, very similar to those one might find on a domestic digital radio-alarm clock or video recorder. This new technology represents just the facade of a completely new set of avionics.

From the outset of F-111 production GDFW saw the

*See 'Cosmic Aardvarks' (Part 3) for a full description of simulator procedures and capabilities.

General Electric Mk. I avionics package as merely a temporary fit pending the successful development of the highly sophisticated Rockwell Mk. II suite (described later in the book) which was intended to be introduced on F-111 No. 100 in late 1968. Mk. II development 'glitches' became so severe that the analogue avionics were eventually installed in no fewer than 277 'Aardvarks', while the Mk. II system did not become available in quantity until 1972. As a compromise, and to meet its near-term requirements, the USAF stepped in and helped to develop a simpler suite of black boxes and

sensors made up of the best features of the Mk. I combined with a selection of the less troubled innovations of the Mk. II, thus creating the Mk. IIB. SAC now had the first digital aircraft on its inventory. The Command was pleased with the FB-111A's new avionics system and went on to add several refinements of its own to cater for long-range operations, adding an extra sensor and enlarging the brain capacity of the beast to fourteen computers!

At the core of this superbly integrated package are two IBM/GD AN/AYK-6 general-purpose computers, either of which is capable of handling all the processing required for navigation and weapons delivery and also of converting analogue data to digital data to make use

**Below: The FB-111A's Mk. IIB cockpit layout, with added 'extras' such as a SATCOM link. (General Dynamics)**

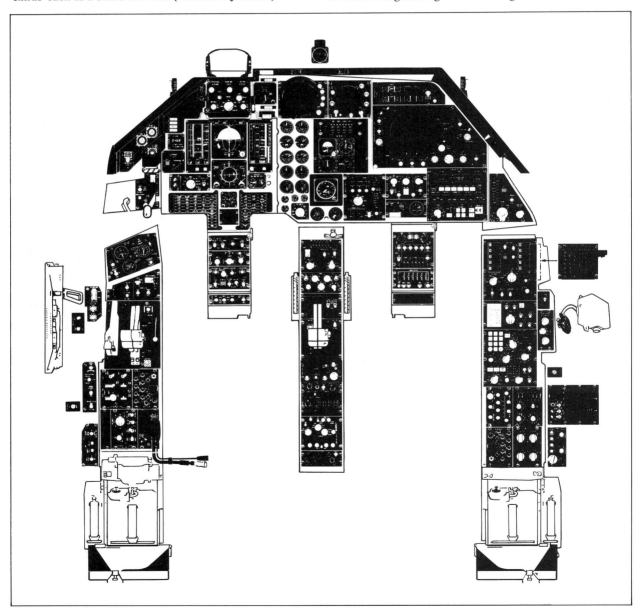

of what the crews consider to be back-up 'dead-reckoning' systems. Keeping the central computers informed are the central air data computer, for true airspeed; a Rockwell AN/AJN-16 inertial platform, capable of furnishing geographic co-ordinates accurate to within 60ft; a Singer-Kearfott feedhorn AN/APN-185 doppler radar, which measures ground speed and drift; a GE AN/APQ-114 attack radar, which offers the traditional 'Ground Manual', 'Ground Auto' and 'Ground Vel' PPI mapping modes with movable cross-hairs as before; and an innovative Litton AN/ASQ-119 Astrocompass which plots the heavens as a passive navaid. A peek at the cockpit with the 'Bullet Bomber' in action best explains the 'switches', and the very different preparation dictated by both the digital technology and the strategic mission.

### Bullet Bomber

Maintaining alert under its steel and concrete Nissen-shaped shelter, an FB-111A lurks with 600 US gallon drop tanks on its outboard pivot-pylons, a pair of glossy white Boeing AGM-69A Short-Range Attack Missiles (SRAMs) on its inboard pylons and two sleek silver B61 gravity bombs in its weapons bay. Unlike a Mk. I-equipped analogue 'Aardvark', which has no clues as to its ultimate destination until the 'Wizzo' 'cranks' in the final target co-ordinates, this jet's Mk. IIB AN/AYK-6 computers 'know' all about these details in advance, even while the bomber sits dormant, but on vigil, at its

**Above: FB-111A No. 15, 68–243, from the 380th BW(M), ambles along the taxiway at speed at Plattsburgh AFB, New York, with dribble-free 600 US gallon drop tanks and an undisclosed weapons bay payload installed. (USAF)**

home-drome. The Operations Division, aided by intelligence personnel and prediction artists and drawing on Chief of Staff Emergency War Order plans, have already laid out a route to the hand-me-down primary (and possibly secondary) targets and have 'cut' a suitable mission type which includes *all* the required waypoints or 'destinations' and offset aiming points – up to 999 co-ordinates in all! With the mission tape prepared, avionics specialists will have already trundled out to the bomber with a 'suitcase' and plugged a lead into the FB-111A to feed the flight plan into the jet's two central computers. This tape may also have fed in extra information pertaining to the types of nuclear weapons carried, information perhaps not already at hand in the computers' 'protected memory', such as 'ballistics'. Digested, the Mk. IIB system 'holds' all the information it needs to fly the mission in a totally 'hands-off' manner, from take-off in the north-eastern United States all the way to the target – and back to recovery. In company with fifteen other FB-111As dotted at SAC's two Medium Bombardment bases and with a host of B-1Bs and B-52s, all allocated specific routes and targets, the aircraft are primed and ready to go at a moment's notice, backed up by a gaggle of Boeing KC-135

Stratotankers at both locations which stand by in a similar posture, ready to 'scramble' and top-up the 'Bullet Bombers' fuel tanks not long after launch.

This state of readiness is maintained twenty-four hours a day, 365 days a year, so that the United States might reply to an act of nuclear aggression with a like response; triggered into action by the President and Joint Chiefs of Staff, the claxons sound and the blue strobe lights flash with synchronized alarm, awakening everything and everybody with rude spontaneity. This call for action may be just an unannounced Operational Readiness Inspection (ORI) to test the Wing's state of alert or it may be the real thing. Often the air crews waiting in the 'ready rooms' have no idea which: all that is in their possession is a handful of sealed orders and a desire to get airborne. Grappling with their crash helmets and flight charts, the crew zoom to their aircraft, vault up the bomber's ladders and strap into the hard seats: a gruelling 7–12hr sortie may be on the cards and it can be positively uncomfortable (SAC is contemplating the installation of 'posterior massagers' in the 'Bullet Bombers'!). Pins are pulled from the aircraft and the engines and electrical systems set in motion; during a routine training flight the engines might already be turning as an incoming and outbound crew exchange 'warm seats' to repeat the pre-programmed 'canned' flight. Extensive pre-flight checks and INS alignment are not possible in alert conditions. The kerosene-bloated KC-135 'Ground-loving old bast****' (GLOBs) are already departing the base in rapid waves, leaving their sooty tell-tale trademarks in an arc up to the clouds, beckoning the 'Bullet Bombers' to join them. With the 'thumbs-up' from the bomber's crew chief confirming that all is well, the TF30-P-107s are spooled up and the bomber lunges forward. With wheels in motion the navigator glances over his switches and the pilot flexes the control surfaces in an integrated chatter-laden frenzy of checks as the FB-111A taxies in a snaked route from its arched shelter to the take-off point, barely stopping for a decent pause before the pilot pushes the throttles all the way forward and commits his jet to the air. In fifth-stage afterburner at night it is an impressive sight – two huge acetylene-type torches of crimson-orange fire. With a sweep setting of 16°, nosewheel steering disengages at 60kts and the pilot pulls back on the stick to rotate at 156kts, unsticking the bomber at 171kts, 3,500ft down the runway. The mission is underway.

Taking a manual tacan fix for a heading to the rendezvous initial point (RZIP) – the tanker top-up co-ordinates, say, 50 miles off the coast of New England at between 20,000 and 22,500ft – the slats are retracted to clean up the wings, which are pulled back to 26°, and the gear tucked up at the flip of a large lollipop lever. 'As if by magic', the nose gear pops into its bay and the rear smooth tractor tyres double up to fold into the main gear well, the last stage in the sequence comprising a momentary but barely perceptible increase in drag as the huge 'barn door' main gear cover flips forward as if to eat the undercarriage before it slams shut. At 360kts and climbing, and with a multitude of tasks to accom-plish, the crew are too busy to reflect on the possible final outcome of the mission; the navigator, in particular, is busy aligning the INS as the aircraft heads for the tanker.

One sensor which is unique to the FB-111A variant is its AN/ASQ-119 astrocompass, mounted flush in the top of the nose in the middle of the anti-dazzle panel. Activated, this system draws on its catalogue of 57 stars to take automatic sextant shots by day or night, to compute aircraft position, used to update the INS. In order for it to function smoothly and accurately the pilot must not haul the FB-111A around the sky in excess of 3g, half the g-limit of the tactical variants; but such 'turns and burns' are out the question at such high weights lest the heavy drop tanks tear off the wings. Even later, and lighter, this apparent disadvantage is far outweighed by the fact that the astrocompass is often the only means by which the INS can be updated: en route to, perhaps, the Soviet Union, over sea and ice-caps, there exists a dearth of readily identifiable radar features with known co-ordinates. The stellar sky changes little.

With the whale-like tanker and sleek bomber in view of one another at the RZIP, the tanker 'drops' on an identical heading and the FB-111A climbs and joins up behind, its dorsal-mounted, off-axis refuelling receptacle awaiting the KC-135's boom. The pilot will hold the aircraft on the GLOB's belly lights while the navigator watches the boom, making suitable suggestions as to what the pilot ought to be doing or confirming that all is well. Some ten tons are transferred usually, over 15 minutes, making good fuel burnt during the energy-consuming take-off and possibly taking the 'Bullet Bomber' up to its maximum in-flight AUW of 122,900lb. A further prod and top-up from a tanker northbound from Iceland will probably be on the flight schedule later.

A free agent once more, and with everything working as advertised and the digital LEDs flickering new numbers, the navigator will key in the next 'destination' and let the aircraft take full control of the proceedings; all the right-seater needs do from this point is to maintain INS alignment by making use of the doppler and astrocompass to correct for drift. The Mk. IIB will do the rest and command automatic changes of headings to the next pre-programmed destinations one after the other; there is no need to reach down to the navigation panel at each waypoint and set the next co-ordinates. The FB-111A will even execute the necessary turns, all by itself. Of course the crew may elect to take a short-cut: for example, they might go from 'Dest 17' to 'Dest 22' or even back home in the event of a gross systems failure – procedures exercised only, in SAC 'press ahead' tradition, in dire circumstances. By 'tapping in' a destination further along the flight plan the avionics will bypass the waypoints in between and command direct steer to that point, again in a 'hands-

**Right: A Plattsburgh crew 'on the boom' to top-up their fuel reserves, with the navigator keeping an eye on the proceedings. (USAF)**

off' manner. The navigator can even tap in a whole new set of co-ordinates to the INS, as would be the case if both central computers failed and the 'mission tape' were lost, although SAC claims the likelihood of this double failure is well under 2 per cent. The pilot is as always free to uncouple the system from the autopilot and take manual headings with stick and rudder but there should be little need for this type of intervention unless the pre-programmed flight plan sends the bomber into the thick of a previously uncharted air defence box, a nuclear electromagnetic cloud or a vicious storm – another detective function of the attack radar. Some bomber ACs have described their role in the digital strategic 'Aardvark' as that of mere 'pickle' button pusher and 'Earthpig' handler during take-offs, refuellings and landings, with only the wing-sweep 'trombone' and throttle controls to play with. The truth is that pilots often uncouple the automatic steering simply because they love to do the flying and they can get quite bored sitting in the command seat with their arms folded while the navigator tinkers silently with his computer keyboards! Perhaps the pilot's most vital function, much like an engineer's, is fuel conservation: without this forward thinking the aircraft might simply fall from the sky, out of gas.

Several waypoints later looms the final decision, and one which must be accomplished in radio silence. In addition to their usual array of scopes and instruments the crew have another vital extra piece of equipment unique to the SAC version – satellite communication (SATCOM), which ties them into the strategic airborne 'Looking Glass' and 'NEACP' emergency command and control posts which orbit over the continental United States with plenty of red telephones. In a 'live' mission, various 'no-go' or 'go' codes would have to be received at the 'Positive Control Turnaround Point', matching the codes in the opened envelope of orders in case the mission proceeds in the face of an abort and culminates in an avoidable international tragedy as a result of poor communications or the belligerent act of a lunatic. This is the oft-quoted supreme advantage of the bomber: it can always be called home. Fitted to the right-hand console from 1979, SATCOM features an LED teletype display together with a comprehensive keyboard into which the navigator can 'tap in' appropriate cues to receive codes or to convey messages. If the 'go' code is received, cross-checked and confirmed the crew will scrutinize their timing and proceed to the primary entry control point – a set of scheduled co-ordinates and times for their ingress into enemy airspace.

As the 'Bullet Bomber' approaches the 'entry point' the pilot's wits are sharpened. The drop tanks, now long expended, need to be punched off to reduce drag and conserve valuable fuel. From their economical cruise height the crew initiate 'auto TF descent' at an initial 10° pitch; as soon as the TFRs 'sense' the LARA lock-on, descent increases to 12° pitch until the bomber levels off at the preset TFR altitude – a procedure identical to that used in the tactical models, with 'ride' selection at their discretion. The anti-flash curtains are lowered over the clamshell hoods as the crew 'go through the weapons switches', readying the bomber's deadly nuclear cargo. The navigator, as always, is intent on the attack radar PPI sweep to monitor the terrain and to ensure the INS is aligned. The Mk. IIB 'holds' all the offsets for the waypoints and target(s), which can be called up using up to four separate OAP buttons located on the NDU, one each for every destination or target if loaded in via the 'mission tape'. By pushing OAP1, OAP2 etc. buttons in turn (typically two offsets are sufficient) the radar crosshairs should fall into place automatically over the preselected radar-significant features one at a time, confirming all is well. The sill-mounted tracking handle may be used to correct offset crosshair position to correct for drift. With the weapons selected and fused, all is then set for a full systems bomb pass.

Redundancy is an important feature of the digital Mk. IIB avionics and an early problem was encountered when crews tended to rely too heavily upon a fully functional aircraft and subsequently failed an ORI. During 80 per cent of routine training sorties specific systems are shut down deliberately to add a strong manual element into the attack sequence. With the INS 'on the blink' for example, the auxiliary flight reference system features a set of gyros for back-up heading indications married with doppler radar to furnish ground speed and position; if both central computers fail, removing automatic ballistics, the INS would be used to keep track of aircraft position and weapons release is effected manually by monitoring target position in the radarscope to 'pickle' the bomb load at the right moment or, if the target is not readily visible in the sweep, by synchronizing two OAP cross-hair positions to produce a 'mean' target position on the display.

## Heavy Metal

Attacks with gravity weapons can be made using a 'radar bombs' delivery in automatic or manual modes, in one of two primary flight profiles, 'loft' or 'laydown'.* 'Loft', as the term implies, is a manoeuvre whereby the FB-111A is hauled up into a high-speed airframe-straining steep climb, heading for the heights. The ADI and gunsight 'command bars' provide the relevant pull-up cue. At the apex of the climb the bomb is released automatically and 'lofted' to the target, soaring skyward in a ballistic arc until it loses momentum and plunges back to earth; during the course of the bomb's flight the crew recover from their inverted attitude in 'idiot loop' fashion, dive, and dash out of the target area in the opposite direction to the bomb's trajectory. 'Laydown' entails a low-level high-speed level overflight performed at 520kts minimum. Following release a parachute retard slows the weapon, which then descends at a leisurely pace towards the target below as the crew dash away, anxious not to be blasted in the bomb's deadly shockwave.

The 'de-safing' of nuclear weapons in flight, prior to the bomb pass, is a simple process but one which must be performed in sequence for the ultimate safety considerations. The navigator has an array of push-buttons on the bottom right of the dashboard on the nuclear gravity 'DCU' weapons consent and select panel, offering ground-burst or air-burst, free-fall or retarded weapons fusing. All nuclear gravity weapons used by the FB-111A and its tactical cousins feature a parachute retard option, a thick fabric drogue chute which can be set to shoot out of the rear of the bomb, or not, as required: in a 'laydown' bomb pass the parabrake is essential; in a 'loft' delivery the navigator will select 'Free-fall' and the drogue will remain stored, enabling the bomb to fly through the air in its ballistic arc in a 'slick' low-drag configuration. 'Air' or 'Ground' burst simply determines when the bomb is going to go off: 'Air' will trigger the nuclear device at a set altitude from the ground, to create mayhem at a supply depot or factory; 'Ground' delays the detonation until the weapon reaches terra firma so that it may direct the greater part of its cataclysmic explosive energy against a specific hardened target such as an underground enemy command bunker or a nuclear missile silo, either of which might be invulnerable to an air-burst attack.

From the outset the 'One-Eleven' was equipped to deliver a variety of these horrific last-resort weapons. In the late 1960s these included the B43 and B57. The follow-on bullet-shaped B61's service début was more or less coincidental with that of the FB-111A and F-111E and has remained the primary nuclear device carried by all American 'Aardvarks' configured for standby nuclear alert (known as 'Victor Alert' in USAFE). SAC tends to employ the most powerful Mod. 1 version while comparatively less devastating tactical variants are available to TAC and USAFE, in Mod. 2 to 5 format, all with TNT-equivalent yields ranging from a still very unpleasant 100 kilotons to a staggering 1 megaton.†

Training with live versions of these most deadly of weapons is of course out of the question: tactical 'One-Elevens' can pound the ranges with conventional weapons to their heart's delight but, for the most part, SAC's 'Bullet Bombers' are obliged to perform most of their 'nuclear' bombing electronically. A series of 'Olive Branch' (OB) sites are scattered around the United States, tuned in to the bombers' computers. Instead of triggering the MAU-12 bomb racks, the aircraft's bomb release impulse can be transmitted as a 'pip'. The OB radar sites then pick up this information and determine accuracy purely on the basis of the strength and timing of the signal. Pseudo-live drops of the B61 can take place within the safety of a range, such as the vast expanses outside Nellis AFB in Nevada. For day-to-day experience, air and ground crews work with a range of glossy white inert 'training shapes' similar in weight and handling to the live silver versions but filled with

---

*A LADD timer is also available – see 'New Dynamics and Ironmongery' in 'Work Smarter, Not Harder' (Part 3).
†In a secret spin-off effort, Sandia Industries has developed a long-range rocket-assisted B61, known as the 'Tiger', which can be 'tossed' or 'lofted' to the target in a stand-off delivery mode, even off-axis from the target.

harmless concrete; for simulated 'laydown' drops of retarded weapons the 700lb Douglas BDU-38/B comes into play.* This, too, is painted white, and behaves just like a 'metal' B61, employing a small explosive to discharge its tailcone and tightly-packed parachute, which then billows out immediately after release to permit the F-111 to egress the 'blast' zone. As a harmless training weapon it has been extremely reliable, though this seemingly innocuous device has caused trouble on occasion: much to the munition handler's disgust, while parked on the ramp at Nellis a BDU-38/B was inadvertently activated, its tailcone smashing through FB-111A 68-259's weapons bay bulkhead and into the main gear well with such force that the aircraft had to be dispatched to GDFW for repairs. The aircraft still flies today, with its unique two-piece bulkheads, and the name 'Gypsy' painted on its flank.

Gravity bombs are not all that the FB-111A totes; it also enjoys the deterrent value of Boeing's AGM-69 SRAM. This solid rocket-boosted 2,230lb, 14ft-long, Mach 3 missile with a maximum stand-off range (variable with launch height and delivery mode) of up to 100 miles was designed originally for use on the B-52 to provide a measure of stand-off capability for this aged aircraft and made its first powered flight in August 1969; the FB-111A subsequently entered the SRAM programme when the Category II trials 'Bullet Bomber', No. 5, took to the skies with polka-dotted test SRAMs. The first supersonic launch was accomplished on 22 September 1970.

Allegedly possessing the radar signature of a bullet, live versions of SRAM joined the FB-111A force in 1973 when Col. Paul W. Maul's 509th 'Enola Gay' Wing embarked on Project 'Bullet Blitz', a series of captive flight tests which culminated in seventeen launches at the White Sands missile range in New Mexico. The 715th BMS 'Eagles' were the first to perform a fully successful live launch, in early 1974, using an inert missile. The live versions, equipping standby aircraft only, are fitted with a near-common W69 warhead which packs a 200-kiloton yield, modest in comparison to the strategic gravity bombs but still highly persuasive! A total of 1,500 SRAMs were produced, with stocks peaking in July 1975 at the close of production when 1,445 were on the inventory.

Unlike the gravity bombs, the million-dollar SRAM is a 'smart' missile, equipped with a Delco computer and a Singer-Kearfott KT-76 inertial measurement unit (IMU). Having set up the navigation and radar switches for an attack the right-seater then 'feeds' in a 'navigation model' from the FB-111A's Mk. IIB nav/attack electronics and 'torques' the missile's IMU by getting the pilot to make small changes of heading to keep the weapon 'thinking' and constantly updated up to the point of release; from the moment of activation the missile must 'know' the positions of the aircraft and the aimpoint so that it may guide itself to target after release. Of course, if the Mk. IIIB system is suffering

'partial systems' or even some kind of major failure SRAM's accuracy is similarly degraded.

To set up a SRAM the navigator has a pair of weapons and SRAM control panels on the right console, permitting him to select station and munitions in the customary manner using revised Mk. IIB push-button controls together with a pair of knobs which are clicked in the desired position to choose either automatic or manual delivery and 'single' or 'train' release. Ballistics are automatic, held in the Mk. IIB computers' 'protected memory'. Automatic firing then commences when the computers 'sense' that the target has come within the missile's launch parameters – its 'strike footprint'. Manual release, as back-up, requires the crew to check the radarscope and SRAM status display panel and to 'pickle' weapons off with well co-ordinated precision: a minute error at launch is multiplied many times by the time the weapon has travelled to the target area, and getting SRAM smack on target at maximum range in these circumstances has been likened to throwing a pellet into a coffee cup from the back of a speeding motorbike. Overlapping missile countdowns can be performed in the automatic mode only, enabling an FB-111A to discharge its typical cargo of two or four

---

*Other 'shapes' include the BDU-12/B and -19/B, used to simulate the B61's predecessors.

missiles within seven seconds in rapid 'train'; manual launches take two to three times as long. In either eventuality SRAM will be preselected to perform one of four different flight profiles to the target, all from an initial low-level 'drop' prior to booster ignition: 'inertial', wherein the FB-111A launches the missile at a 'canned' set altitude and bearing to the target for optimum accuracy; 'terrain sensor', in which SRAM employs its radar altimeter to skim over the topography en route to target to avoid detection; 'combined' inertial and terrain-following; and 'semi-ballistic', in which the weapon flies up and over to the target in an elliptical, guided, ballistic arc, for maximum range. The choice is dependent on systems availability and the trade-offs between accuracy, covert missile ingress and stand-off launch range: an area target requires less precision, a hardened one or a small fixed site absolute precision.

Many SRAM updates have taken place over the years, particularly to its IMU, and plans were afoot to produce a more powerful AGM-69B version. This has now given way to a completely new longer-range model called SRAM II, about two-thirds the size of the AGM-69 variant and due to achieve IOC in 1992. It is not certain whether the 'Bullet Bomber' will receive an allocation of the weapons because of the voracious appetite of SAC's rotary launcher-equipped B-1Bs and new Northrop B-2As, both of which carry revolver-loads of the missiles, but the possibilities are there.

### Swing-Wing Crow Defendere
'School' forms a major component of the FB-111A training programme in which students and qualified crews alike are constantly briefed and rebriefed on the Warsaw Pact (WARPAC) threats: none of the flyers has any illusions that if war did break out they could expect to confront the most sinister and lethal air defences at the enemy's disposal. These lessons would become all the more important as the crew ambled, on guard, through enemy-dominated airspace.

During the early days of the FB-111A programme many of the navigators came from the defensive systems 'office' of the Hustler or B-52 and to a large extent many

Below: A delightful study of a Plattsburgh 'Bullet Bomber' ingressing an 'Olive Branch' range in New England in 'Auto TF descent' mode. Note the zinc chromate-coloured replacement strake component. (USAF photo by Walt Weible)

of today's right-hand seaters see themselves as electronic warfare specialists ('Crows') first and navigators second. As more than one senior member of the 'Old Crows', USAF's prestigious club of Electronic Warfare Officers (EWOs), explained, it is not possible to rely purely on wits, the TFR and effective terrain masking to penetrate deep into hostile skies. First of all there may be no available masking terrain, and secondly the Soviets maintain an enormous quantity of missiles and fighters for home defence. If the Soviets launched all their bare-metal fighters the skies would shine like a huge mirror'. Even as old weapons systems fade into obsolescence many are recapped with a nuclear warhead to make good their inaccuracy. USAF crews joke that some of the latest highly manoeuvrable SAMs such as the SA-12 Gladiator, effective at altitudes as low as 300ft and at ranges of up to 50 miles, might snap around in the air and come back for a second attempt if they miss the first time! The general consensus is that low-level flying is vital but provides only part of the answer: the effective use of countermeasures is equally crucial,

and this involves careful timing. SAC specifies 'ECM transmit start' points so that the loosely knitted waves of bombers overwhelm the radar defences in a coordinated fashion.

During the course of its development and service inauguration the 'Bullet Bomber' was equipped with passive Loral AN/ALR-39 and later -41 'See Sam' superheterodyne devices which supplemented the fincap-mounted AN/AAR-34 CMRS to provide 'lamp' warning of a missile launch and to help the navigator decide when to 'pop' appropriate decoys from the AN/ALE-28 CMDS. Dalmo-Victor's AN/APS-109 RHAWS provided strobe lines on the crystal video display, adjacent to the TFR scope, as a means of identifying threat range and bearing. It was all soon outmoded and the digital era generated renewed impetus for a modern self-protection package. Starting in 1977 a new range of black boxes and antennae was wired into the FB-111A fleet comprising the Dalmo-Victor AN/ALR-62 radar warning receiver (RWR), which introduced a prominent 'knob' under the forward fuselage, working in harmony with a Sanders AN/ALQ-137 radar deception-jammer, a heavily modified AN/ALQ-94. In place of the old needles and strobes was a revised, concentrically ringed video which displays the threats in readily digested alphanumerics. A little '12' in the display, for example, denotes that an SA-12 tracking radar is locking on to the aircraft, the symbol's position in the display indicating the range and bearing; if it starts flashing, a Gladiator missile is on its way! To cope with a densely

Below: FB-111A No. 28, 68-256, at present assigned to the 509th BW(M) at Pease AFB, New Hampshire, displays its four 600 US gallon drop tanks and open bomb bay doors. All is left within easy reach to enable ground crews to 'pull the pins' from the BDU-38/B B61 simulator bolted inside the aircraft's belly. The FB-111A's AN/ALE-28 CMDS is now being replaced by the Tracor AN/ALE-40 'Square Shooter' dispenser. (Mil-Slides)

**Above: A 'Swing Wing Crow Defendere' performing trials with four Boeing AGM-69A SRAM missiles, in this instance polka-dotted inert examples used for cinematic calibration purposes. The 100-mile-range SRAM is assigned a target by the Mk. IIB FB-111A navigation system and can be launched against radar sites with some help from the electronic warfare kit. (USAF)**

saturated electromagnetic environment, at the turn of a knob the navigator can 'prioritize' the display, junking the lower-priority threats from the video to highlight the real dangers. This piece of kit, in its latest 'glitch-free' updated format, has proved to be so successful and reliable that it has since been retrofitted to the entire F-111 fleet.

Track-breaking deception-jamming is the function of the AN/ALQ-137, whose receive and transmit antennae are mounted flush within the nose, wing glove and 'speed bumps'. Electronic warfare is such a dynamic science that several upgrades to the equipment have taken place over the years, and many 'Strategic Crows' would like to see a new jammer to counter the latest radars, but plans to incorporate such technology were abandoned as part of the recent 'budget crunch'.* For the time being, they must make do with the existing kit, which is constantly updated with a catalogue of potential threats provided by SAC's 'snoopers' – the RC-135, SR-71A and U-2R/TR-1 'ferrets' – and programmed into the FB-111A's jammer and RWR by on-base avionics technicians. As part-recompense, under the latest FB-111A modernization initiative (dealt with later in the book), the old AN/ALE-28 CMDS is giving way to the near USAF-standard Tracor AN/ALE-40 'Square Shooter', tied to an updated cryogenic receiver. The 'Square Shooter' can pack a large capacity of 8in 'RR' chaff and 'MJU' flare cartridges and will soon be able to dispense Loral Loralei mini-decoys to lure SAMs away from the aircraft. The now trustworthy Cincinnati Electronics AN/AAR-34 receiver is being similarly 'revisited' by the USAF 'to incorporate 1980s technology, including state-of-the-art cryogenics, greatly

---

*Plans were in hand to install either the Sanders AN/ALQ-189 or a derivative of the ITT/Westinghouse AN/ALQ-165 Advanced Self-Programming Jammer.

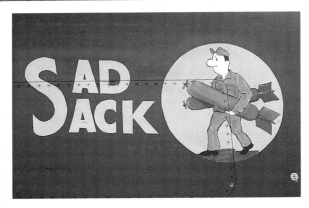

'Nose art' (actually applied to the flanks) of FB-111As of the 380th BW(M) based at Plattsburgh AFB, New York: 68-269 is titled 'Sad Sack', 68-239 is 'Rough Night', 68-260 bears the well-known acronym SNAFU ('Situation Normal, All F***** Up!'), 68-250 is 'Silver Lady' and 68-244 is 'Lucky Strike'. The blue and red background discs of all but 'Lucky Strike' (which is painted on a white disc with a red outline) denote the relevant squadron, the 528th BMS or 529th BMS respectively. All the aircraft were painted in the new two-tone dark colour scheme. (USAF)

enhancing performance and reliability', say the suppliers.

One more obvious defensive tactic that has often been mooted is 'torching': creating a fire streamer in the bomber's wake by discharging kerosene through the outlet nozzle located between the engine exhausts. Several veteran air crews quizzed on this issue have all denied its efficacy categorically: whereas flares drop away from the aircraft in a decoying arc, distracting, say, heat-seeking air-to-air missiles or SAMs with terminal infra-red guidance, 'torching' might well attract a missile, and no enemy fighter jock 'is going to [get so close as to] play dog and sniff your a** so you can roast him!' One of them did concede that 'torching' by a lead jet might be effective at helping stray wingmen re-formate at night. It makes for heart-stopping air-show material at any event.

Befitting SAC's steel fist emblem is the ultimate countermeasure: to fire SRAMs at enemy radar sites in a strategic 'Wild Weasel' role, possibly in support of the 'heavies', prior to a break and bid for freedom. SAC crews talk about 'rolling back' the defences as part of their all-important Single Integrated Operations Plan or SIOP, using up their pair of wing-mounted AGM-69s to silence concentrations of radars en route to the primary target, which is then dispatched using the remaining pair of weapons. To meet this requirement SRAM was designed to incorporate the Sylvania AN/ALR-37 Radiating Site Target Acquisition System (RASTAS), specifically to turn the missile into a stand-off, nuclear-tipped anti-radar weapon, and an interface between the RWRs, radarscope and SRAM does exist, able to lock the missiles on to radars with accuracies measured within half a mile, for use in the strategic defence-suppression role. It is uncertain whether RASTAS was incorporated in production SRAMs but it is known that the navigator can select a 'RHAWS bomb' instead of 'radar bomb' navigation model mode to put a sudden end to the opposition!

**Tiger tails**
In much the same way that the USAF's 'Aggressor' squadrons get into the 'psyche' of emulating Soviet fighter pilots by drinking the occasional vodka and wearing hammer and sickle emblems, so the men tasked with the 'swing-wing' strategic offensive role – and their tactical F-111E/F brothers on 'Victor Alert' duties in USAFE – have fun with trinkets and emblems reminding them of their thankfully so far academic nuclear capability; in this era of East–West *détente* some consider the 'Warsaw Pact Central Heating' plaques, ashtrays, mugs and glasses dotted around the squadron buildings a little insensitive, but they are intended only as good-natured jibes – the rather ludicrous media image of American pilots drooling at the chance to drop 'the big one' is far removed from reality. The flyers are all highly motivated professionals, all of whom love flying, and the Air Force – particularly SAC – is quick to weed out emotionally unbalanced people from its ranks. None can deny, however, that performing the standby nuclear alert job provides a strange combination of tension and boredom, and not a few reflective moments either; with such awesome power at their fingertips the nuclear flyers have become some of the world's greatest philosophers!

The sharpening of skills is a non-stop affair. In addition to 'canned' training flights over New England (many of which require express FAA and even tacit environmentalist approval) the itinerary includes no-notice inspections by 'hard-hatted' SAC chiefs, the minimum of an annual gruelling ORI which includes a mass launch and, just to keep in touch with their peers elsewhere in the Air Force, participation in major events and exercises on away matches. These embrace 'Red Flag' and 'Green Flag' wargames at Nellis, NATO manoeuvres and meets and the aptly named SAC 'Prairie Vortex'. SAC runs a very rigid disciplined system and has its own brand of competitive wargame in which strict emphasis is placed on timing, navigation and the accuracy of bomb delivery and where honours and cups are to be had for the top scores – the SAC 'Bomb and Nav Comp'. The 'Bullet Bomber' has always excelled. Its digital technology provided an edge over the lumbering B-52s and Royal Air Force Vulcans against which it competed in the 'Giant Voice' events of the 1970s. In the microchip era the RAF Tornado GR.1 has presented a major challenge to the Americans, often sweeping the board as winner with its newer technology. The Tornado does, however, have several severe limitations, not least of which are range and payload.* The good natured 'pokes' directed at the RAF are a friendly mark of respect; no pilot will ever openly flatter anything but his own brand of flying machine.

Until 1 January 1975 SAC's FB-111As were assigned to the Second Air Force, and they were initiated in their first 'Giant Voice' 'Bomb Comp' in 1970 at McCoy AFB, Florida, with large 'flying deuces' painted on their fins, ready to show off to the B-52s. As one might expect, the SAC Bomb Comp was nothing short of impressive in scope. It could last up to three months and involve the participation of units from all branches of the Air Force as well as 'guest' entries from the RAF. The two 'Bullet Bomber' Wings have always achieved top scores, capturing and often holding the highly prized Meyer, Mathis and LeMay Trophies. In the late 1980s the Bomb Comp continues to be a major event involving a very large percentage of the Command, with four crews from every flying unit selected by SAC's 1st Combat Evaluation Group. Notification of the personnel nominated for the event comes only five days ahead of the first round of the competition, to rule out special preparations. In 1987 there was even an award for the smartest aeroplane, collected by a 509th fixer. On a reciprocal basis with the British, the FB-111As have made appearances at the RAF's Bombing Competition since April 1971, when Carswell and Pease each dispatched an aircraft to participate in a demonstrative capacity.

Now part of the Eighth Air Force headquartered at Barksdale AFB, Louisiana, SAC's FB-111As bear Second World War style artwork on their flanks and undercarriage doors with pride, while the 393rd BMS takes full advantage of its squadron nickname to venture to Europe to participate in the flamboyant 'Tiger Meet', where units from all NATO member countries with a feline ancestry congregate for a big fight, tooth and claw, for top honours. The 1978 meet at Kleine Brogel, Belgium, produced a 'Bullet Bomber' entry whose entire fin was adorned in tiger colours, a tradition preserved in more modest form (confined to the rudders of FB-111A participants) nine years later at the 1987 meet at Montigo AB, Portugal. The FB-111s are destined to return to Europe with increasing regularity.

In the years 1977–1979, before the Reagan Administration took office and reinstated the Rockwell B-1 VG super-bomber, several plans were mooted for a much-modified 'Aardvark'. In two similar proposals, both eventually discarded, engineering drawings were prepared for a possible FB-111A 'stretch', a create a derivative capable of carrying the same payload over the same distance as the venerable B-52G. GDFW's brochures even talked of an AN/AWG-9 sea lane defence model, in an attempt to resurrect the F-111B, and had visions of withdrawing at least one tactical

---

*See 'Into the Twenty-First Century' (Part 3).

Above: 'Tiger Meets' always engender elaborate colour schemes, even on the normally sombre 'One-Eleven' participants. FB-111A No. 19, 68-247, of Pease's 393rd BMS 'Tigers', took part in the June 1978 meet at Klein Brogel, Belgium, with an appropriately striped tail. (MAP)

variant – the troublesome F-111D in particular – to provide the extra airframes required.* The latest Rockwell B-1B and the stealthy Northrop B-2A 'flying wing' will shortly supplant the FB-111A in SAC service, and the type is destined for transfer over to the tactical forces by 1991.

This nominal switch from a strategic to a tactical role must be viewed in the light of the Intermediate Nuclear Forces (INF) Treaty, under which the USA has agreed to remove its Pershing II and ground-launched cruise missiles from Western Europe. According to the USAF press statement made in July 1988, sixty FB-111As are to be 'converted' to – given added provisions for conventional weapons – F-111Gs and will be forward-deployed to England to bolster NATO's 'flexible response' strategy.† The USAF describes the projected F-111G as being capable of carrying air-launched missiles – in all probability the AGM-69 SRAM or its new Boeing successor SRAM II. The old 'Bullet Bomber' has a secure future.

---

*The original proposals in 1977 called for converting the FB-111As to an FB-111H configuration. The near-identical 1979 plans proposed producing 89 FB-111Bs from F-111Ds and 66 FB-111Cs from 'Bullet Bomber' stocks. The rebuilt GE F101-powered models were designed to lug up to twelve SRAMs or 52 conventional bombs.
†The reallocation of the 'Bullet Bombers' to USAFE is subject to authorization. Under the proposals of the Ribicoff-Edwards committee, Pease AFB is to be closed after January 1990.

# Aardvarks Down Under

'We are small in size but we're good. We believe we have the talent and capability to make full use of the F-111 force'. The determined words from the CO of No. 6 Squadron RAAF sum up his unit's allegiance to Australia's most capable strike aircraft. Amberley air base, fifty miles west of Brisbane, has two 'One-Eleven' squadrons supported by 1,000 'tech troops': No. 1 (call-sign 'Buckshot') with the F-111C; and No. 6 (call-sign 'Falcon'), a hybrid operational and training unit, with the F-111C, four specialized RF-111Cs and four ex-USAF F-111A attrition replacements.

When the first of Australia's 24 F-111Cs (A8-125) arrived on Amberley's runway on 1 June 1973 the event must have seemed almost unreal to those present. It had been on 'pause' for five years and at times looked as if it would never happen. Following an order for two dozen F-111A models on 24 October 1963 Australia became the first and only foreign customer for the 'swing-winger'. GD had attempted to sell their expensive and sophisticated product to NATO and even drafted a scaled-down model for Germany at half the F-111A's weight. Britain was the main sales target, with hopes raised by prolonged uncertainty over the TSR.2 project. Australia in fact originally wanted TSR.2 to replace its British Canberras but resorted to the alternative 'One-Eleven' – then only a 'paper' aeroplane – because of doubts surrounding TSR.2's future. The Australians were well advised: TSR.2 was cancelled on 6 April 1965 and Britain also turned to General Dynamics. Both customers joined forces to finalize contracts for substantially similar purchases. Both wanted variants based on the FB-111A airframe with its extended wings and beefed-up landing gear but the Australian F-111C was to have Mk. I avionics (the original 'Charlie' was indistinguishable from the American 'Alpha' inside) and the British F-111K version different Mk. II systems, making cross-maintenance impossible.* The British Labour Government however went through another series of U-turns and cancelled its order on 17 January 1968.

The F-111C evolved into an aircraft which is identical to the FB-111A in gross weight and is powered by the TF30-P-3 engines of the much lighter F-111A. This has never been a problem but there were plenty of other difficulties. When contracts were finalized in May 1966, on a promised A$3.8 million unit cost, RAAF Amberley embarked on a two-year field extension. Ground crews began training, systems rigs were installed and a Link simulator was ordered. The first F-111C flew from Fort Worth in July 1968 with Dick Johnson at the controls and was handed over on 6 September. Subsequent

aircraft were to have been flown to SMALC by RAAF crews who would then ferry them to Australia, after familiarization flights. Sadly there were no further deliveries for nearly a year. The failure of the static-test WCTB in September 1968 caused all the F-111Cs to be placed into long-term storage pending modification.† Australia's Defence Ministry decided that it could not afford to risk accepting the aircraft without extensive structural testing. While GD did their best to find solutions the RAAF had to sit and watch their purchases gather dust and treble in price. Heated negotiations in November 1969 resulted in an agreement to accept the F-111Cs on condition that any subsequent improvements, as a result of testing, would be built into the aircraft; these included the new WCTB boron-epoxy composite doubler plates for much improved strength. To be totally sure, the Australians demanded a 16,000hr test run on the new wing box. GD felt this to be excessive but proceeded anyhow, taking an F-111C wing box to 32,000hrs and an F-111A sample to 40,000hrs. It took much time and trouble to devise adequate test procedures and deliveries could not recommence before the spring of 1970. In Australia the whole issue became a major political scrap and the 1969 election campaign contained a strong cancellation lobby.

Prime Minister John Gorton decided to short-cut further dissent and have the aircraft reactivated and delivered. The first F-111C started through the rework programme on 16 December 1969 but only six days later the harrowing wing-loss at Nellis grounded the entire F-111 fleet – the fifth grounding since April 1968. The F-111Cs subsequently remained in storage while cancellation was debated once again. The original contract made no provision for compensation but the Americans agreed to buy back the 24 aircraft, subject to Congressional approval, at around half price. As an interim measure two dozen F-4E Phantoms would be leased to the RAAF on favourable terms with an option for another 24 if the F-111C was cancelled. The F-4Es arrived at Amberley in 1970 and became very popular with the Australians, introducing a Litton inertial platform and radar-guided air-to-air missiles, plus an

---

*See 'Cosmic Aardvarks' (Part 3) for a description of the Mk. II avionics suite.
†Official GDFW customer deliveries comprised one F-111C in September 1968, four in August 1969, thirteen in September 1969 and the final four in November 1969 but all the aircraft were stored. At the first hand-over ceremony USAF Chief of Staff Gen. J. P. McConnell announced that the F-111A was ready to return to Vietnam, a decision reversed the next day when the wing box failed!

Above: F-111C No. 20, A8-144, displays its long-span wings and Triple Plow I inlets. A senior RAAF officer described the RAAF version as 'a hybrid', with the inlets, engines and nav/attack avionics of the F-111A, the self-protect systems of the F-111E, the wings and undercarriage of the FB-111A and the WCTBs of the late USAF models. Significant updates have taken place since this photograph was taken. (MAP)

Below: One of Amberley's F-111Cs poses with the full range of weapons currently applicable to the type and with its determined-looking crewmen. Behind the array of Sidewinder AIM-9Bs, 20mm gun ammunition and Mk. 82 'slick' and Snakeye bombs can be found Mk. 82 GBU-12 and Mk. 84 GBU-10 Paveway II laser-guided devices, Australian cluster bomb units, AGM-84 Harpoon anti-ship missiles and GBU-15 electro-optical 'smart' bombs. (RAAF)

'uncanned' visual 'dive–toss' weapons computer system – aeons ahead of the old Canberra and its Second World War style reclining bombardier through-the-looking-glass approach to attack. The RAAF chiefs stood their ground, however, adamant that they wanted the all-weather long-range F-111C.

By mid-1971 the only 'One-Elevens' to have touched the Australian tarmac were a delegation of 430th TFS 'Tigers' from Nellis, calling in for the RAAF's 50th birthday. Meanwhile the F-111Cs received some 200 upgrade modifications resulting from the test programme, including the new WCTB. Lt. Gen. John O'Neill of USAF Systems Command estimated that the US would lose $500,000 per aircraft and arguments rumbled on until December 1973 when Australia elected a new government. Labour Defence Secretary Lance Barnard had been very critical of the F-111 in opposition but he grudgingly conceded that his administration would honour the deal. Crew training resumed at Nellis on 29 January 1973 and on 14 March Barnard announced that the F-111Cs would indeed be accepted. Delivery of the first six aircraft began at McClellan AFB, California, on 28 May in a programme code-named 'Peace Lamb' (as a conciliatory gesture?). The jets were ferried out via Hawaii and Samoa, arriving on 1 June, three lots of six more following on 27 July, 28 September and 12 December. By 22 June the last F-4E had left Amberley, to many people's regret, and the 'One-Eleven' era had begun in earnest.

No. 82 SW at RAAF Amberley set about recouping lost time. It staged an impressive flypast for the Royal opening of the Sydney Opera House in October and participated in joint-service exercises early in 1974. In April that year No. 6 Squadron's commanding officer, Wg. Cdr. Ray Funnell (now Chief of Air Staff) and Sqn. Ldr. John Miller marked the fiftieth anniversary of the first round-Australia flight. They took 12½ hours,

Above: Trailing fire and condensation, F-111E No. 1, 67-115, from the USAF AFFTC in California, gives a 'torching' display at the 1983 Edwards Open Day. This technique is also an RAAF speciality. It has been mooted as a means of decoying infra-red heat-seeking missiles, but is of questionable value: flares drop away from the jet, decoying the enemy missiles away from the F-111; dumping fire might assist in target acquisition! (T. Shia)

spread over two days, knocking 42 days off the 1924 record. Further inter-city records were set in 1976. The 'Aardvarks' then began to venture further afield: A8-143 lit up the skies at the 1977 RAF Jubilee Review at Finningley with a 'torching' flypast (an RAAF speciality, created by dumping fuel into the afterburners' fiery wake); quartets of F-111Cs were dispatched to join their USAF counterparts at 'Red Flag' exercises at Nellis; and others participated in SAC's 'Giant Voice' competition.

In September 1979, to keep apace of technology in the Northern Hemisphere, the RAAF initiated a study of new weapons for use on their F-111s. This has since led to the acquisition of American 'Pave' family systems, including the all-weather Ford Aerospace AN/AVQ-26 Pave Tack targeting pod, Texas Instruments Paveway laser-guided bombs and Pave Strike-derived Rockwell GBU-15 glide bombs.* In June 1982 Fort Worth received an F-111C to flight-test the Pave Tack pod for Australia and was given a contract to produce nineteen conversion kits. Modifying the test-bed took until January 1983 and was followed by a year of intensive flight-test operations, directed at perfecting a purpose-built interface to mate the digital Pave Tack with the analogue F-111C. The radar display was 'cleaned up' by a new digital scan converter able to handle all the

*See 'Statue De Libya Raiders' (Part 3) for a description of the various 'Pave' weapons and sensors.

alphanumeric symbology generated by the new device and wiring was added for the new 'smart' bombs. In addition the entire stores management system was upgraded to enable other new weapons to be carried, some of which have given the Australians an edge over their American 'swing-wing' peers.

## Missileers

One of the major tasks undertaken by No. 1 Squadron is maritime strike. Australia has been described as a 'coastline country' and her responsibilities extend far across the Pacific, west into the Indian Ocean and north beyond the Timor Sea to Indonesia and Malaysia, where ships abound. By contrast, bombing ships is not a job that the USAF 'One-Eleven' crews consider desirable, partly on the grounds of inter-service rivalry ('It's really a Navy job') and partly because they consider the mission somewhat suicidal. Maj. Dick Brown USAF, with 3,900 hours in various models of the F-111 at the time of writing, was very frank about this subject: 'Boats

are really tough because there's nothing to hide behind. Your line of sight on radar is probably where you're going to get caught. I wouldn't like to do it – not without some sort of stand-off weapon like Exocet.' Capt. George Kelman USAF, an aggressive flyer nicknamed 'Kelmaniac' by his contemporaries, summed it up: 'It's more for the boat to find us, or not to find us, than for us to find the boat.' These thoughts are echoed by F-111 crewmen throughout the USAF whose job it is to go deep into enemy territory toting iron, cluster, laser and electro-optical bombs, using radar-masking to best advantage. Attacking a heavily defended, high-value target in a broad expanse of open water is 'kind of scary'. The Soviet ships' sensors can tell if an aircraft, say, switches to 'Ground Vel' radar attack mode and can 'zap' the interdictor long before it has come within toss-bombing range. The RAAF are well aware of these hazards and have taken appropriate steps. Joining the F-111C repertoire to provide both extra reach and that much-needed stand-off capability to fulfil the maritime

Above: Under a major rework and modernization initiative, the RAAF's F-111Cs received the Ford Aerospace AN/AVQ-26 Pave Tack targeting and designating pod, seen here deployed from the weapons bay of a No. 1 Squadron 'One-Eleven'. The aircraft also totes an SUU-20 practice dispenser and a baggage pod. (RAAF)

task are two weapons systems which have been combat-proven by the US Navy in recent clashes in the Middle East – Harpoon and HARM.

The aptly named McDonnell Douglas Astronautics AGM-84A Harpoon is a 1,145lb, 12.6ft-long turbojet-powered anti-ship missile which packs a hefty 488.5lb high-explosive blast-type warhead capable of remaining intact after ship-hull penetration to poke and tear enemy warships, with the added bonus of a high probability of triggering secondary internal explosions. It has demonstrated 95 per cent reliability in the 'Gulf'. Target range and bearing acquired on the F-111C's radar during a brief pre-launch pop-up are handed over to the weapon via the Harpoon Aircraft Command and Launch Subsystem, giving the missile all the preliminary data it needs to set up a kill. The range at which this is accomplished is classified, but estimates of 40nm or more are probably accurate, presenting a deadly threat to the 'floaters'. Following release the F-111C breaks away, back to safety; meanwhile mid-course missile guidance employing a three-axis attitude reference system married to a digital computer and radar altimeter for sea-skimming flight takes the weapon to the target area, at which point the missile pops up so that its active radar dish can pick up and lock on to the target. Harpoon was first developed in June 1971 and entered service with the US Navy eight years later, and the RAAF joined the league in August 1985 when it sent one of its 'Charlies' to the Point Mugu missile range in California for live trials. Follow-on tests were performed by the full-time trials workhorse A8-132 at the RAAF Air Research Development Unit (ARDU) located at

RAAF Edinburgh in South Australia, and all surviving RAAF 'One-Elevens' are to be updated with the requisite wiring and control panels, providing a capability which will deter any seaborne aggressor.

In an Australian-based counterpart to the USAF Foreign Weapons Evaluation Program, ARDU's white-bellied F-111C is constantly in the throes of testing new American systems for possible acquisition. The Texas Instruments rocket-powered AGM-88 High-Speed Anti-Radiation Missile (HARM) is another such weapon that has recently gained priority status on the RAAF's shopping list, in this case a device honed to the defence suppression mission: to destroy land or sea-borne radars and thus deny the enemy effective anti-aircraft capability. The 13.75ft-long, 800lb HARM will perhaps be interfaced with the F-111C's newly updated Dalmo-Victor AN/ALR-62 RWR at some stage in the future for launch in the 'Self-Protect' mode but this has not yet been accomplished; instead the AGM-88 is launched in a 'Target of Opportunity' mode when the situation dictates or in a 'Pre-Brief' mode in support of colleagues or prior to target ingress, relying on the missile's own AWG-25 passive radar-detecting seeker to acquire and 'lock up' on the target dish. Maximum range is classified and varies with launch height (tree-top to FL400) and delivery mode (level, dive or loft), but 40 miles is a fair estimate. The initial F-111C AGM-88 trials were completed in 1988 and the procurement of an undisclosed number of HARMs is in prospect.

More upgrades are taking shape, including an indigenous analogue-to-digital nav/attack refit similar to the up-and-coming USAF/Grumman F-111A/E Avionics Modernization Program (AMP), to enable the RAAF

Left: The McDonnell Douglas AGM-84A Harpoon has a particular place in the Australian defence scenario. Here four of these long-range anti-ship missiles appear beneath ARDU's F-111C No. 8, A8-132. The white-bellied jet is painted with calibration markings and carries a GE M61A1 20mm 'Gat' gun. The pristine finish has become charred and glazed by weapons trials in recent months. (RAAF)

Above: The ARDU workhorse from RAAF Edinburgh, South Australia, in flight with a pair of highly decorated Rockwell GBU-15 glide bombs. GBU-15 packs a 2,000lb warhead and is considered to be the most accurate 'smart' bomb in the world. (RAAF)

'Aardvarks' to soldier on into the twenty-first century.* Indeed, despite their small numbers, the Amberley-based 'One-Elevens' represent the most potent single concentration of strike air power in the Pacific. It is an expensive business though. As one officer put it, 'To be in this league requires commitment. You can't penny-pinch. You're either in this league or you're not. And that must be the message – crap or get off the pot!'

No. 6 Squadron runs a conversion course which comprises 76 flying hours for pilots and 65 for navigators. The overall approach is similar to that of the USAF, with detailed preparation and analysis for each sortie. Flight refuelling is practised, much of this provided by USAF tankers assigned to Pacific Air Forces (PACAF). Crew training tasks are organized within the squadrons for day-to-day operations, and from higher authority when broader tasking is required. The Australians are not the ones to spend a lot of time at home, and they get out and about on multinational exercises such as the 'Triad' events with PACAF and RNZAF. 'Triad 84' in New Zealand, for example, involved four F-111Cs, PACAF F-15 and F-16 'Teenagers', ten RAAF Mirages and RNZAF A-4 Skyhawks and Strikemasters, entangled in an air combat man-

oeuvre, with the 'Charlies' operating out of Christchurch Airport in support of both 'Blue Force' and 'Orange Force' as required. Combined manoeuvres of this type require substantial pre-positioning of support equipment and ample fuel reserves. With a fuel load equivalent to the maximum weight of a Jaguar GR.1 the F-111C needs to be at well-supported locations (such as international airports!).

Logistics support is never a problem when the units can operate from their home base, as they did for Exercise 'Coral Sea' in October 1985. As one senior 'One-Eleven' pilot has remarked,

You know, you can get into an F-111C in Brisbane on a black and nasty night and fly south through the Great Dividing Range, down through the Perisher Valley and deliver bombs on a target in, say, Melbourne – all at 200ft AGL without ever seeing the ground. You can use it on an anti-shipping strike in the morning against a target in the vicinity of Cocos Island and against a land target 2,000 miles distant from that on the same evening.

For 'Coral Sea', F-111 squadrons provided 'Orange Force' strike elements flying ground-attack and anti-shipping missions in company with sharkmouthed F-4Es from PACAF's 3rd TFW which provided CAP cover. The F-111Cs operated in pairs against 'targets' such as dams, bridges and power stations, evading the

*See 'TAB-V Pigs' (Part 3) for a fuller explanation of the AMP effort. The RAAF will fit their machines with a digital computer complex managed by a Mil-Std 1553 databus.

interceptor force of PACAF 18th TFW F-15 Eagles and RAAF No. 77 Squadron Mirages particularly well. In attacks on maritime targets the F-111Cs practised ripple-firing four AGM-84As, a typical load for this kind of mission, working with P-3C Orions which performed the initial sea-scouting function. Pre-strike reconnaissance was also provided by Amberley, using its RF-111C element.

## Photo Vark

The RF-111C, a special conversion with an equally chequered past, merits further discussion. In July 1966 the RAAF announced that it was to purchase six 'swing-role' RF-111Cs, to be converted at a later date from 'C' stock starting to take shape on the GDFW assembly lines. Commonality was the name of the game and from August 1964 GD had begun to explore a TFX-R offshoot which would offer vastly superior capability and much greater growth potential over the contemporary range of reconnaissance jets, made possible by the F-111's capacious airframe and its unmatched endurance. The subsequent $118 million GD RF-111A programme, backed in related studies by the RAAF, involved reworking RDT&E F-111A No. 11 (63-9776) with a dedicated reconnaissance pallet faired into the weapons bay, eventually comprising a comprehensive array of Hycon KA-55 12in high-altitude and Fairchild KA-56 low-altitude panoramic cameras, an unspecified infrared linescanner, framing cameras synchronized with flares for night-time operations and a twin set of Westinghouse Electric AN/APD-8 sideways-looking airborne radars (SLARs) mounted in slim radomes facing abeam, all managed by a North American Rockwell digital Recon Control Computer System for accurate cueing. Flight-test operations commenced on 17 December 1967 and the package showed consider-

able promise, the F-111's stability-augmented flight control system proving that it provided the perfect stable platform for the recce mission. But two years later the entire 'One-Eleven' fleet was grounded indefinitely; Australia's new aircraft were mothballed, along with plans for the recce derivative, and the follow-on Wing-sized force of 60 USAF RF-111Ds envisaged at the time was not proceeded with, axed by budget cuts. The RAAF and GD shelved the whole RF-111 effort in dismay, while the demodified test-bed later found a new home perched on a concrete pedestal as a gate guardian to the 366th TFW at Mountain Home AFB, Idaho, where it can still be seen today.*

Not surprisingly, Australia's interest in an RF-111C was rekindled with the arrival of its rehabilitated 'Charlies' four years later. Although serious consideration had been given to retaining the stop-gap F-4Es and supplementing them with further examples together with eight RF-4E Photo-Phantoms, the advent of the 'swing-winger' proved that it would be more desirable to allocate a select number of F-111Cs to the task as originally planned. Project definition was established initially in 1975 by a joint GDFW and RAAF team headed by J. R. Goodman, with full Governmental approval following in July 1977. F-111C A8-126 was flown over and modified to the test-bed role at Fort

*Wearing the spurious tail number 66-022. An RF-111B variant was proposed to the US Navy but was terminated alongside the F-111B.

Below: A Pave Tack-equipped F-111C tries a Texas Instruments AGM-88 HARM anti-radar missile out for size, fitted to an Aero 5A rail bolted to the inner starboard pivot-pylon (station 5). The AGM-88 is now being manufactured in 'B' format, with destructive 'cubes' for improved warhead lethality. (Texas Instruments)

Worth, rolling out on 18 April 1979 ready for a four-month flight-test programme in Texas.

The modification involved adding a new TV tube and recon controls to the cockpit and deleting the weapons bay doors plus MAU-12 bomb racks, with virtually everything redesigned from scratch: a new, large, permanent pallet housing all the reconnaissance gear was installed which hinged down from the starboard side of the bay to provide access to the sensor suite; a smaller companion hinged door on the port side ensured that the pallet was not too wide to prevent the 'tech troops' from gaining easy access to any of the equipment, to provide forward field operability. Initial trials, with RAAF crewmen Sqn. Ldr. Kevin Leo and Flt. Lt. Andy Kemble at the helm, were begun at Fort Worth and then proceeded to RAAF Darwin in Northern Territory for a two-month follow-on evaluation extended through to December, so that mission procedures could be laid down and the operating manuals written up. Once the trials had been given the 'thumbs-up' an additional three F-111Cs, A8-134, -143 and -146, were modified to the task the following year by RAAF personnel from No. 482 Squadron and No. 3 Aircraft Depot using retrofit kits fabricated at Fort Worth. Now operational for eight years, and 'mature' from a systems and operations standpoint, the RAAF RF-111Cs are considered to be one of Australia's greatest national assets, capable of producing 'some remarkable results'. Crews assigned to the mission come from the RAAF's top 'Earthpig' people, converting to the added controls and mission requirements with little difficulty under a separate 'mini' training programme administered by No. 6 Squadron.

The heart of the system with which the new crews come to grips comprises a number of sensors designed specifically for either high- or low-altitude work. Peeping from the rear portholes are a pair of CAI recon-optical KS-87C day and night framing cameras, which take semi-oblique snapshots using 3in, 6in, 12in or 18in focal length lenses, depending on altitude and the required area coverage; and bigger Fairchild KA-56E low-altitude and KA-93A4 high-altitude panoramic cameras, contained in the ventral 'doghouse' and forward bay, supplement the framing cameras by providing strip photography compressed cleverly into a frame, covering an area ranging in size from a small patch of ground to a complete horizon-to-horizon view. These cameras produce excellent results in the clear, idyllic antipodean skies; for night photography a Honeywell AN/AAD-5 variable-swath infra-red linescanner is activated from behind a shutter during an overflight manoeuvre, to detect forces cloaked by darkness or vegetation. The final piece of kit comprises a TV viewfinder and airborne video tape recorder (AVTR) tied to the 'real-time' TV display located on the dashboard under the TFR and RWR scopes. The TV viewfinder is an essential mission aid, assisting with line-up over target and sensor cueing during overflight and parallel oblique recce passes, and it comes with optional wide or narrow zoom fields of view (FOV) adjustable at the twist of a knob. To back up the pallet's

tray of tricks, additional intelligence may be garnered from the regular nose-mounted KB-18A strike camera and cockpit RSP camera – the attack radar providing a useful forward-looking substitute for a SLAR sensor as well as aiding in normal all-weather navigation. Sensor controls are grouped on the revised right-hand console and new dashboard CRT panel, enabling the navigator to select his stations and activate the sensors.

To ease sensor interpretation and make sense of the huge quantity of exposed film, the RF-111C's central air data computer is interfaced with a data display set to annotate the standard 4.5in-wide celluloid with time and date, lat/long co-ordinates, radar or pressure altitude, drift, heading, pitch, roll and the mission number plus its security classification. Film annotation is of vital importance because oblique and panoramic camera photography introduces considerable perspective into the camera frames; interpretation would be near impossible without this information.

A typical reconnaissance mission is planned in much the same fashion as a strike sortie, using point-to-point flight routes and drawing on situation reports ('sit reps'), intelligence reports, other crews' debriefs, RSP and predictions and good old-fashioned maps and charts, on assignments directed by higher authority – HQ

Operational Command (continental), HQ Support Command (overseas), Defence, Air Force Office ('Defair') – or No. 6 Squadron headquarters but with the emphasis placed on the photo-snapping job. The RF-111C is, in common with the basic 'Charlie' version, the longest-legged of all the tactical 'One-Elevens' and is capable of operating unrefuelled, without drop tanks, over an impressive 1,000nm radius in tropical conditions – and with a significant portion of the mission conducted at low level. This profile typically calls for a take-off and climb to 27,000ft for optimum cruise, a drop to low-level TFR at 200ft AGL over a 400nm radius, with pop-up to the required altitude for the reconnaissance pass, and then a return home at cruise height using a mirrored profile. External tanks and AAR support from PACAF KC-10s and KC-135s are options on offer and may be used to extend the aircraft's duration. Following aircraft recovery the pallet is simply swung down, providing the 'tech bods' access to the tapes and chunky metallic-blue film magazines, which are duly processed in the mobile but large Processing and Interpretation Cabin complex. TV viewfinder imagery may also be replayed once the cassette has been unplugged from the AVTR, providing a vital tool during debrief. This often consumes up to two or so hours and

will reveal further intelligence to add to the torrent of sensor-based recce products based on visual or radar sightings, RWR indications and more obvious pointers such as enemy aircraft, AAA or SAM activity which will serve to highlight the 'hot spots'.

The RF-111C is a true dual-mission aircraft. As one RAAF officer noted, 'The modifications involved the weapons bay and cockpit only – the exterior of the aircraft is virtually unchanged. It can carry the same weapons load through the same attack profiles in the same weather as the strike aircraft. All we have lost is the gun, weapons bay fuel tanks and luggage space' – and, of course, beer-carrying capacity! External pods are now used for personal essentials. The full conventional attack capability is retained, utilizing the onboard Litton AN/AJQ-20A Mk. I NCU/INS and BCU of the 'vanilla' F-111A/C, so that missions can conceivably involve a composite tasking – reconnaissance-strike. RF-111C crews are kept current on all aspects of attack;

**Below: F-111C No. 2, A8-126, became the 'Photo Vark' test-bed in 1979; three additional RF-111Cs were created the following year, using kits supplied by GDFW. The cameras are housed in the modified weapons bay. (General Dynamics)**

**Above: The 'office' of RF-111C A8-143. It retains the full Mk. I nav/attack capability of the F-111C (note the chunky stores and station select knobs on the right-hand WCP) but was fitted with a new sensor control panel (forward of the WCP) and a TV display located on the dashboard console under the TFR E-scan tube and RHAWS display. The RAAF have upgraded the RHAWS to the latest Dalmo-Victor AN/ALR-62 alphanumeric RWR system. (RAAF)**

in fact the original programme authorization was justified on the grounds that the weapons delivery capability would in no way be compromised, and the machines and their crews are true 'swing-wing swing-rolers'.

Gauging RF-111C readiness is a continuing task assigned to No. 6 Squadron and is in many respects easier to manage than with the interdictor-only aircraft: reconnaissance is fundamentally the same whether flying in peace or war, celluloid is cheaper than 'smart' bombs or missiles and the flyers themselves (mostly instructors) are highly skilled in their art. Products obtained during exercises are self-explanatory; a team coming home without the goods will likely soon have red faces and will learn quickly from any mistakes made! Gauging effectiveness however is considerably more difficult. Integrating such a small team into Australia's defence strategy requires considerable exper-

tise and planning to maximize the nation's limited resources: RAAF F/A-18 Hornets may back up the F-111Cs in the strike role should urgent new targets crop up for example, but sending the RF-111Cs off in the wrong direction could prove disastrous given the vast geographic responsibilities placed on 82 SW's shoulders and the RAAF's limited back-up recce capability.* The Australians are now enjoying increased liaison with the United States to aid this process and 'Boomerang Squadron's crews participate on a regular basis in US-sponsored exercises and competitions, including the prestigious biennial Reconnaissance Air Meet (RAM) held at Bergstrom AFB, Texas, home of the USAF's tac-recon forces. The first RAM was fought out in November 1986, and although the RF-111C contingent have not yet gained possession of the cup they trailed just a few points behind the winners at both RAM-86 and -88 and are developing new tactics. No. 6 Squad-ron's motto is 'Nous Reviendrons', and doubtless they will be participating in future RAMs to test their skills again. Peer pressure from competition generates the extra adrenalin: RAM-88 involved nine teams with three aircraft apiece and included a dozen low-level high-speed day and night sorties spread out over nine days. No. 6 Squadron's trio of 'Photo Varks' held first place after the initial five night missions but proved vulnerable to 'enemy' F-4D and F-15A 'Aggressors' by day; each 'kill' carried a loss of 150 points for the victim team and the Australians must have wished they carried all-aspect, heat-seeking air-to-air missiles to keep the opposition at bay – at present the 'Charlies' are equipped with the rather primitive AIM-9B.† More recently, 'Photo Vark' capabilities were demonstrated to their full in Exercise 'Pitch Black 87', a multinational Pacific combat manoeuvre embracing American Phantoms and B-52s plus RAN P-3C Orions alongside the RAAF's strike-reconnaissance contingent. Two RF-111Cs flew a string of sorties of up to five hours' duration gathering prospective target data which was processed in the field by a tent-based interpretation team. Specialized high-speed long-range recce work is a fairly new game to the RAAF but the crews know their business. Regular exchange postings with the USAF have proved to be mutually beneficial.

The F-111C has earned a good reputation for reliability and safety. The early problems with cracks in the nosewheel assembly, and a total nosewheel collapse in April 1978, prompted the possibility of using domestically manufactured spares (the RAAF fitted bird-proof windshields in advance of the USAF), both to take advantage of local skills and to reduce costs associated with shipping components from the major *matériel* manager, SMALC in California. In all there have been six losses in fifteen years of operations. No. 6 Squadron lost A8-136 in April 1977 after an in-flight turbine failure and explosion, the crew managing to part company from the stricken machine. The second loss, that of A8-133, occurred five months later at Evans Head, New South Wales, while in October 1978 A8-141 went into the Hawaki Gulf off Auckland, New Zealand. There was another sad loss in August 1979 when A8-137 ingested water on take-off from Ohakea in New Zealand and ran off the runway and burned out. This spate of write-offs was followed by nearly six mishap-free years, broken by the crash of A8-139 in the sea off Montaga Island, New South Wales, and the demise of

A8-128 which tumbled into the terrain during a night TFR flight near Testerfield, NSW, on 2 April 1987. With such a small force of 'One-Elevens' at hand each aircraft is of great intrinsic value and attrition replacements are sought whenever possible. The only realistic option is off-the-shelf F-111As. Four were requested and granted in 1980 and to achieve optimum commonality with the rest of Australia's fleet they received extended wing-tips and a strengthened undercarriage. Ferried to Amberley between February and April 1982, they now serve with No. 6 Squadron, proudly bearing its blue lightning bolt fin insignia (No. 1 Squadron has the same bold design in golden yellow).‡

The restructuring of the Royal Australian Air Force in the late 1980s has made even better use of its updated and mixed force of F-111s. In 1988 Air Marshal Ray Funnell announced that Amberley's 82 Strike Wing would become the Strike and Recon Group of the

---

*'Real-time' transmission of digitally processed camera and infra-red linescan pictures using charged coupled devices and other 'converters' could become a feature of the RF-111C in the near future. The CAI Recon Optical KS-87 is now available with a dual real-time, data-link and regular film magazine capability while the Honeywell AN/AAD-5 linescanner offers a similar capability in its latest D-500 format. Digitalized sensor data could be broadcasted to ground receiving stations over the RF-111C's existing HF and UHF radio antennae. The main problem for the RAAF would be to forward-base a sufficient quantity of the expensive ground processing stations used to decode the signals back into photographs.
†See 'Winders and Gats' in 'Cosmic Aardvarks' (Part 3) for a fuller explanation of air-to-air defensive tactics.
‡F-111As 67-109 and 67-112 to -114 inclusive.

**Below: The sensor pallet of the RF-111C comprises two KS-87C framing cameras, two panoramic cameras (a KA-56E and -93A4), an AAD-5 infra-red linescanner and a TV viewfinder which swings down to afford good access to any of the equipment. Note the large film magazines. The interior of the bay is painted white, with metallic-blue sensors. (RAAF)**

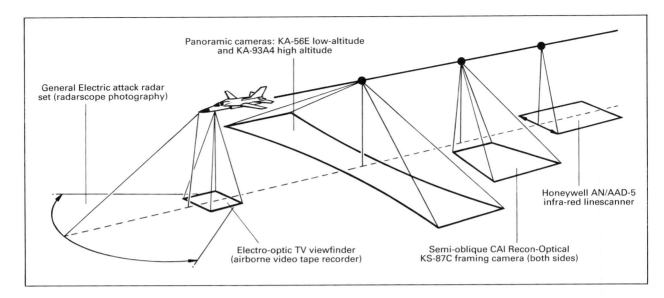

Panoramic cameras: KA-56E low-altitude
and KA-93A4 high altitude

General Electric attack radar
set (radarscope photography)

Honeywell AN/AAD-5
infra-red linescanner

Electro-optic TV viewfinder
(airborne video tape recorder)

Semi-oblique CAI Recon-Optical
KS-87C framing camera (both sides)

**Above: RF-111C sensor operation in level flight. Stand-off oblique photography can be effected by banking the wings.**

RAAF, providing an umbrella for the entire continent. A system of advanced bases such as that at Curtin near Derby, which offers hangar protection against the extreme heat for half a dozen 'Aardvarks', has been established so that aircraft can be forward-positioned to cover most of the potential enemy approach routes. Six such bare bases are to be built in the north, each run on a caretaker basis with fuel and weapons pre-positioned

for action, to meet Australia's new mobile, flexible defence doctrine. Australia stayed with the F-111 despite its distressing early years and her good faith has paid off. Some say the aircraft is rather too sophisticated for her immediate needs but there are few criticisms to be heard. No. 6 Squadron's CO did admit to one shortcoming: comparing his aircraft with the DC-9 airliner (which is comparable in gross weight) he commented that the F-111C 'loses out badly on hostess service!'

# Raven

Just months after the first F-111Cs touched down at RAAF Amberley a very brief but bitter air war was sparked off on the other side of the globe in the skies above the Suez Canal and the Golan Heights. In the midst of Israeli observance of Yom Kippur in 1973 the Egyptians and Syrians launched a massive offensive to crush the young State. Logistics and courage determined the final outcome in favour of the Israelis yet it was a very close finish: the Soviets had introduced a horrifying mix-and-match, layered, integrated air defence network which sorely challenged the Israeli-flown, US-supplied state-of-the-art fighter-bombers' countermeasures equipment. The terrible aircraft losses shook the US Department of Defense. America's sole land-based dedicated electronic combat aircraft which might be used to safeguard her own flyers in a similar scenario was the Douglas EB-66 Destroyer blanket-barrage noise-jammer; this venerable jet was on the verge of total withdrawal in early 1974 and had been deemed obsolete several years before even 'Linebacker', despite its truly gallant efforts in those operations. The United States was obliged to find solutions, and she therefore embarked on a massive series of defence-suppression, stand-off weapons-delivery and electronic combat programmes, collectively referred to as 'Pave Strike', to counter the new Soviet anti-aircraft weaponry.*

One of the top priorities was to build a replacement for the Destroyer able to neutralize enemy electronic defences with carefully tuned and directed spot-noise-jamming, to obscure friendly aircraft positions during the heat of an attack by selectively blotting out radar-scope displays with 'snow' and swamping automatic gain receivers with electromagnetic interference, to deny the enemy both Ground Control Intercept (GCI) vectors for their fighters and reliable radar acquisition for their SAMs and precision-laid AAA – thereby enabling the 'friendlies' to perform their strike mission relatively unmolested; strap-on podded jammers bolted to the strike force, although vital in helping to defeat the 'terminal threats' (those emitters actually guiding missiles or flak), simply lack the power and sophistication to match the opposition and offered no element of surprise.

US Navy Grumman EA-6B Prowlers, which had performed a similar aerial supportive task during 'Linebacker II' operations in Vietnam, possessed this eagerly sought capability. Using computer-tuned, high-gain, closed-loop jamming directed at the Sino-Soviet-supplied defences from their radical Eaton AIL AN/ALQ-99 underwing pods, in turn cued by their receptive fintop 'footballs', the Prowlers were able to help screen swarms of B-52s from attack, 'providing just enough cover', as Navy skipper Cdr. R. F. Rollins noted, before the enemy became wise to their tactics and broke through. The US Air Force were impressed. Different operational requirements – namely the Air Force demand for a penetration jammer – ruled out the possibility of purchasing the slow-moving EA-6B, but not its jamming equipment.† With reports and papers in hand the USAF set about investigating the means of repackaging this combat-proven equipment internally in a new, more sophisticated AN/ALQ-99E guise aboard a supersonic-capable aircraft, one which could perform both long-range TFR penetration and stand-off, long-endurance subsonic loiter operations. The natural choice was the 'Aardvark': its huge, slender airframe offered growth to accommodate all the bulky receivers and transmitters, and with a greater degree of automation built into the system its solo right-seat EWO would be able to handle the job undertaken previously by two or three Navy 'spark heads'.

As suppliers of the AN/ALQ-99E Jamming Sub-System (JSS), Eaton AIL at Deer Park, New York, would inevitably emerge as victors. As for the airframe integration work, there were two clear contenders. On 8 January 1974 the USAF issued Phase 1A competitive design study contracts to GDFW and Grumman. Grumman had the edge: it too possessed experience with the 'One-Eleven', it had already developed two electronic jamming derivatives of the A-6 Intruder for the US Navy and Marine Corps and it had the luxury of its own privately run, expensive anechoic test facility at Calverton, considered to be one of the best in the country.‡ F-111A No. 59 (66-041) was flown in from Nellis and spent four weeks suspended on cables in the electronic shed as a guinea pig. Antenna pattern, electromagnetic interference (EMI) and environmental control tests were all performed in time fo the paper

---

*Project 'Pave Strike' also embraced, *inter alia*, the McAir F-4G 'Advanced Wild Weasel', equipped with the AN/APR-38 homing and warning computer to seek out radar sites for destruction with anti-radar missiles and cluster bombs, and the Rockwell GBU-15 glide bombs.

†USAF proposals to adopt the EA-6B had already been explored; inter-service rivalry and funding priorities had killed them all, but they were hastily resurrected in the light of Israeli experience in Yom Kippur.

‡The Navy/Marine/Eaton AIL AN/ALQ-99-equipped EA-6B Prowler, and Marine/Bunker-Ramo AN/ALQ-86-equipped EA-6A. The EA-6A carried various external countermeasures pods activated by the right-seater and cannot be classed as a true 'closed loop' jamming system.

Above: F-111A No. 59, 66-041, performed Phase 1A and Phase 1B trials at Calverton from 1974 under the guidance of Gruman EF-111A Program Manager Tom Street. It is seen here with the 16ft canoe modification, and dayglo red stripes on its nose, wing tips and tail. It retains its old 'Roadrunners' tail-code, 'NA', but wears an AFSC badge in place of the customary TAC insignia. (Grumman Corporation)

Right, top: In Ghost Gray and red trim, article M-2, 66-041, spent much of its time during Phase 1B of the development effort in Grumman's Calverton-based anechoic chamber for electronic trials. The pyramid-shaped devices are a 'combination of animal hair and other substances which

absorb radio frequency radiation, thereby preventing reflections that could distort test data', say Grumman. The anechoic tests confirmed that the JSS, separated by the bay and fin arrangement, could operate successfully in a 'lookthrough', 'closed loop' manner. (Grumman Corporation)

Right, bottom: The weapons bay of the 'Electronic Fox' swings down to reveal the bank of five exciters (the bigger, rectangular shapes), plus an array of computer, power supply and coupler 'black boxes'. The ten JSS jamming antennae are on the other side of the pallet, behind the 'canoe' radome. (Grumman Corporation)

submissions which were due in by August. Under Phase 1B, on 26 December the USAF awarded Grumman a contract to build two of the newly designated EF-111A 'Electronic Foxes'.

## Spark Vark
Integrating the JSS into the two test-beds, 66-041 and newcomer 66-049, was a mammoth task. The majority of the receiver equipment was mounted in an established 'football' design atop the fin while the 2½ tons of jamming exciters and antennae were fitted to a pallet which swung down from the modified weapons bay, its ten, physically steerable, 1,000W transmitters poking out underneath and covered by a 16ft-long plastic 'canoe'. The problems were immense: power supply, aerodynamic stability, centre of gravity, fatigue stresses and the cooling of the powerful JSS all generated major

obstacles for the Grumman and Eaton engineers. Ballast amounting to 700lb was placed in the nosewheel bay to compensate for the tail-heavy configuration, massive plumbing for ram-air heat exchanger and liquid-cooling provisions were incorporated into the weapons bay and taileron roots, to keep the equipment at a cool 40°F, and the F-111A's regular, engine-driven 60kVa generators were boosted to 90kVa capacity to drive the JSS – sufficient and reliable power is crucial to the electronic warfare (EW) mission. A series of non-stop ground and airborne tests lay ahead; started on 30 January 1975, this was gradually completed in step-by-step stages over the course of the ensuing 38 months.

The first machine to get airborne was 66-041 on 15 December 1975, with just the ventral 'canoe' to start with and sporting large red high-visibility markings on its control surfaces. The trials and tribulations of the

Above: M-1, 66-049, served as an aerodynamic test-bed after it was discovered that dedicated flight trials were required to perfect the fin installation. Here, with wings set at 72.5°, the 'Spark Vark' makes a high-speed dash over the Atlantic Ocean. (Via Rick Matteis)

following months highlighted several more obstacles. Col. Rick Matteis, USAF Ret., who went on from his F-111 tours in Nellis, Takhli and Upper Heyford to manage the EF-111A flight-test programme and was eventually to lead the whole EF-111A effort at the Aeronautical Systems Division (ASD) at Wright-Patterson AFB in Ohio, described the biggest initial problem of all, which concerned the fin:

> The original beef-up design turned out to be inadequate to support the 800lb of receiver equipment on top of the vertical tail. This required a schedule slip and a redesign and re-test. Originally we planned to build two prototypes into the full-up jamming configuration but the tail problem made it necessary to keep one aircraft as a pure aerodynamic test-bed.

M-1 (66-049) would serve as the aerodynamic trials machine, painted in a decorative red, white and blue finish and stuffed with ballast, while M-2 (66-041), finished in a warlike two-tone matt grey scheme with black trim on its radome and antennae covers, acted as the systems test-bed. In fact M-1's maiden hop on 10 March 1977 was cut short when the pilot of the chase aircraft saw what he thought were wrinkles on the fin. This turned out to be untrue, but it highlights the paranoia surrounding what should have been one of the less complex conversion tasks!

Following the engineering revisions, the re-beefed, even heavier fin worked well. On 17 May M-2 took to the skies, and both machines were pushed into a gruelling flight-test effort to make up for lost time. Grumman alone spent 3½ months engaged in 84 sorties (215 flight-hours) fine-tuning their new product,

followed by the USAF's Development Test and Evaluation (DT&E) at Eglin which pushed No. 2 through 78 sorties totalling 258 hours under a six month-long work-out. Aerodynamically the EF-111A behaved surprisingly well. Stability augmentation helps of course, as will the brand new GDFW digital flight control system currently under development for all 'One-Elevens'.* Most pilots describe the 'Electronic Fox' as 'identical to an F-111A with a 6,000lb payload', and 'full' 6g manoeuvres are possible. The 'football' in fact tends to reduce rather than increase any tendency to wallow at high speeds but it does impose certain limits in the landing pattern, due to side-slip in crosswinds. The normal crosswind limit for the 'Aardvark' is 35kts maximum, using a wing-low, rudder correction technique and a maximum 'crab' angle of 10°, reduced to about 15–20kts in a no-flap no-slat approach.† The EF-111A is restricted to 28kts, which cuts the margins in an emergency situation. For the early DT&E tests the 'interim beef' machine was limited to Mach 0.9, while its test instrumentation reduced the maximum crew weight differential to 40lb in order to guarantee that the capsule would work if

*The digital flight control system will be tested at Edwards AFFTC on board an EF-111A and an FB-111A starting in 1989. Contracts for a further 400 sets are envisaged.
†Restricted by side-loads on the main gear.

needed – not that any test crew dared even contemplate abandoning this single-copy multi-million dollar jet!

From a systems point of view, 66-041 heralded the dawn of a new electronic combat capability which remains unmatched to this day, jamming in up to seven different radar-operating wavebands simultaneously and covering anything from early-warning 'Spoon Rest' systems to 'Pat Hand' SA-4 acquisition radars. Grumman claimed that four or five 'Electronic Foxes', properly pre-positioned in 'race-track' orbits, could generate 'an unbroken electronic screen across Europe, from the Baltic to the Adriatic'. On one occasion during the active trials against simulated radar threats '041 simultaneously and accidentally blanketed out all commercial radio, taffic control and TV systems along the West Coast!', an error which was misinterpreted by some people as a major flaw in the package. The idea behind the AN/ALQ-99E spot-noise system was for it to tune its jamming power precisely at the operating frequencies of the threats and not barrage-jam like the old Destroyer, perhaps disrupting friendly electronic activities at the same time. Moreover the system had to work in true 'look-through' mode – to receive and process the threats being picked up while actually performing the jamming, something the Navy EA-6B equivalent had problems doing on occasion. The Defense Systems Acquisition Review Council (DSARC, or Defense Acquisition Board, DAB) wanted further reassurances, some of its number convinced that the JSS was an expensive 'Heath Robinson' creation. Rick Matteis:

> The test program was described by the US Congress and DoD as the most extensive test of an electronic warfare system ever attempted, but as inadequate. There was an element in our government that was trying to make a point of the fact that we did not have test ranges that would fully test a system such as this prior to committing to production. The rest of us felt that you would have to actually go to war, or at least ask the Russians to let us fly over their ground-based systems, to satisfy those people that were looking for complete realism!

To validate the machinery the USAF proceeded with a huge Initial Operational Test and Evaluation program under DAB's scrutiny. Detachment 3 of the Eglin Tactical Air Warfare Center (TAWC) was formed at Mountain Home AFB, Idaho, in April 1977 and commenced field trials with 66-041 starting that September. Flying over Florida against the TAWC's Consolidated Eglin Real-Time System to gauge jamming effectiveness, and moving on to Mountain Home that December, the aircraft and its Det 3 crew jetted their way around the United States, taking part in everything vaguely 'electronic' to wring out the aircraft's systems, wargames over Tonopah at Nellis AFB, Nevada, and integrated 'hunt and kill' missions with the George AFB, Californian F-4G 'Advanced Wild Weasel' radar-killers among them. Selective jamming was demonstrated on numerous occasions, blotting out all hostile emitters successfully with minimum disruption to its electronic colleagues; at one point an opposing Air National Guard unit requested the 'Electronic Fox' to turn off its jammers so that the controllers could locate their own aircraft for safety reasons.

DAB remained dissatisfied. Up to that point, they argued, Det 3 maintenance personnel had been aided by Grumman technical representatives who knew the EF-111A intimately and on 10 February 1979 they issued a memo insisting on proper 'blue shirt' (simulated air base) Follow-On Test and Evaluation trials, with Air Force maintenance people in complete charge. A modest half-dozen 'Electronic Fox' conversions were authorized in March, while from April through to October the USAF flew a further 86 sorties (261 flight-hours) to establish a firm foothold for the EF-111A. The crew chiefs and their technical specialist aides from the support shops were able to keep the jet airborne without any hitches: it required less than 20 maintenance man-hours per flight-hour (MMH/FH); mean time between failures (MTBF) was double that predicted, at 5.7hrs; and ground crews took an average of only 2.4hrs to isolate and repair faults – half that anticipated. Even the abort rate of 5 per cent was due largely to the fact that the hard-worked test-bed M-2 had skipped a scheduled depot-level overhaul and tended to suffer from minor fuel leaks. The electronics worked like a dream and the first supersonic systems run was made by M-2 on 25 July with Det 3 crew Maj. Thomas Heyde and Lt. Col. Donald Rich at the controls, clearing the bird for all-weather, all-speed operations. DAB relented, the ASD breathed a sigh of relief and the budgets for Fiscal Years 1979–1983 allowed for a further 34 aircraft, including the rework of the two test-beds to the full operational configuration.* Go-ahead!

'Alphas' selected for conversion were withdrawn from operations at Mountain Home AFB and flown direct to Calverton. Stripped of paint and torn down, each aircraft required an average nine-month gestative cycle to emerge at the other end as a fully fledged radar-jammer, the matt lemon zinc chromate primer topped with a coat of 'Ghost Gray' paint better suited to low- to medium-altitude operations. The job was described by Grumman as a '25 per cent change to the aircraft', embracing the installation of completely new wiring (totalling some 25,000 cables) and some 100 antennae associated with the JSS, the new Dalmo-Victor AN/ALR-62(V)4 Terminal Threat Warning System (TTWS) receiver and the Sanders AN/ALQ-137(V)4 Self-Protection System (SPS) jammer, collectively known as the Tactical Jamming System or TJS. A complete depot-type overhaul was thrown in for good measure. The EF-111A was virtually a brand new aircraft, and it needed a new name. In due deference to the vital role of the right-seat EWO or 'Crow', and to the aircraft's electronic mission, the USAF dubbed the EF-111A the 'Raven' – a name with strong electronic combat traditions. Many in the 'Aardvark' community refer to it simply as the 'Gray Airplane', with mixed respect and admiration.

Each Raven was put through extensive pre-accep-

---

*Twenty-one kits in FY79, 80 and 81, which included the two test-beds, twelve in FY82 and a final nine in FY83. The average cost was about $21 million an aircraft.

Aerodynamic trials machine M-1, 66-049, in its pretty decor of glossy white with red and pale blue trim and a yellow lightning bolt. Note the test boom on the nose and the absence of nosewheel doors. M-1 was later reworked to the full operational configuration and it returned to service on 20 November 1981. (Via Rick Matteis)

Above: A pair of 390th ECS, 366th TFW Ravens, with A-6, 66-019, nearest the camera. In common with four other Ravens, '019 is an ex 'Combat Lancer' 'Alpha'. Lt. Col. Tom Pickering was the 390th ECS's first CO; the present commander is Lt. Col. Richard M. Meeboer. (Mil-Slides)

Below: On the ramp at Nellis preparatory to a 'Green Flag'

wargame, this 390th ECS Raven displays its two-tone Ghost Gray camouflage to good effect, a scheme introduced to mask the EF-111A in its cloudy, medium-altitude habitat. Note the pivot-pylon, which is used for fuel or baggage but will soon tote HARM anti-radar missiles and Tacit Rainbow radar harassment drones. (Frank B. Mormillo)

tance trials, starting with DITMCO circuit analyses at Calverton and followed up by a series of up to six test flights in the hands of Grumman and USAF test pilots. A typical check flight started with a post-launch orbit at 15,000ft to pitch the TJS against Grumman's Electronic Warfare Test Range, located within the Calverton facility and called the 'Campsite'. This would be followed by a 500kt low-level run against 'No Man's Land', an island off the southern tip of Martha's Vineyard, Massachussetts, whose 60ft sheer cliff exercised the TFRs. A climb to 35,000ft for a dive and supersonic dash in fifth-stage afterburner was next on the roster, culminating in low-speed instrument landing system alignments and various wing and flap and slat settings during practice approaches in the landing circuit around Suffolk County Airport, prior to touchdown back at Calverton. Crews were then debriefed and any discrepancies noted, for fixing. Each machine took about 30 days to polish prior to acceptance – a very thorough check-out for a tactical aircraft. In total, 42 aircraft were passed fit and signed for between 4 November 1981 and 23 December 1985.*

### Gunfighters

The first unit to receive the new type for operations was Lt. Col. Herbert Tom Pickering Jr.'s 388th Electronic Combat Squadron (ECS), 366th TFW, located at Mountain Home AFB. The 388th ECS 'Griffins' had been formed on 1 July 1981 and were already in the throes of training new air crews for the mission by the time the first Raven, article A-3 (66-051), was greeted by the welcoming reception on 5 November. A prerequisite for the initial batch of trainees, all destined to be instructors, was 'prior experience in the Vark'. In practice candidates offered an average of 2,000hrs in the 'One-Eleven'. Men like the CO Tom Pickering had combat experience in both the EB-66C/E and F-111A; his Ops Officer EWO Maj. Robert Osterloh, for example, who was to assume command of the unit two years after its formation (and who was one of very few EWOs to have a major command position) had 442 combat hours in the old Destroyer. This wealth of experience provided a pool of eleven top-echelon crews by July 1982. All of them underwent a five-week, 200hr instruction course on Grumman's System Integrated Test Station, then a short flying phase with experienced Raven handlers from TAWC's Det 3, backed-up by extra hours in the Cockpit Familiarization Trainer (CFT). The CFT was crude but effective, comprising a mock-up of the EF-

*Shop Nos. A-3 to A-42. M-1 and M-2 were reworked and handed over on 20 November 1981 and 23 May 1984 respectively.

**366th TFW (12th AF, TAC)**
**Mountain Home AFB, Idaho**

| Squadron | Colour | Nickname | Code | Aircraft |
|----------|--------|----------|------|----------|
| 389th TFTS | Gold | Thunderbolts | } MO | F-111A |
| 391st TFS | Blue | Bold Tigers | | |
| 390th ECS | Red | Ravens | MO | EF-111A |

The 366th TFW 'Gunfighters' formed initially with F-111Fs, taking the aircraft over from the 347th TFW, under three squadrons, the 389th TFS (original code 'MP'), 390th TFS (original code 'MQ') and 391st TFS. The Wing converted to F-111As in 1977. In July 1981 the 388th ECS was formed but its designation was changed to 390th ECS in December 1982. The 390th ECS does not use the red squadron colour on its aircraft.

111A cockpit which permitted the flyers to learn all about the switches and controls. Pending the introduction of the fully-fledged AAI/Sperry Raven Operational Flight Trainer, in which a complete mission can be practised, including full EW threat and response simulation, some extras were added to the makeshift CFT, including what Tom Pickering described as a 'synergistic effect' – a videotape recorder and TV with sight-and-sound placed in front of the windshield to give the air crews a 'feel' for the live aircraft.

On 15 December 1982 the 388th ECS became the 390th ECS, taking up the designation of a resident fighter squadron which had been disbanded on 1 October to make F-111As available for conversion. Still using the 'Wild Boar' insignia but now the more appropriate motto 'Deny, Deceive, Defeat', the squadron set about filling up its ranks. Three years later, on the day before Christmas Eve, the last conversion, A-42 (67-044), was accepted at Calverton, the 390th ECS had 30 pairs of qualified air crews on strength, flying an authorized two dozen Ravens, and the 366th TFW 'Gunfighters' were back up to full strength, with 27 EF-111As and 43 'vanilla' models parked on the snowy ramp.

The background story bears telling, as the Mountain Home establishment has seen many 'firsts' and many changes over the years. The base started its 'One-Eleven' career with the definitive F-111F version under the aegis of the 347th TFW in September 1971, the month after GDFW test pilot R. E. Myrann took 'Foxtrot' No. 1 (70-2362) up on her maiden hop. The 366th TFW 'Gunfighters' assumed control of the force on 31 October 1972, with seventy F-111Fs equipping the 389th 'Thunderbolts', 390th 'Wild Boars', and 391st 'Bold Tigers'.* During their brief tenure in Idaho the F-111Fs

**Right: The 'office' of the 'Spark Vark', looking first at the accommodation, comprising olive brown-green seats, red head-rests and grey-brown straps, and then at the business end: the left-hand side of the dashboard console is virtually identical to all but the F-111D, apart from the absence of a coaming-mounted ODS/LCOS gunsight; the right-hand side was stripped out and gutted completely to make room for the new TJS controls. Note the DDI display tube and pedestal keyboard. The unhooded radar display is to the top left of the DDI, with the radar tracking handle relocated precariously between the capsule ejection levers. (Grumman Corporation)**

held down a worldwide reinforcement commitment and were used to travelling, often at short notice. In Operation 'Cape Train' Detachment 1 of the 'Gunfighters' was sent to Taegu AB, South Korea, at a time of tension there in August 1976. The North Koreans had violated the Neutral Zone separating the two States and things began to heat up uncomfortably. Within 31½hrs of the deployment execution order eight F-111Fs with 20mm gunpacks and AN/ALQ-87 ECM pods on board were standing by with Mk. 82 'iron' bombs, having made the voyage in 11½hrs with four AAR hook-ups; twenty machines in all were dispatched within 6½hrs, requiring 21 cargo aircraft to 'trash haul' the spares. Mission orders were drafted and the 'tapes cut' for their Mk. IIB avionics but things cooled down considerably with the presence of the 'Aardvarks'. The aircraft, mostly from the 390th TFS, returned to Idaho in October via RAAF Amberley. In the year following the Korean showdown and American Bicentennial celebrations Operation 'Ready Switch' brought an abrupt end to F-111F activities at Mountain Home: all 'Foxtrots' were transferred to USAFE while the 'Gunfighters' took over the 'Roadrunners' F-111As, completing the transfer by 6 August; the 474th TFW, in turn, converted to F-4D Phantoms pending the introduction of the next GDFW

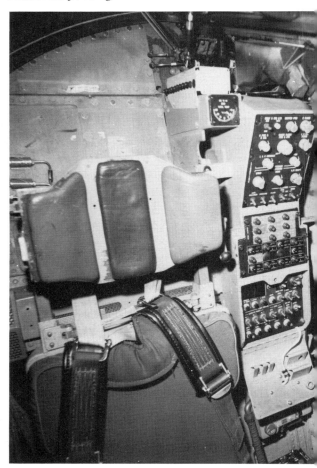

product, the F-16 Fighting Falcon.† Switching to analogue systems, the 366th TFW saw its Wing heavily denuded as aircraft were made available for conversion to EF-111A standard and then increase once more as the reworked Ravens returned.

Today, as ever, fledgeling Raven pilots must be experienced 'One-Eleven' flyers: the EF-111A has only one set of flight controls and during the heat of an electronic battle, when the EWO is preoccupied with the enemy defences, the AC is obliged to take charge of navigation and the self-protect systems all by himself. The radar tracking handle, the PPI radar display presented by the modified AN/APQ-160 ARS and the analogue NCU/INS panel were moved to the centre console and mid-dashboard position to put them within easy reach of either crew member. The left-hand side of the cockpit remained virtually intact, minus the ODS lead-computing sight, and pilots should be able to step out of an F-111A and into an EF-111A and 'go through the switches' blindfolded.

Prospective EWOs are usually drawn from candidates with about 1,500hrs as 'Wizzos' in the strike fleet yet an increasing number of promising candidates straight out of the Mather AFB, California, 'Fightergator College' are now joining up. They must undergo the complete F-111A WSO course and then an extra 127hrs of academics, 30hrs of simulator time and 20 flying hours with Lt. Col. Richard M. Meeboer's 390th ECS before being deemed anywhere near mission-ready.‡ This extra tuition is vital: the right-hand portion of the 'office' was altered radically and is the real business branch of the aircraft. Dominating the EWO's field of vision is a large 11in tube or detail display indicator (DDI), a new DDI control pedestal keyboard which replaced the stick, and an extensively revised right-hand console turned over to 'jammer control' and 'receiver control' panels comprising rows of switches and knobs to prime any or all of the ten antennae under the 'canoe' and to activate the receivers mounted in the 'football'.

---

*The 347th TFW had formed at Mountain Home on 15 May 1971. Official F-111F customer acceptance dates involved 28 F-111Fs between September and December 1971, 42 between January and June 1972 and a further 36 examples in dribs and drabs between February 1973 and November 1976. F-111F No. 106 (74-0188) was the last all-new 'One-Eleven' to be delivered and marked the end of 'Aardvark' production.
†The 474th TFW is to disband in 1989, bringing an end to the pioneering F-111 Wing. See page 153 *et seq.* for more details regarding Operation 'Ready Switch'.
‡See 'Cosmic Aardvarks' (Part 3) for a description of F-111 training, for both pilots and 'Wizzos'.

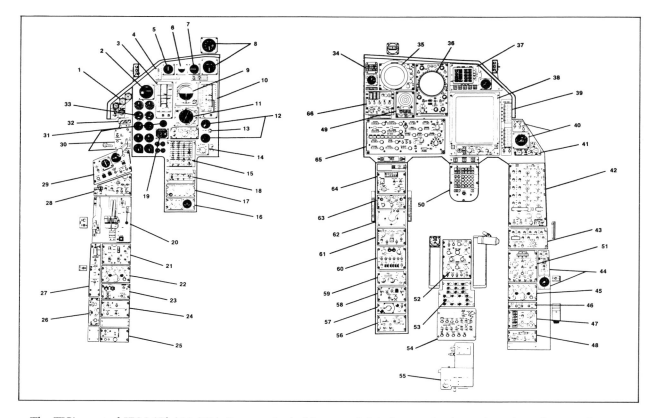

The TJS's central IBM 4Pi AN-AYA-6 computer holds all the information on the envisaged threats in its 'memory read' chips. New information can be fed in to supplement this either through the tedious process of tapping in entries on the EWO's DDI control pedestal keyboard or more speedily by changing the computer software. The latter is accomplished prior to the mission and takes only about five minutes if a pre-programmed module containing all the essentials is plugged in. The EWO is then free to call up a suitable menu on the DDI, check the programme and make corrections if necessary. These cockpit check-lists and BIT checks are a particular speciality of the ground-based avionics technicians, who can 'prime' a Raven ready for the EWO. Computer 'mission modelling' is also used – a high-tech 'game' which replaces the old maps, pins and threads with a console simulation of the envisaged radar opposition and how it can best be countered.

Once the Raven is airborne the receivers 'sweep' across the selected wavebands (ranging, approximately, from A to J bands, or around 0.1 to over 10.5Gc), listening for hostile radar emissions. Threats picked up which match the catalogue of pre-programmed radars – including any unidentified but potentially hostile ones – are then flashed up on the DDI. In this display mode the horizontal axis of the DDI corresponds to relative 'target' bearing, and the vertical axis indicates frequency. With the jammers selected and the bank of status lights adjacent to the DDI confirming that the systems are operational, high-power spot-noise and

modulated pseudo-deception jamming, radiated in selected 'widths', will later be accomplished automatically by the JSS on command. The screen displays the jamming cursor laid over the appropriate threat symbol; a giant thumb switch at the bottom of the DDI keyboard, similar in many respects to a control stick trim button, enables the EWO to override the automatic selection of the JSS by moving the jammer cursor on to another threat within its waveband limits – one the EWO considers more dangerous. Either way, with the jammers earmarked for specific radars and holding their position on the 'contacts' using antenna steering course corrections from the Raven's INS and computers, the EWO has simply to monitor the proceedings and ensure that his box of tricks is ready to radiate.

The initiation of jamming is usually accomplished at a given range or time – a delicate trade-off between 'announcing' a strike mission by jamming too early and inadequate cover by jamming too late – by activating the master radiate switch. All preselected jammers are then sequenced into play a few milli-seconds apart, a measure designed to avoid a sudden 'vertical' drop in the power supply curve which might cause the IBM computer to 'hiccup' and switch itself off. From this moment the 'closed loop' systems enables the JSS to be left in complete control, to counter new 'contacts' as they emerge: a jammer will only radiate for as long as the assigned threat is on the airwaves – as soon as the receiver, listening in 'lookthrough', informs the computer that the threat has turned off, so the relevant

**Left: The EF-111A Raven cockpit.** The pilot's side of the cockpit is very similar to that of all other marks of the F-111 save the 'Delta', with the exception of the bank of engine status needles which were shifted *en bloc* to the left side of the dashboard. The navigation and radar controls and displays were moved to the centre of the cockpit to make room for the new receiver and jamming controls and displays, at right. 1. Jettison, and engine fire warning switches and lamps. 2. Wing-sweep and flap/slat position indicator. 3. Airspeed and mach indicator. 4. Threat lamps. 5. Standby airspeed indicator. 6. Standby attitude indicator. 7. Standby vertical velocity indicator. 8. Radar altimeter indicator. 9. Attitude director indicator (ADI). 10. Altitude-vertical velocity indicator. 11. Horizontal situation indicator (HSI). 12. Fuel quantity. 13. Fuel quantity test button. 14. Fuel quantity indicator selector knob. 15. Main caution lamp panel. 16. Ram doors/oil quantity panel. 17. Instrument landing system control panel. 18. Auxiliary caution indicator panel. 19. Control surface indicator. 20. Throttle control panel. 21. Autopilot damper panel. 22. Interphone control panel. 23. Auxiliary flight control panel. 24. Windshield rain remove and anti-ice controls. 25. Oxygen and anti-*g* suit control. 26. Compass control panel.

27. Flight control test panel. 28. Misc. switch panel. 29. Landing gear control. 30. Landing gear control. 31. True airspeed indicator. 32. Barrier arresting hook and external stores jettison panel. 33. Engine status indicator panel. 34. Annunciator indicator panel. 35. TFR video. 36. Unhooded radarscope. 37. JSS/SPS caution panel. 38. Digital display indicator (DDI). 39. Jammer status panel. 40. JSS modes select and bearing/distance/heading indicator. 41. Jammer power and test panel. 42. Jammer control panel. 43. Receiver control panel. 44. Power monitor panel. 45. Interphone control panel. 46. Antenna select: UHF, tacan and IFF. 47. AN/ALE-28 CMDS control panel. 48. AN/AAR-34 CMRS control panel. 49. AN/ALR-62 TTWS indicator. 50. DDI control pedestal. 51. AN/ALQ-137 SPS control. 52. Lighting control. 53. Crew module DC power panel. 54. Ground check panel. 55. Oxygen and suit control. 56. Air conditioning control. 57. HF control panel. 58. Generator control. 59. Tacan control. 60. IFF control. 61. ARS radar mode controls. 62. Radar tracking handle. 63. TFR ride mode and clearance select panel. 64. Fuel control. 65. NCU/INS computer controls and 'windows'. 66. UHF radio control panel. (Gumman Corporation)

jammer is deactivated or assigned a new threat as one crops up. In a 'low-threat' area boredom might even creep in as the EWO passively and hypnotically watches the JSS in action against just two or three emitters; in a dense electromagnetic environment – an 'electronic thicket' – there will probably exist many more threats than the JSS can cope with unaided and manual intervention will be necessary to assign jammers to the radars presenting the greatest hazards to the 'friendlies'. This electronic battle of wits between the 'Crow' and his adversaries on the ground has been likened to a 'cat and mouse game'; given the ferocity of the defences, which are aiming to reply with a barrage of SAMs, some of which might be tailored to home on the Raven's powerful JSS, the phrase 'duelling mongoose and cobra' more readily springs to mind!

The order of priorities that the EWO must take into account changes not only with the degree of enemy radar activity but also according to the nature of the Raven's assignment, be it 'barrier stand-off', 'close-in' or 'primary' jamming, in which the same radars assume a different order in the threat hierarchy. 'Stand-off', the 'safe mission', involves two or three Ravens orbiting in 'race-track' patterns at up to 50 miles behind the Forward Edge of the Battle Area or Forward Line of Troops (FEBA or FLOT). Cruising at a blasé 15,000–20,000ft with their wings spread out at 16° for maximum cruise economy, they can maintain their circuitous loiter for up to four hours at a stretch. Between them they put out a 'maximum jam footprint' to generate an electronic 'barrier' or 'screen' to obscure the position of strike packages of fighter-bombers preparing to enter enemy-dominated airspace, and provide cover for vulnerable E-3 Sentry AWACS and even GLOBs performing refuelling operations. The essence is surprise: numbers, routes and timing are hidden, to keep the enemy guessing.

'Close-in' tasks a solo jet or pair of Ravens close to the FEBA at more discreet altitudes of around 500ft, to support the A-10 'Warthog' and Harrier 'mud movers' engaged in close air support (CAS) work, sheltering them from all but the heat-seeking jeep- and shoulder-launched missiles, manual AAA and small-arms fire – the unpredictable. The CAS aircraft can thus concentrate on dropping their bundles of chaff and flares and deliver cannon shells, rockets and bombs on target.

'Primary', the mission exclusive to the USAF EF-111A and the one considered to be its forte, requires deep penetration as escorts on interdiction operations way behind the forward lines or against second-echelon forces on battlefield area interdiction (BAI) missions. A pair of Ravens may precede, accompany or even trail behind a loosely knit strike package, staying low in TFR mode and then 'popping up' to 500ft for brief bursts of mid- to high-band radar-jamming activity, to cover their colleagues during the heat of the bomb runs when they are most vulnerable to attack from 'terminal threat' systems. The JSS has to be stepped into action quickly and it is customary to have everything switched on and ready to transmit before the 'pop'. For a bigger interdiction strike – a latter-day Ploesti or loosely routed 'Victor Alert' 'WARPAC heating' mission – further grey birds would orbit at the rear as 'barrier' sentries to cover the 'TF-ing' package as it entered and exited the thick, heavily defended first- and second-echelon electronic defences.

These wide-ranging requirements, in support of numerous types of aircraft, are what make the computer-assisted jamming job so challenging. It would be disastrous, for example, to jam a ZSU-23/4 'Gundish' whose high-velocity cannon were beyond reach of the 'friendlies' in preference to a SAM which is able to pepper or blast a colleague. The 'whats, wheres and whens' of jamming are the true test of a 'Crow'.

All Raveneers are introduced to the mission over Mountain Home's 109,468-acre Saylor Creek bombing and electronic warfare range in Southern Idaho, which contains several surprises managed by the 392nd Elec-

**Above: The 42nd ECS at Upper Heyford, England, formed initially under the jurisdiction of the 20th TFW, under the leadership of Lt. Col. Dave L. Vesely. Here article A-32, 67-052, displays slats and Fowler flaps in action. The streamlined fairings above the wing glove house some of the receivers for the AN/ALQ-137 SPS and AN/ALR-62 TTWS; other SPS and TTWS antennae are located anonymously behind the sleek pale grey nose. Another 'Heyford Raven, 66-057, was one of two which provided stand-off jamming during Operation 'El Dorado Canyon' in April 1986. (USAFE photo by Sgt. David S. Nolan)**

tronic Combat Range Squadron.* The 392nd ECRS runs a mini Integrated Air Defense System (IADS), which includes mobile simulated AAA, acquisition, GCI, height-finder, surveillance and SAM terminal threat radars, all wired up to emulate a Soviet IADS. The EWO's jamming response to the simulators – including reactions against the latest Multiple Threat Emitter Simulators (MUTES) – is duly judged using Electronic Warfare Evaluation Program (EWEP) techniques, by processing the data from the MUTES and MSR-T4 analyzers. The results are available for the flyers' perusal, enabling tactics and procedures to be refined and to highlight the novices' strengths and weaknesses.

The readiness of the 390th ECS is another facet of their performance which is constantly under review; it is gauged in the Air Force's oldest, most customary manner – on the basis of total sorties generated. Every F-111 base has its placards listing monthly sortie goals, with missions flown, abort rates and so forth, as an announcement of each squadron's week-to-week performance. For Mountain Home's 'Red Squadron' (a colour not actually seen on the EF-111As, but only displayed by its red-capped Aircraft Maintenance Unit, the 'Raven Keepers') the first test came in early October 1983 when the 390th ECS was thrown into Exercise 'Run Fast 83-7', designed to test the unit's ability to respond quickly to orders for action – a 'surge' event which aims to get the maximum number of mission-ready crews and jets airborne and ready for battle. The 390th ECS have since progressed beyond advance-notice 'Run Fast' and no-notice 'Showdown' launches

to take their jets elsewhere for training, to Nellis AFB, Nevada, for 'Flag' wargames, out of State on major TAC manoeuvres such as 'Amalgam Warrior' and even on transoceanic, globetrotting excursions. Their first trip to Europe took place in the late summer of 1986 when a half dozen aircraft flew to RAF Boscombe Down, England, for four weeks as part of 'Coronet Papago'. More significant was the type's first 'Coronet West' deployment to the Pacific region, from 14 March to 10 April 1988 – the first time that Ravens had ventured to the Orient. A quartet of EF-111As led by Detachment Commander Maj. Emmet Beeker III flew to and staged out of MCAS Iwakuni, Japan, to take part in the local 'Cope Max' and bigger combined US and South Korean (ROK) 'Team Spirit 88' exercises, supported by elements of the 392nd ECRS. The major impetuses of 'Coronet West' were to familiarize Raven-handlers with the Pacific environment and to train the resident PACAF and ROK fighter units in the use of complex combat electronics, on a 'two-way street' basis, as Maj. Beeker described it. More deployments to South Korea and Japan are planned.

Up to full strength for four years, in a typical month the 390th ECS generates some 200–220 sorties. In FY86 Col. Dennis C. Sammer's 'Gunfighters' used up 28.5 million gallons of JP-4 fuel to fly 7,952 sorties for a total of 18,127 flying hours, the 28-strong Raven establishment accounting for 39 per cent of that tally for an average of 112 sorties or 255hrs per aircraft. Two years later CO Col. Richard G. Hellier's 'Gunfighters' are continuing to burn rubber and jet fuel at an equally dramatic rate, to hone their skills and maintain a steady flow of qualified analogue strike and electronic warfare crews.†

### Let 'em eat Crow
As USAFE take time to remind everyone, Mountain Home is not the sole bastion of electronic combat capability. In March 1982 a Site Activation Task Force (SATAF) was established at RAF Upper Heyford, England, to prepare the base ('bed it down') for Ravens. In common with the SATAF in Idaho, this included a complete review of maintenance procedures and the fielding of Grumman AN/ALM-204 automatic test

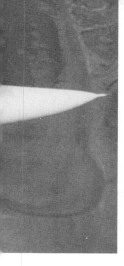

equipment benches, comprising six consoles which perform electronic checks on the EF-111A's 49 separate TJS line replaceable units (LRUs) or 'black boxes', which can be unplugged for shop-level repairs to keep the radiating Ravens on the wing.

The new squadron revived the title of the 42nd Tactical Electronic Warfare Squadron, which had been deactivated as the last EB-66C barrage-jammer outfit on 15 March 1974. Bearing a new emblem and re-labelled the 42nd ECS, the unit came into formation on 1 July 1983 under the command of Lt. Col. David L. Vesely, an experienced helicopter and F-111F pilot. Briefings with the SATAF followed as the 42nd ECS took over a

portion of the aerodrome (an established 'One-Eleven' base) and boosted maintenance facilities, which included the creation of an extra flight-line Aircraft Generation Squadron.‡ Finally, after a seven-hour transatlantic flight and two in-flight top-ups, at around 3 p.m. on 3 February 1984 David Vesely and Maj. Roger W. Brooks (as Lt. Col., the current CO) brought EF-111A 66-037 into gentle contact with Upper Heyford's main runway. A reception committee from the parent F-111E-equipped 20th TFW and USAF 'top brass', including ASD Systems Program Office Director Col. Rick Matteis were there to greet 'NATO Raven One', the nickname daubed on the aircraft's pale grey underwing baggage pod. Over the course of the next eighteen months the Raven outfit would expand to encompass 60 squadron members and 225 specialists, using ten F-111Es as companion trainers pending the final arrival of its full complement of a dozen EF-111As.§

On 1 July 1985 the 42nd ECS became part of the 66th ECW, 65th Air Division, headquartered at Sembach AB in West Germany as a component of the Seventeenth

---

*The unit previously operated at Gila Bend, Arizona, and became operational in Idaho in November 1982. Attached to the 366th TFW as the 4492nd ECRS from 1 July 1984, it became known as the 392nd ECRS on 1 April 1985. The unit spends at least half the year on tour around the United States and, further afield at Cold Lake, Canada, takes part in 'Maple Flag' wargames in the forests and icy open country of the north.

†Under the Ribicoff-Edwards committee base closure plans, George AFB, California, is to be closed and its 37th TFW F-4G Wild Weasels are to be consolidated into an electronic battle organization alongside the 390th ECS EF-111As at Mountain Home. The bulk of the 366th TFW's F-111As are to be transferred to Cannon AFB, New Mexico, in mid-1991, where all F-111 conversion training will be centred in the next decade.

‡See 'Work Smarter, Not Harder' and 'TAB-V Pigs' (Part 3).

§The full unit strength has fluctuated between eleven and thirteen Ravens. Aircraft have recently been exchanged with Mountain Home as USAFE examples became due for depot-level overhauls in California.

**Below: Making a clean take-off from 'Heyford's runway with its updated TF30-P-109 engines in action, EF-111A A-32, 67-052, heads for the ranges. It is nicknamed 'Cherry Bomb', a sobriquet used previously by a 42nd TEWS EB-66C in Vietnam. The 42nd TEWS was given recent fame in the film *Bat 21*, which portrays Lt. Col. Iceal E. Hambleton's ordeal after having been shot down in his Destroyer. (Tim Laming)**

Air Force, USAFE, to develop a 'unified strategy to coordinate electronic combat assets'. This integrated structure is what makes the European Ravens' mission so different from that of their colleagues in the 'Gem State'. As David Vesely noted during the inauguration of 42nd ECS operations, 'We are NATO committed and the NATO emblem on our squadron patch symbolizes that undertaking'. Upper Heyford's crews attend classes to familiarize themselves with European military procedures before participating in multinational manoeuvres. At Upper Heyford the Raveneers lead an almost separate existence from the co-located F-111E strike Wing, despite the social liaisons, and are just as likely to be seen flying alongside other USAFE aircraft or with Dutch, Luftwaffe or RAF machines as they are to be found escorting the tan and green 'Echoes' on joint sorties from the home-drome. The first off-base NATO event in which Ravens participated took place in May 1985 when two EF-111As and twenty crew members flew to Italy to provide jamming cover in Exercise 'Distant Hammer 85', a joint effort with the Fifth Allied Tactical Air Force. Combined operations have since expanded to embrace the Second and Fourth ATAFs in the north, though the Raven's good endurance means it can often fly directly from its specially allocated shelters in Oxfordshire; needless to say this was accomplished during a major 'feet-wet', live jamming operation in April 1986.*

USAFE takes its electronic business very seriously and, under the 65th AD, combined operations are the name of the game: working with F-4G 'Advanced Wild Weasel' radar-killers from Spangdahlem's 52nd TFW; providing a stream of incoming and outgoing data with the 6910th Electronic Security Wing; and joint jamming missions with their tan cousins from Sembach – five giant, lumbering 43rd ECS Lockheed EC-130H 'Compass Call' Command, Control, Communications Counter-measures ($C^3$/CM or 'Comjam') Hercules, outfitted with powerful communications receiver and jamming equipment.† Weaving these aircraft into action without any one disrupting the other is a complex task: if not careful, for example, the Raven might block the nostrils of 'Weasels' seeking to acquire an emitter's position for a missile attack, or disrupt the 'Compass Calls' sensitive receiver equipment – or even foul a protective CAP F-15 Eagle's intercept radar. This tangy, multi-layered electronic sandwich has to be spliced together very carefully to counter the Soviet IADS. Realistic training, however, presents very difficult problems. The Polygone electronic warfare range, situated on the German border, contains many MUTES and Army air defence batteries eager for a scrap with electrons but, just as with bombs, clearance is required from the Range Safety Officer (and, in this instance, civil authorities) prior to jamming, in case the Ravens and 'Compass Calls' play havoc with the congested commercial airline traffic or disrupt citizens' enjoyment of prime-time radio and TV! Europe is simply too congested, and considerable restrictions are placed on the units.

Ex-'Thunderbirds' leader and TAWC commander

Gen. Tom Swalm was well aware of these limitations and in 1982 initiated a special electronic warfare exercise called 'Green Flag' as an adjunct to the already successful 'Red Flag' wargames. Held at Nellis on a regular basis, deep in the American desert in a relatively unpopulated area, the aircraft can have a free run on their equipment. It is not to be confused with 'Red Flag'. As 1Lt. Steven Solmonson noted, 'It's as different from "Red Flag" as the Rolling Stones are to Michael Jackson . . . a TAC management initiative led by TAWC to provide centralized direction of all aspects of electronic combat'. It comprises three combined combat support tasks – EW, $C^3$/CM and the suppression of enemy air defences. Both Raven squadrons, along with EC-130Hs from Sembach and Davis-Monthan AFB, Arizona, SAC RC-135s, F-4G Weasels from George and Spangdahlem, TAC E-3 Sentries, RF-4C 'TEREC' passive-only radar plotters and Navy/Marines EA-6B Prowlers, fly in a frenzied electronic battle that lasts six weeks. Flying as the 'Blue' force, they must counter a Soviet-like 'Red' force IADS, which employs fighters and GCI, and acres of simulated threats run by the 554th Range Group, with Army and Guard Hawk and Roland SAM batteries thrown into the mêlée for good measure. The 'threats' include mind-boggling devices like the Raytheon 'ADEWS' and Tracor 'MJBs', capable of jamming the aircraft's navigation, communication and IFF transponders (and which will soon be able to jam the F-111s' TFRs!) and an array of radars ranging from captured Soviet 'Height Finder' and early-warning scanners to the MSQ-T13 which emulates the 'Straight Flush' acquisition and tracking system of the deadly SA-6 'Gainful' and 23g-capable SA-11 'Gadfly' SAMs. It is a very busy affair, as turboprop-, turbojet- and turbofan-powered machines jostle into position with their electronic gear activated: the cloud-splitting 'Compass Calls' take on the data links and communications and the prancing, eager 'Weasels' the SAM and AAA sites, tasking the sensitive Ravens to jam the SAM acquisition radars and to screen all friendlies from early-warning GCI systems that provide vectors for opposing F-5E and F-16 'Aggressor' interceptors.

'Green Flag' has not only provided an opportunity for the multifarious electronic combat aircraft to learn how to work together; it has also rendered them all the more potent. For example, if a radar 'teases' an EF-111A or is required to stay on the air for much longer than is desirable in order to acquire the 'Blue' force through the jamming, it becomes more susceptible to attack by the 'Weasels', who will load and fire their HARM missiles, each of which is capable of 'remembering' where the threat is even if the radar is turned off.

---

*See 'North Africa Bomb Competition' in 'Statue De Libya Raiders' (Part 3).
†Unlike the Navy/Marines EA-6B Prowlers, which also carry AN/ALQ-92 or AN/ASQ-191 Comjam equipment, the Raven is a pure radar-jammer and leaves the Comjam task to the 'Compass Calls'. In addition to the five EC-130Hs flown by the 43rd ECS, 66th ECW, a further five operate with the 41st ECS, 355th TFW, at Davis-Monthan AFB in Arizona. A further six EC-130Hs are to be fielded but no plans exist for further EF-111A conversions.

Conversely, if a 'Weasel' has bitten off more than he can chew the Raven EWO can take manual control of his JSS to provide a carefully laid-down screen, permitting the radar-killer to egress safely and recompose himself, ready to jump back at the enemy once more. 'Green Flag' is popular with the electronic people and generates a lot of sorties. In 'Green Flag 88-3', held from 20 February through to 16 April, for example, 34 different units, 1,400 air crew and 4,230 support personnel generated 3,774 sorties! The Ravens accounted for a big slice of the action, the Idaho establishment alone sending a clutch of EF-111As, 280 'Raven Keepers', and members from the 392nd ECRS and TAWC's Det 3, with 390th ECS crew members rotating in and out of the battle to broaden its participation. The results were reviewed and tabulated and the relative effectiveness of

each participant gauged accordingly. As might be expected, the EF-111As were a key ingredient, and they soon find new challenges. To add extra spice the event will soon embrace the USAF's recently unveiled 4450th Tactical Group Lockheed F-117A 'Senior Trend' covert stealth strike aircraft; these passive sensor-equipped jets will require selective, stand-off noise-jamming to mask the occasional radar 'glitter' from their radical, angular airframes and the Raven has been described as a perfect mission companion. New tactics and new doctrines are evolving constantly.

Hardware and software modifications to the JSS have also been in the pipeline for some years. In October 1984 the USAF awarded Eaton AIL and GDFW a contract to develop a new range of modular exciters, signal processors and modified receivers for the 'Spark Vark', to expand and 'tailor' waveband coverage according to the immediate mission requirements. In this manner, for example, an EF-111A might be fitted and programmed to launch with all ten jammers directed at just two or three bands. A 390th ECS EF-111A, 66-038, was flown to Carswell AFB, Texas, on 6 November 1985 and towed to GDFW for integration trials. The difficult development feat was to be accomplished in concert with the large Air Force Electronic

**Below: 'Let 'Em Eat Crow', A-38, 67-034, is the 42nd ECS 'flagship', assigned at the time of this photograph to Lt. Col. Bill McAdams. The current CO is Lt. Col. Roger Brooks. Note the spurious '642' painted on the nose-gear door. References to 'Crows' are part of the history of the electronic warfare world and the connection no doubt influenced the choice of 'Ye Olde Crow' for sister-ship 67-035. (Tim Laming)**

Above: A pair of 42nd ECS Ravens on the wing, in the
landing pattern around Upper Heyford: 67-032 is nearest
and '055 leads. The aircraft are officially part of the 66th
ECW headquartered at Sembach AB, West Germany, who
have the befitting motto 'Omnia' ('We Observe All'), under
the direction of Maj. Gen. Robert L. Rutherford's
Seventeenth Air Force, USAFE. (MAP)

Below: Article A-9, 66-013, is one of two Ravens assigned to
full-time follow-on development work with Detachment 3 of
the 4485th 'Combat Echo' test squadron, normally forward-
located at Mountain Home but frequently to be found at the
parent TAWC base, Eglin AFB, Florida. Note the open bay
and 'canoe', the TAWC badges, the 'OT' code and the black
and white chequered fin stripe. (MAP)

Warfare Evaluation System and the new General Dynamics anechoic facility at Fort Worth but problems soon arose, eventually leading to cost overruns and schedule slippages which killed the whole effort: a stop-work order went into effect on 20 May 1988.* Much to everyone's embarrassment, a 26-member team headed by CMSgt. David Caron had already been dispatched from Mountain Home on 17 March, and it spent three weeks restoring the aircraft back to its former glory. Both the team and the Raven returned to Idaho on 8 April.

TAWC's Det 3, 4485th Operational Test Squadron, still actively engaged in trials with their pair of 'OT'-coded EF-111As at both Mountain Home and Eglin, are now scratching around for an alternative update. Grumman, who lost out on the TJS upgrade bid, have been studying the problem in depth and believe they can effect a once-and-forever hardware change, to keep the aircraft viable well into the early twenty-first century. Their plans, still on 'hold' because of recent budget constraints, include replacing the computer complex with a bigger-capacity AN/AYK-14-6B system and moving to 'high order' computer languages. In the past minor Raven updates referred to as 'software' changes have actually involved changing 'memory read' microchips; with the new system the EF-111A could be updated on a regular basis purely by flight-line reprogramming.

## Tacit Rainbow

Several less conspicuous updates have so far survived the fiscal axe. In the pilot's quest for extra power, P&W and the USAF have developed a kit which permits the Propulsion Branches at Mountain Home and Upper Heyford to modify the TF30-P-103 engines to P-109 standard, boosting total maximum thrust by an extra 4,680lb and total military thrust to 24,860lb at minimum cost. This much-welcomed update has been applied to all EF-111As and will do much to compensate for the new array of weaponry planned for the type and designed to sharpen the Raven's talons.† At present the aircraft carry only baggage pods (and on rare occasions a pair of drop tanks) but they will soon be sporting Side-winder air-to-air missiles for self-defence, HARM anti-radar missiles to enable the type to decommission rather than merely jam the opposition and – the most sophisticated strap-on of them all – Tacit Rainbow.

Bearing a remarkable similarity to a cruise missile, upon which this air-breathing, winged anti-radar 'harassment drone' is based, Tacit Rainbow carries enough fuel to cruise for up to 1½hrs, permitting it to loiter for an extended period over the enemy radar network after launch. On receipt of a threat picked up by its wide-spectrum 'sniffer', the missile switches to attack mode and guides itself to the 'contact'; should the opposition shut down to avoid being struck, Tacit Rainbow breaks off its attack and resumes its loiter, awaiting a new threat. The weapon is still in development but the USAF envisages Ravens pre-programming and launching up to two such weapons per sortie, supported by numerous strike aircraft which will fill the skies with the device preparatory to big air strikes. With Tacit Rainbow orbiting on guard beyond the FEBA ready to knock out any hostile radars, and the newly adapted Unisys AN/APR-47-equipped F-4G 'Weasels' trolling the area with HARMs and electro-optically guided Maverick missiles, come the next possible call for action the Ravens might well have an easy job to perform. Such, no doubt, is wishful thinking; counter-countermeasures are often very cheap to develop and field, and few people share the pretence that anything but a whole new unknown array of anti-aircraft systems awaits to challenge the cunning 'Electronic Fox'!

---

*Plans to upgrade the SPS jammer to Sanders AN/ALQ-189 or ITT/Westinghouse AN/ALQ-165 standard, in common with the FB-111A update, have been shelved.
†USAF F-111As and F-111Es are similarly switching to TF30-P-109 powerplants.

# 3. BEARING THE FLAG

## 'Work Smarter, Not Harder'

Typically, it was raining on 12 September 1970 when Col. Grant A. Smith, 20th TFW commander, led in the first pair of F-111Es to Upper Heyford, England.* The trip from Langley AFB, Virginia, had taken 6hrs 43mins with a single tanker prod en route. The two drab 'swingers' squatted on damp concrete for the perusal of those who braved the weather to see the new shape in town. Despite their anonymous appearance, the only markings being national insignia and camouflaged serials, this initial brace was due for the 79th TFS, the 'Tigers'. They were nominated in October 1969 as the first USAFE F-111 unit and went on to achieve full IOC a year later – a few months ahead of Nellis and in spite of the suspension of deliveries in the first six months of 1970, held up by WCTB problems.†

The BCU-equipped 'Harvest Reaper' jets had served well as F-111E test-beds and 'Alpha' No. 38 (66-020) had received a thorough 'Tac-Eval' at Cannon AFB in late 1968, wringing out the new AN/AAR-34 CMRS and AN/APS-109 RHAWS self-protect systems, ECPs and TOs which would be applied to production F-111Es and retrofitted to the F-111As respectively. A year later fourteen fully fledged F-111Es were operational with the 422nd FWS at Nellis, providing conversion training for new flyers alongside ground crews under the auspices of Field Training Detachment 916S.

There were mixed feelings among 'Tiger' pilots as they saw their F-100 Super Sabres distributed to other squadrons. They had only moved in from RAF Wethersfield six months previously and still regarded their 'Hun' as a fairly 'hot' ship on a base whose history was full of lumbering bombers with names like Hyderabad, Hinaidi Hendon, Hereford – and Heyford. Upper Heyford had bombing in its blood and the F-111 looked pretty much like a bomber too. The 'Tigers' had won seven battle honours in the Second World War, earning the nickname the 'Loco Squadron' for 193 locomotives destroyed by their P-38s and P-51s. After eighteen further years with the F-84 and F-100 they were not anxious to be seen flying a 'pregnant duck with a dubious past'. Fighters also have guns as a rule and it would have distressed pilots who were used to a quartet of 20mm shooting-irons to know that the 'Gat-pack' that the F-111E was supposed to carry would hardly ever be used. Worst of all was the idea of having to share a cockpit with a 'whizz-kid', especially one where the pilot was not clearly placed in the front seat! However, on entering the cockpit (never an easy task), they found that the changes were all improvements. Despite its AUW of 45–50 tons the aircraft lacked none of the F-100's agility, while its vastly improved stability took all

the luck and guesswork out of bombing; above all, the aircraft's systems appeared to be from a different century.

By January 1971 the 79th TFS was up to strength and the 55th TFS had received its first aircraft (68-019). A month later the last four 'Huns' blazed out and by April 54 F-111Es were on base, moving rapidly towards a total of 78. The last unit to convert was the 77th TFS, who assumed an operational role on 27 July. As the Wing reached full strength command passed to Col. Richard M. Baughn, an Iowan and an 'old head' in fighters. With the prodigious endurance available from the 'Vark' it became necessary to establish a series of combat profile missions (CPMs) to give realistic long-range sorties. Eleven 'packages' were established, taking F-111Es on routes ranging from northern Scotland to France, southern Spain, the Baltic and the Adriatic. A CPM involved a low-level high-speed day or night flight on a precise, timed route. These CPMs established a pattern which remains much the same to this day.

New technology meant massive logistical expansion. Numbers on the base's payroll rose to 3,500, 350 of whom were concerned with the new bird's avionics. Singer's Link Division supplied a flight simulator based on the GPB-4 computer. Large engine maintenance shops arose, fuel storage was expanded to meet the long-range newcomer's thirst and new hangars were constructed, leading eventually to the modern, second-generation monolithic TAB-V (Theater Air Base, Vulnerability) shelters, whose 124ft × 82ft floor area provides space to tend and re-arm each and every F-111E behind massive external doors and beneath a thick reinforced concrete shell.

### Thunderbolts

At the time of writing the Wing flies 76 aircraft under the command of Col. Graham E. Shirley, whose motto 'Work Smarter, Not Harder' pervades the base with a crisp air of efficiency but friendliness.‡ His analogue F-111Es are to all intents and purposes younger-build F-111As with Triple Plow II inlets and a revised right-hand WCP: neat push-buttons replaced the 'Alpha's

---

*Of that first pair of arrivals, only F-111E 68-035 flies on today. Sadly, in December 1979, 68-045 took its crew to the bottom of the Wash.

†Official F-111E acceptance dates comprised 31 between August and December 1969, 53 between July and December 1970 and 10 between January and May 1971. Most of the initial batch went to the 27th TFW before being reassigned to the 20th TFW – see 'Cosmic Aardvarks' (Part 3).

‡An additional six F-111Es are in the USA. Fourteen had been stricken at the time of writing.

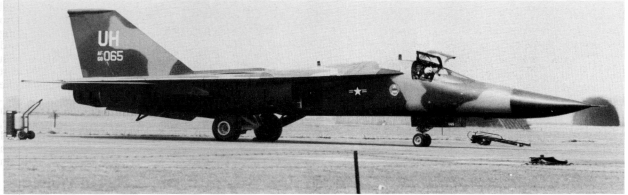

Top: With a barely visible but nevertheless rather rude 'zap' on its nose, F-111E No. 77, 68-067, taxies at Upper Heyford, June 1971. The aircraft belongs to the 77th TFS 'Gamblers'. Codes were standardized as 'UH' in the following summer. (Robin A. Walker)

Above: F-111E No. 75, 68-065, rolling at Upper Heyford in typical mid-1970s markings. From 1977 through to April 1988 familiarization training was managed by a Consolidated Training Unit or CTU, comprising some ten instructors drawn from all three squadrons; today each squadron handles its own transition training requirements. (Robin A. Walker)

chunky stores station, fuse and release mode select knobs but the dashboard radar and NCU/INS switchology and weapons sequencing remain unchanged. This commonality with the F-111A enables the 20th TFW to hold down its mission in USAFE without the encumbrance of having to provide a full RTU facility for newcomers. Instead, by far the bulk of inbound flyers first undergo the 'Long' or 'Short' training courses run by Lt. Col. Alan J. Coleman's 389th TFTS 'Thunderbolts', 366th TFW, at Mountain Home AFB, Idaho. 'Long' (or 'Basic') is for people straight out of FLIT at Holloman, New Mexico, or ATC instructors with no fighter experience; 'Short' (or 'Transition') comprises a series of 're-qual' or refresher training programmes for experienced crewmen who have been out of the cockpit for a while or who are transitioning from other fighter

types.* Reporting to Building 291, fledgeling 'Earthpig' pilots and 'Wizzos' earn their spurs over the course of an extensive six-month training schedule. F-111A handling, emergency procedures, capsule egress, nav/attack 'switches', basic attack profiles and a transition from day to night TFR are all included, with a few 'hard' mountain rides thrown in for experience. A significant portion of the syllabus is handled in the classroom, working with simulators, part-task trainers, audio-visuals and papers, but the flying is the ultimate test, taking the pilots up and over the north-western terrain in Idaho and Montana; WSOs too are taught basic handling and emergency procedures and are permitted to fly the aircraft at above 1,000ft AGL. Bomb practice takes place over the nearby Saylor Creek range. 'It's a good training program; Mountain Home and the "local terrain" offers a bit of everything'.

Lt. Col. Alan J. Coleman's instructors like to boast about the accuracy with which they can get their apprentices to put bombs on target; however, official figures detailing F-111 CEPs (circular error probables) and the 'shack' rate achieved (the number of times the crews achieve a first-pass bull's-eye) remain a closely guarded secret. Given that an F-111 can reduce a whole installation to rubble in one fell swoop, minute varia-

*See 'We have the mobility' in 'Cosmic Aardvarks' (Part 3) for a full account of the Stateside training 'Tracks'. Some training is performed by the 391st TFS 'Bold Tigers'.

| Squadron | Colour | Nickname | 1970 | Codes From Jan. 1971 | From July 1972 | Aircraft |
|---|---|---|---|---|---|---|
| 55th TFS | Blue | Fightin' Fifty-Fifth | – | JS | UH | F-111E |
| 77th TFS | Red | Gamblers | UT | JT | UH | |
| 79th TFS | Gold | Tigers | UR | JR | UH | |
| 42nd ECS | Gray | – | – | – | UH | EF-111A |

**20th TFW (3rd AF, USAFE)**
**RAF Upper Heyford, Oxon., England**

The change from potential 55th TFS 'US' to 'JS' codes took place before the squadron received aircraft, so the former was never used. The blue fin caps were later changed to a blue and white chequered pattern. The 79th TFS wears a yellow fincap with tiger stripes. The 42nd ECS is based at Upper Heyford but is assigned to the 66th ECW headquartered at Sembach AB, West Germany, with USAFE's Seventeenth Air Force.

**Below: The SUU-20 dispenser can house up to six practice bombs and four FFARs. It is standard equipment for all Stateside 'One-Elevens', including the strategic models. 'Slick', low-drag BDU-33 25lb practice bombs are installed. (Frank B. Mormillo)**

**Bottom: The low-drag SUU-21 dispenser features sliding doors to improve its aerodynamic properties and houses up to six practice bombs in two compartments, in this instance orange Mk. 106 high-drag 5lb bombs. Like the SUU-20 it can be fitted to any of the pivot-pylons (stations 3, 4, 5 and 6). (Authors)**

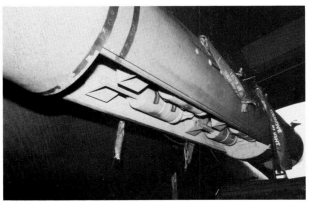

tions in the accuracy of weapons delivery are somewhat academic! To prevent the 'One-Eleven' undergraduates (and, indeed, mission-qualified flyers) from demolishing every practice range in Christendom the birds are launched with little bombs under their big wings which make little holes in the ground instead. Two types of modestly priced bombs are used for routine training, the 25lb low-drag BDU-33, which is painted blue and bears a remarkable similarity to a mortar round, and the tubby Mk. 106 high-drag 5lb munition, painted in gaudy 'dayglo' orange; both are carried in a dispenser. These pods also come in two configurations: the SUU-20 is a squat, open-bottomed device which can carry up to six practice bombs and four 2.75in folding-fin rockets (FFARs); the tubular SUU-21 model has no provision for FFARs but has an identical bomb capacity, split between two compartments, and incorporates ventral bay doors which improve its aerodynamics.* The ballistic properties of the BDU-33 and Mk. 106 are such that they can be used to simulate 'slick' or 'retard' high-drag bombs respectively, enabling the flyers to maintain proficiency between the occasional full-sized drops.

After having peppered the Saylor Creek range over the course of some 30 sorties the flyers become fully fledged 'One-Eleven' team-mates and have two primary options – to remain at Mountain Home, assigned to Lt. Col. William D. Patton's 391st TFS 'Bold Tigers' for possible deployment worldwide in times of crisis, or to be posted to RAF Upper Heyford in support of NATO.

*Units stationed in the USA still use the SUU-20, USAFE the -21 only.

## Out on the Range

For the 20th TFW's newcomers and old hands alike, getting time over Britain's crowded ranges these days is a real problem. All NATO's attack crews want low-level practice so the F-111 crews often find themselves using their extra fuel to reach Northern Scottish ranges like Tain rather than the Wash which is being pounded heavily by the RAF. Range work forms the core of a training programme which begins with a familiarization process for 'new guys'. There are F-111E upgrade training, academics, simulator and three or four rides to learn the complexities of local flying rules. One unique aspect of the 20th TFW's Mission Qualification programme was that from 1977 it was managed by a pool of the 20th TFW's most experienced instructors, who wore the CTU (Consolidated Training Unit) patch. In April 1988 the CTU was devolved back into a squadron basis. After satisfactorily completing the 'Mission Qual' phase, followed by five sorties and a check-ride with the Standardization and Evaluation Division, there is a 4–5 day period to cover certification on other 'special' mission areas. They are then deemed 'mission-ready normal soldiers'. As Lt. Col. Dave Skakal, 77th TFS Operations Officer, explained to the authors, 'Our goal is to check 'em out in 45 working days after they have arrived; sometimes we meet that, depending on weather and exercises'. The crews then accumulate hours and work towards attaining 'flight lead' status, commanding two-, three- or possibly four-ship missions, later going on to gain new credentials as project officers or instructors, with the possibility of graduating from an

Above: 'Gunfighters' F-111A No. 122, 67-077, taking off with empty BRUs and practice-bomb-filled SUU-20 dispensers. The 366th TFW 'ready switched' to F-111As in the summer of 1977 and now flies two squadrons of 'Alphas': the 389th TFTS 'Thunderbolts', commanded by Lt. Col. Alan J. Coleman, and the 391st TFS 'Bold Tigers', commanded by Lt. Col. William D. Patton. The 'Thunderbolts' fulfil the 'analog RTU' role for both TAC and USAFE. (Frank B. Mormillo)

assignment to the six-week-long Tactical Leadership Program (TLP, or 'battle management' course), run by NATO at Jever, West Germany, or the twelve week-long Fighter Weapons School, run at Cannon. It is a combat proficiency- and career-orientated ladder which crews climb as they clock up further hours, geared towards people as much as the mission – though there does exist a liberal sprinkling of 'high-time' 'old head' captains and majors throughout the 'One-Eleven' community who have no desire to be promoted out of the F-111's cockpit to behind a desk!

Exercises are a dominant feature of life at any USAFE base and they give everyone an idea of the pressures of a wartime scenario. They include regular NATO 'Tac-Evals' when all aspects of the Wing's activities are scrutinized. The 20th TFW did particularly well in their May 1988 'Tac-Eval', emerging as the best unit in NATO. 'Hammer' exercises generate mass launches of aircraft: 'Hammer 87/1' on 19 May 1987 saw no fewer than 58 F-111Es and EF-111As roar down 'Heyford's tarmac; simultaneously Lakenheath put up 51 F-111Fs

Above: F-111A No. 106, 67-061 from the 'Bold Tigers', cruising with its wings locked out at 26° and carrying four BRUs each toting a sextet of Mk. 82 'slick' bombs. Drops of full-sized live and inert ordnance are performed at least once a year during WTDs. (USAF photo by Ken Hackman)

in forty minutes for their 'Aardvark Amble'.* These quick-reaction launches are a powerful reminder of the Wing's pivotal role in any potential European conflict.

'Excalibur' manoeuvres are exclusively USAFE, rotating on a six-monthly basis among the Third, Sixteenth and Seventeenth Air Forces, and comprise low-level navigation and weapons delivery with 5-second time gates, on a no-notice basis, in association with reconnaissance, CAP and defence-suppression jets from the other American Wings. In the April 1988 'Excalibur III' the 20th TFW's four-ship team came first and second for timing. Capt. Greg Lowrimore, with 1,500hrs of F-111 radarscope-peering time in his logs, proudly recalled that 'Both the F-111 Wings beat every F-16 Wing, and they have a system which is ten times better than ours. A lot of that was due to the two-versus-one crew'; the only casualty was F-111E 68-051 which suffered lightning-strike damage to its nose and fin-tip. The previous year Upper Heyford's 55th TFS 'D Flight' came in only four points behind the Lakenheath team in 'Excalibur II' at Hahn AB, West Germany. Again they beat the resident F-16s in the low-angle/low-drag section of the bombing despite one aircraft losing its systems on approach to the range. Capt. Mark Sullivan, 20th TFW Weapons Officer, felt their performance was 'Excellent, considering we were competing against digital aircraft'.

Training elements have also involved the 'One-Eleven' community in many of the delicately named

'Mallet Blow' exercises of the last decade. These take place at the Otterburn range, the popularity of which with NATO ordnance distributors means booking two years in advance. At 'Mallet Blow' F-111 crews gain experience of simulated interception by Rapier SAM missiles below them and CAP F-4s above, with an E-3A Sentry tracking their movements. Otterburn offers a selection of armour, aircraft and 'runway' targets though the most difficult objective for crews is to keep within the strict height, visibility and set-heading parameters specified by range safety requirements.

Working on the UK's predominantly over-water ranges with practice bombs is a reasonable way of maintaining basic proficiency but, as Capt. Greg Lowrimore pointed out, 'It's just a raft with a reflector on it. With the land/water contrast on radar it's just a blip – very simple to bomb'. All F-111s have a 'beacon' plotting mode and this too produces a recognizable 'blip' on the radar-scope. Broadcasted by ground-based FAC, it may be used as an offset when supporting the Army – not a major part of the F-111's brief, but there to be had if needed.

Crews have a requirement to drop a hefty load of the real stuff at least once a year. To this end, Weapons Training Deployments (WTDs) are much in demand. Such major events are planned by the 20th TFW for Garvey Island, Zaragosa or a German land range. Zaragosa was developed via Project 'Creek Step' in 1970 after the Libyan Revolutionary Council obliged the USA to relinquish its base at Wheelus in North Africa. The range itself is at Bardenas Reales, maintained by the 406th TFTW which has no aircraft of its own but which

*See 'Statue De Libya Raiders' (Part 3) for a full description of 48th TFW training and accomplishments.

hosts an air rescue detachment and tankers on TDY. Both USAFE F-111 Wings send aircraft whenever possible to drop live and inert bombs and 'training shapes' on the huge, raked concentric 'dartboard' and strip targets. Upper Heyford frequently dispatches up to six visitors at a time.

Training often takes the F-111s on longer excursions. In the 1970s the regular 'Midlink' exercises took them alternatively to Pakistan and Iran in support of CENTO. Manoeuvres of this kind are ideal ways of demonstrating the 'One-Eleven's capabilities. At a NATO 'Reforger' exercise the F-111 contingent flew 166 out of the 194 sorties they were allocated, most of them in weather which grounded the other tactical machines. The F-111s were originally allocated only 30 per cent of the sorties but clocked-up 86 per cent of the successful missions flown by all participants; of those missions, 145 were right on target.

**Red Flag**

Weather is seldom a factor at the exercise venue most crews regard as closest to the real thing – 'Red Flag'. Admittedly several 20th TFW crews got even closer by visiting the 474th TFW in Thailand to study 'Linebacker' combat operations in 1972 but 'Red Flag' at

Nellis is today's combat. 'Aardvarks' from USAFE, TAC or SAC have invariably appeared at these six-week-long desert work-outs. They began in 1975 as a result of extensive interviews with air crews during and after the Vietnam conflict and they enable crews to push their skills to the limit in the face of F-5E and F-16 'Aggressor' pilots who know all the tricks (several are ex-F-111 jocks). On a range of immense size, totalling some three million acres, the visiting crews get the chance to face realistic air-to-air and ground-to-air threats including simulated 'Smoky SAM' launches, AAA and the full range of WARPAC radar emissions. Attacks can be made on 'airfield', 'industrial' or armour targets constructed from plywood, junk or obsolete material retrieved from the scrap-heap.

Perhaps the ultimate threat is the desert itself, though less so to the 'TF-ing' F-111. Out of 34 aircraft of all types which 'bought the farm' in the first ten years of 'Red Flag', 23 simply flew into the terrain. Pilots are restricted to a 300ft minimum altitude during their first week, with the chance of a 100ft minimum in the second before they hand over to a replacement crew. Maj. Dick Brown is very enthusiastic about 'Red Flag':

> I think it's as close to combat as you can get. It's all mind projection in the sense of *thinking* it's like that, except that they don't kill you. The difference between 450kts at 250ft over Europe and 600–700kts at 100ft in the desert is like day and night: it's like driving slowly through town and then going out on the motorway for the first time.

Aircraft bombing from below 5,000ft are exempt from pursuit by fighters because of the risk of debris from exploding ordnance. Another limit for all those air-

Below: 20th TFW CO Col. Graham E. Shirley's jet, F-111E No. 6, 67-120, appropriately nicknamed 'The Chief', with spoilers, slats and flaps deployed. The four-colour fin-cap represents, from front to rear, the 79th TFS 'Tigers' (yellow), the 55th TFS 'Fightin' Fifty-Fifth' (blue), the 77th TFS 'Gamblers' (red) and the tenant 42nd ECS (grey). (Authors)

Above: 'Gamblers' (from left to right) Lt. Col. Dave Skakal, Capt. Greg Lowrimore, Capt. George Kelman and 1Lt. Chris Ross, by their 'Red Squadron' insignia in the 77th TFS briefing room at Upper Heyford, England. Dave Skakal is a former Ramstein F-4E pilot, Greg Lowrimore is an F-111D WSO who at the time of writing was about to go to Mountain Home to convert to the job of EWO in the EF-111A, George Kelman is a former F-4G 'Wild Weasel' EWO or 'Bear' who switched jobs to that of 'One-Eleven' pilot and Chris Ross is on his first operational tour. (Authors)

Below: A 55th TFS F-111E (No. 85, 68-075, nicknamed 'Galleon') makes a touch-and-go at Upper Heyford in April 1988. Downwind approach in the circuit is made at about 350kts with 10° on the angle of attack indicator. Pilots execute a 30° bank into finals, bleed off speed, then apply power just prior to touch-down to kill the sink rate, contacting the concrete at around 140kts – at normal flap and slat settings with the wings at 16°. The smell of burnt rubber pervades the strip after such a manoeuvre, particularly when the brakes are applied, but the huge tyres last for about 100 sorties' worth of rolling and pounding. (Authors)

borne is a 3,000ft radial separation from broadcasting EF-111A Ravens, to avoid sterilization! The F-111s usually form the core of an INT (interdiction) package involving CAP fighters, EF-111As and other back-up types rather than flying the independent solo sorties which 'Aardvark' flyers prefer. Air crews have unprecedented opportunities, through joint mission planning, to understand the jobs of the other people they work with, be they F-15 Eagle pilots, F-4G 'Wild Weasel' crews or RF-4C recce crews.

A 'Red Flag' outing starts with 18 months' advance notice and the period of participation includes the journey to Nellis, which must be fast and direct as in a real wartime deployment. The organization of a squadron's 'Red Flag' visit falls to a serving officer. In addition to his TLP patch, fame as the 77th TFS's resident song publisher and 'ownership' of F-111E 68-061 'The Big Dealer', Capt. George Kelman arranged his squadron's 'Red Flag 88-1' appearance, which lasted from 6 January to 23 February. Getting things ready is not merely a matter of patting one's colleagues on the back and saying 'Let's go!'. The deployment of six aircraft and 70 crew chiefs, with squadron air crews appearing on rotation for ten-day sessions, produced a mass of paperwork. Two months after the unit returned there were still bills for billeting and car rental to clear up and a whole network of spares and logistics supply channels to remember for the next time.

Of all the exercises, 'Red Flag' demands close co-ordination from the 'Aardvark's' crew. Usually crews are kept together for a whole tour and rely heavily on the cockpit rapport they develop. George Kelman recalls:

The first day at Red Flag people were out there just flying around. By the second day we realized we had to sit down and talk about what we were going to do at every point. By the third day it was like one person even though it's a two-man airplane.

Avoiding the interceptors is always a major challenge and getting caught is embarrassing, but the F-111 is very capable

at defeating threats and hitting a target on time. In our two weeks there we never missed a target by more than 15–20 seconds – in contrast to one F-16 unit who were 1½ minutes late! By flying together as a crew you can think as one person.

After 1,200hrs in the F-111 he should know. In the desert, as elsewhere, the 'Earthpig' relies on transonic speeds at tree-top heights to evade capture. If the attacker can be detected in the RWR scope or even in the row of four rear-view mirrors, fitted as a partial solution to the 60° cone of blindness to the rear, 'speed of heat' flying is the best move. Few fighters can get a missile lock-on to an F-111 flying at TFR minimum altitude out of afterburner. One of the 79th TFS aircraft, F-111E 68-062, recently sported a large angry fish on its nose and the name 'Land Shark'. As its crew chief reported, when seeking approval for the artwork, 'When flying low over the desert at "Red Flag" the only visible sign of the F-111 was the vertical fin. The "enemy" Aggressors nicknamed the F-111 a land shark'. 'Hard Ride' might be selected also to avoid 'ballooning' over the tops of more relaxed terrain where the F-111 would present a clear silhouette against the sky.

The fighters present a major challenge. Among the current batch of US adversaries, Maj. Dick Brown rates the F-16 as the nastiest:

If that sees you, you're dead. I mean, an idiot can get in there. If a good flyer gets in that airplane it's scary because there's nothing you can do in an aircraft like this. The F/A-18 and F-15 are even deadlier because of their beyond visual range [BVR] radar missile capability. They kill you before you see them.

*Above: DCC SSgt. Larry J. Casteel's personal charge, F-111E No. 50 (68-040), nicknamed 'The Other Woman' and assigned to the 79th TFS/AMU 'Tigers' in 1987. (David Robinson)*

A 'coffin' symbol appears over the F-111 on the large Air Combat Maneuvering Instrumented display screen back on the ground at Nellis and the console officer calls on the radio: 'Blue [whatever] you're dead!' Up against the modern range of all-weather fighters, F-111 drivers must develop a whole range of defensive tricks. Speed and the self-protect pyrotechnics go some way, and then there is BIF – bomb-in-face. Lt. Col. Tom G. Runge, affectionately known to his colleagues as 'Grunge', reckoned that the RAF Buccaneer pilots who pioneered this sneaky trick 'Must have practiced it for real the first time!' He added that it 'isn't something that we could go out and practice, but our guys are definitely taught the specifics of how to go about using it.' If under pursuit at low level an 'Aardvark' crew would 'pickle' off a live bomb and hope that the fighter on their tail would get shredded in the blast. A further trick in the wily 'Aardvark's catalogue of defensive tactics is selective use of wing-sweep, something the auto-sweep fighters like the F-14 Tomcat and Tornado F.3 cannot do, as George Kelman explains:

You can use your wings very tactically to help you out. You can set them *exactly* where you want them if you study the curves enough to give you the best maneuverability in the airplane. Plus you can set them to fake somebody out. If someone's attacking and they see the big airplane down there and see his wings back, even though you're going at a relatively slow speed, say 480kt, he may think you're going

600kt and leave you alone; whereas if he sees them forward he'll deduce you're going slow and then he may commit and try and jump you.

Drawing on his 'Red Flag' experience in the F-111, Lt. Col. Tom G. Runge noted:

Range operations are conducted with the wings set at 35°–45°, and only fully back if you are trying to go *very* fast. Automatic wing sweep? With the F-14, as soon as the wings start to sweep forward, you know you've got him.

Capt. Mike Conway added: 'He does a real nice bat-turn but all of a sudden he starts to run out of energy – he can do it *once!*'

## Over the bog and green

Most of the day-to-day training takes place in areas which are much wetter, darker and steeper than the desert around Las Vegas, Nevada. While crews occasionally take in 'Maple Flag' (similar to 'Red Flag' but over the forests of Canada) they are more likely to be seen thundering through the Welsh or Scottish valleys in the UK. New arrivals at Upper Heyford learn about that pretty soon. Like all 'Aardvarks' the F-111E is rated as a pleasant aircraft to fly. George Kelman is very complimentary:

It's a very easy airplane to fly, but hard to fly very well because it's doing things on its own with the computers. It's a Cadillac, very smooth, very reliable, and it can get down low and stay out of trouble. The only thing that'll really bite you is wing sweep. That'll induce a lot of problems if the pilot forgets his wing sweep or tries to manuever with the wing aft or forward.

The 'new guys' soon gain confidence in understanding the 'Vark's habits and let it negotiate its natural habitat, down among the heather and the lochs.

Although most Upper Heyford crews average little more than 15–20hrs of flying a month, a training flight is actually a full day's work. The 'Crew Show' is usually four hours prior to take-off. An hour and a half of that will be spent on mission planning, an hour briefing the flight and about an hour stepping out to the aircraft and 'pre-flighting' it. On a typical three-hour sortie at around 900fs the bird covers a lot of ground and everything has to be carefully planned. Capt. George Kelman observes that 'When you're blasting along that fast and somebody doesn't know what's going to happen next it gets dangerous'. The WSO makes use of the film library to plot his offsets using RSP, predictions or stills from the nose-mounted KB-18 strike camera and sets about drawing up the route. Planning is very much a team effort:

If one person's eating his lunch when he should be drawing little threads on a map it may be the reason why we lose an airplane and a crew. Everyone takes their job very seriously. When you're hyped up like that you're prepared. You know that when you come across this ridge there's a ground threat here and an Army division over here so I have to sneak down this river line, best I can. You're really 'up' and you know it's going to be there, so you're excited about it. But it's all part of the plan – you don't just take off and say we're going to head over there and go for it.

The current analogue systems in the F-111A and E mean greater workloads for crews than the later digital models. Greg Lowrimore explains that they still have to 'spin the dials' and crank in the waypoints one at a time, based on a pre-flight computer print-out which lists the co-ordinates. 'It still has the same *capability* as the digital models, it's just that you work harder. We can't simply plug in a tape and go and fly'. The '3-destinations' capability is seldom used.

Having drafted the details of the sortie the crew will go to their allotted F-111E and discuss its health with the crew chief. The pre-flight checks require that both crew members accept the aircraft as serviceable. Any doubts by pilot or WSO means it stays at home – 'There's no majority vote!' On a night TFR run virtually everything has to be 100 per cent, though slightly degraded INS and radar may be acceptable for clear-weather daylight sorties. Chances cannot be taken. On a mass launch in March 1986 six out of 42 aircraft were 'runway aborts', though they would probably have proceeded with the mission had it been a genuine combat launch. Crew chiefs preside over the F-111s' departure, orchestrating the whole show. SSgt. James Colson from the 77th Aircraft Maintenance Unit (AMU) outlines the process of releasing 'his' 'swing-winger' from its arched den:

The power unit is set up then the crew come out, do a walk-around, and review the forms. They climb in and ask for electrical power and compressed air to start up the systems, and run through their checks. They then call up and say 'Ready for a start, Chief'. The Chief confirms that the area behind the jet is clear. You say 'air on two' and start the number two engine. Sometimes the other engine is started by cross-feed from the running engine, sometimes a power unit is used. 'Cart-start', using cartridges, is used if a power unit isn't available, for example at a British base where they have different equipment.

If everything is running by the book the F-111 can then emerge from the TAB-V shelter and proceed to the pre-take-off hold for exterior 'last chance' checks and for weapons 'de-safing'. These tasks are performed by a composite team of one or two crew chiefs and an avionics technician. It is a visual check-list job, in contact with the air crew via an intercom lead. With the pins pulled out the sortie is underway, and at the end of the runway the F-111E can be held on its powerful brakes with the TF-30-P-103s blasting in fifth-stage afterburner. Take-off is normally conducted in pairs, with rotation occurring at around 142kts and lift-off at 157kts, based on normal weights. The TF30s are marginally quieter than the turbojets of the older-generation fighters; even so, jet noise is not the sound of freedom to everybody. When the 20th TFW were temporarily based at RAF Greenham Common in 1976 a local headmaster attributed his school's 50 per cent reduction in exam passes to the distractions on the nearby runway. Recent protests in Oxfordshire have resulted in modified departure routes from Upper Heyford.

**Right: Low Angle Drogue Delivery (LADD) attack profile.**

## New dynamics and ironmongery

The F-111E has a tactical radius of nearly 1,000nm to work with. In various hypothetical conflict situations, that could cover all of Poland and Czechoslovakia or, operating from airfields in the Mediterranean, Russia's Caucasian oilfields. In wartime the battlefield area interdiction (BAI) mission would see the 20th TFW operating counter-air strikes against airfields, fuel stores and munitions dumps. Their talents would be in great demand. 'Salty Nation' exercises at the F-111 bases place much emphasis on maintaining Emergency War Order duties, right up to the 'Nuclear Black' alarm state, in protective wear. 'Interdiction' missions would be flown against bridges and other sources of resupply to the enemy, while 'strike' implies a last-resort nuclear delivery sortie if conventional weapons failed to contain the enemy advance.

To meet these requirements the attack profiles used today embrace modes which only came into regular use in the period following the Vietnam War, when more aggressive manoeuvres were added to the old, mainly straight-and-level act. All these options were available back in the 'Combat Lancer' and 'Linebacker' eras, made possible by the 'uncanned' ballistics computer, but the F-111's early teething problems caused the Air Force to err on the side of caution and restrict the aircraft to less strenuous g-loadings – at least as far as conventional weapons delivery was concerned. As the swing-wing community's pioneers rose through the ranks to the higher echelons of the USAF, so the old restrictions were relaxed and the F-111 really came into its own, using tactics developed by the Fighter Weapons School. Employing the same switchology as before, except for a new dashboard 'offset box' which can hold up to six sets of offset co-ordinates, stepped in one set at a time alongside appropriate offset range and bearing in the normal manner, the delivery options now embrace 'level', 'angular', 'loft', 'toss' and 'low-angle drogue delivery' (LADD). Lt. Col. Dave Skakal explains that

We practice primarily for the night, weather, radar delivery, which is 'worst case'. Delivery can also be completely visual, using the sight, and we also have a timer delivery which we can do either radar or visual. We are beginning to train for 'toss' and we do all of the 'angular' patterns: beginning at 5°, then 10°, then 15°.

LADD employs a timer, a separate item from the standard BCU, and is considered a nuclear option: 'We push the "pickle" button and the timer runs and gives us pull-up indications'. Flying at minimum TFR at top speed, at a preset range to target TFR is disengaged and the pilot pulls the aircraft up in a 4g climb, leaving the clock to 'pop off' a Mk. 106, BDU-38/B or retard nuclear weapon on schedule. With the bomb gone the screaming 'Earthpig' is rolled inverted and nosed back towards terra firma, followed rapidly by a wings-level roll to recover the jet as it nears the ground. The crew then dart out of the target area with TFR re-engaged, as the high-drag weapon drifts to earth at a safe distance way behind them.

'Toss' is even more energetic. At an altitude of 200ft and some four or more miles from the target the aircraft is hauled up in a shallow climb at high speed with the bomb 'pickled'. As soon as the BCU commands bomb release the pilot immediately pulls a straining 3–4g left wing-over to avoid overflying the aimpoint. The low-drag BDU-33s or 'slick' bombs are thus flung to the target using only kinetic energy. Accuracy is surprisingly good and averages of 75ft are often demonstrated. What is particularly impressive about these dynamic manoeuvres is that they can be performed at night 'in the weather' at around 550kts, possibly in the midst of mountains or valleys, and with the TFR uncoupled, using a considerable amount of hand-flying! There is no other aircraft on the inventory capable of doing this. It is hardly surprising that the 'One-Eleven' is the most feared aircraft in Europe and that flying the beast to its full demands considerable nerve and derring-do.

To make the most of these expanded attack profiles a new range of munitions has joined the force. Capt. Greg Lowrimore emphasizes the value of the new iron-mongery: 'For the first time we're finally getting weapons that were *designed* for the F-111'. Large, 'slick' iron bombs like the Mk. 84 required the F-111 to pull

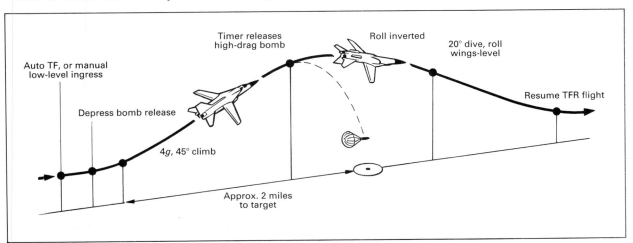

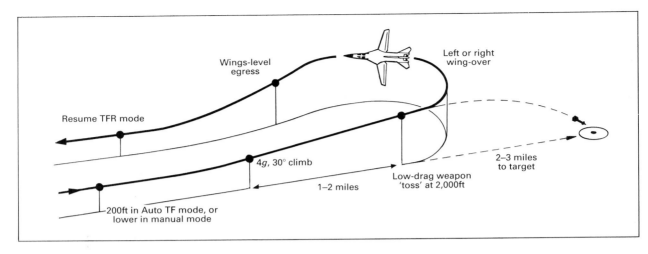

**Above: 'Toss' attack profile.**

off the target in reheat to avoid being rattled and punctured by its own ordnance; even the low-level, steel airbrake-retarded Snakeye Mk. 82 which could be delivered with more discretion imposed a 500kt-maximum limitation, forcing crews to go relatively slowly in the thick of enemy defences. The hard lessons learned in SEA forced a major rethink and munitions development effort for the postwar fast-and-low Air Force.

One of the most important new weapons to emerge from the melting pot was the Air Inflatable Retard, referred to as the 'AIR', which recently replaced the old Mk. 82 'slick' and Snakeye plug-on tailfins with a more reliable dual-mode BSU-49 tube containing a canvas balloon-cum-parachute nicknamed the 'Ballute'. The humble iron bomb was transformed. Of greater significance, a large BSU-50 tail was designed for the previously 'slick'-only Mk. 84 2,000-pounder, moving this weapon into the transonic tree-top lay-down game. Sgt. Dotson, 'Loadeo' champion, elaborates:

The BSUs have a spring-loaded cover on the back and when the bomb's dropped the lanyards, hooked to solenoids, pull the pin out of the back and the 60lb spring-loaded cover pops off. The 'chute then shoots out about four feet to give you your retard capability. In the clean, low-drag mode the AIR arrangement is set to remain stored and the bomb comes off and behaves like the old 'slick'.

The AIR not only radically improves F-111 survivability but also greatly simplifies bomb assembly in times of crisis. Once in full swing, the weapons assemblers can roll 'Ballutes' off the line at a rate of about one every 30 seconds, ready to 'bomb-up' the big fighters. The flyers are the ones who are really impressed though. Maj. Dick Brown's verdict:

You can drop it lower and faster, which is really good. It's about the best improvement we've had. You can use it at 100ft at the speed of heat – as fast as the old jet will go. The 2,000lb version is particularly impressive – best bomb we've got. Just drop it and it makes a mini mushroom!*

Joining company with the 'Ballutes' in the ordnance

---

*For use against hardened targets, the Eglin-based 3246th Test Wing are at present perfecting Lockheed's I-for-improved I-2000, a brand new type of Mk. 84 bomb capable of punching through 8ft-thick reinforced concrete at oblique angles of up to 60°.

storage bunkers are a range of new special-purpose munitions, the CBU-87/B CEM, Gator Mine and BLU-107/B Durandal. The Aerojet CBU-87/B Combined Effects Munition and Honeywell Gator Mines are area weapons, replacing vintage CBU-58 cluster bombs with packaged submunitions tailored for particular jobs. More specifically, CEM is a 950lb canister which can be 'tossed' at near supersonic speed and at low level. Post-release, pop-out fins spin the canister so that it sprinkles its 202 shaped-charge bomblets on to enemy armour, to create an instant tank-demolition derby. The Gator Mine is a 500lb class 'toe popper' which has a delayed-action effect. The canister splits and dispenses a mixture of 94 anti-armour and anti-personnel mines which self-arm after touching down, to create a minefield. The philosophy of the weapon is to halt or channel enemy ground forces into bottlenecks where they can be picked off by long-range artillery and rockets.

Designed specifically for the counter-air mission is the French Matra BLU-107/B Durandal, tested and selected for the F-111 under the ADTC's novel Foreign Weapons Evaluation Program (FWEP), which resulted in an order for 5,000 of the weapons. Durandal is a 'one-shot, one-hole', low-drag, torpedo-shaped device with an all-up weight of 430lb, capable of being delivered during a high-speed level run in much the same fashion as an AIR but with one major difference: following its parachute retard sequence, a rocket motor ignites to send the weapon charging into the enemy airfield with considerable force, enabling it to penetrate the top surface before detonating. During their recent deployment to 'Red Flag', crews from the 20th TFW were given the opportunity to check the weapons out for effect. Capt. George Kelman, who organized the whole show, explains:

As a Wing we dropped 24 – eight per squadron. The weapons came from here at Upper Heyford and we shipped them over; they were the oldest lots in the Air Force as we wanted to see how they stored and handled. So we loaded them up at Nellis and went out and dropped them on a soft target, a special range where they had seismic sensors in the ground – unfortunately, no one will let us blow up their

runway! We filmed the release from the air to evaluate the effectiveness of the weapon. It doesn't do everything we want it to do, or we're not really sure if we're using it the right way, so we're addressing some ways of fixing our operational use of it and trying to get the Air Force to release some more so we can do some more testing. But there is *nothing* better at destroying a runway than a Durandal. The only problem is, can you get it on the runway? Depending on the weather and certain other factors it would be a problem getting enough of the weapons to do the damage you wanted to do.

Flying in the 'fast lane' over a target measuring a few hundred feet wide at most demands absolute precision, and the pilot's visual acquisition as an aid to weapons delivery is a tremendous help in ensuring correct off-axis line-up on the runway strip; this however is exactly the type of mission the 'Triple-One' was designed to do. Lt. Col. Dave Skakal thinks that it is 'a very compatible mission and weapon for the F-111'. Capt. Greg Lowrimore concurred:

There's not that much drag, compared with carrying around fat CBUs to spread little bomblets all over the field. Realistically, you can go and spread stuff like the CBUs and it will take a little while to clean it up, but a couple of bulldozers later they're set to go. But if you tear up their runway they just have to sit there and figure out what they're going to do next. It's hard to take off with holes all over the place!

**Below, far left: Mk. 82/BSU-49 500lb AIRs on a bomb trolley; the rear spring-loaded cover pops off after release to extract a 'Ballute' retarding device. The bombs can be released as low as 100ft and as fast as the F-111 can go – though high-subsonic speed laydowns are customary. (Authors)**

**Below centre: A Mk. 84/BSU-50 2,000lb AIR strapped to an MJ-1 weapons loader. This is the biggest 'Ballute' on the inventory, capable of creating 'a mini mushroom'. (Authors)**

**Below right: Inert training rounds of the Matra BLU-107/B Durandal anti-runway munition. A typical mission load would comprise a dozen Durandals, six each on two pivot-pylons. (Authors)**

Top: The 'short', two-band Westinghouse AN/ALQ-119(V) 'Compass Tie' noise- and deception-jamming pod was the standard USAFE self-protect strap-on for F-111E/Fs in the period c.1977–82, painted all-black or black and white and located between the ventral strakes. This device superseded the noise-only AN/ALQ-87 jammer. (Robin A. Walker)

Above: The olive green, 'shallow', two-band Westinghouse AN/ALQ-131(V)-13 replaced the AN/ALQ-119(V) and features 'power management' to apportion power to the most dangerous radar threats. The pods are loaded with a 'jamming strategy' provided by the CNPA division and jam in bands 4 and 5, in up to forty different waveforms, to counter the 'terminal threat' radars which guide lethal SAMs to target, for example the 'Straight Flush' illuminator. Note the mini pylon located between the strakes. (Authors)

### Sparks and electrons

Part of the 20th TFW's 1988 'Red Flag' deployment also involved staging through Florida for an Electronic Warfare Evaluation Program, a process that has endured since 'Combat Trident'. The Eglin complex includes sophisticated threat simulators and electronic warfare evaluative systems similar to the Saylor Creek and Polygone facilities, against which crews are able to gauge the effectiveness of their electronic self-protect gear but with fewer restrictions. Unlike the other TACAIR units, which lean on feed-back from TAWC's 4485th 'Combat Echo' full-time operational test squadron, the tightly knit 'One-Eleven' community is much more self-reliant and tends to organize most of its own follow-on trials: the extra Durandal tests being sought are one example, EWEP another. Capt. George Kelman, Project Officer for the exercise and an ex-F-4G 'Wild

Weasel' EWO with considerable knowledge of electronic warfare, describes the procedures:

> We designed it for ourselves to test our electronic combat capability after a long flight, to make sure that the pods and whatever else we carry will work after having traveled a long way. The first airplane started its run at about 9 hours 40 minutes after take-off and it took about an hour to get all six airplanes through and on the ground. Basically we wanted to be sure that the devices would work after that much flying time at altitude where it's nice and cold. The results were tabulated along with some other data from ground testing.

Tactical 'Earthpig' pen-aids wrung out at EWEP remain largely unchanged since the engineering modifications of late 1968, with the exception of the addition of the improved, digital Dalmo-Victor AN/ALR-62 RWR and a new ECM strap-on – the Westinghouse AN/ALQ-131(V)13 jamming pod, in shallow twin-band configuration, designed to supplement the comparatively antiquated internal Sanders AN/ALQ-94.* The modular AN/ALQ-131 first entered the inventory in 1979, ex-ploiting the latest rapid-response travelling wave technology to counter the new range of Soviet-built radar emitters, including the lethal 'Straight Flush' and its successors. Attached to the aft hadpoint between the strakes like a phallic appendage, the pod is able to perform both noise- and deception-jamming and may be updated with the data on the latest threats by ground crews from CNPA, the Communications, Navigation and Penetration Aids branch. CNPA employ portable fault-finding 'suitcases' which can be plugged into the pod's Centrally Integrated Test System to tweak the electronics and up-load a new 'jamming strategy' in less than 30 minutes.

The low-slung olive drab AN/ALQ-131 itself is a powerful piece of kit, emblazoned with radiation hazard stencils. Deception techniques available are believed to comprise what are known as 'transponder' and 're-peater' modes, the former generating signals matched to the threat but transmitted back with an increasing delay to provide spurious range indications and the latter producing modulated copy-cat signals out of phase to provide false azimuth or to break the lock of conical-scan radar threats. Noise modes are effective against all radar types as 'power management' is used by the pod to apportion the limited available transmit power against the priority threats, fogging radar screens, confusing dopplers and confounding the enemy's automatic gain receivers. The number of radar types the pod can take on is classified but includes all the terminal threats – the missile guiders – likely to be encountered. Automation is necessary nowadays as the opposition can respond so quickly, before the air crews can manually decipher the waveforms and intervene. As one senior ex-EWO, a member of the 'Old Crows', told the

---

*The AN/ALQ-131 has superseded the AN/ALQ-87 and later, 'short' AN/ALQ-119 ECM pods. Other standard mission aids include the AN/AAR--34 and AN/ALE-28, the AN/APX-64 identification friend or foe, and 'ARC' UHF and HF radios. As is the case with the FB-111A, the AN/ALE-28 is being replaced by the Tracor AN/ALE-40 and the AN/AAR-34 is being improved.

authors: 'The electronic environment gets so saturated with signals that you'd have to take your boots off and work the switches with your toes, because everything's so time-compressed – especially in the thick of it when you're trying to get things set up for a weapons pass'.

The attitude towards ECM has also changed a great deal since Vietnam: crews like to be reassured that the self-protect systems work, so that they can be switched on and left to respond on their own when required, and this in turn imposes training problems. Lt. Col. Dave Skakal points out that there are considerable restrictions concerning the use of 'wartime' ECM settings, and full-blown trials like EWEP and the special 'Green Flag' events at Nellis are a heavily booked rarity for the crews:

We're tasked with the capability of loading up the pods with actual wartime settings but of course we don't transmit them because it would compromise what's in there. So, when we do actually transmit we load them up with a 'training tape' and transmit training settings. We *do* exercise those often. We go to the Polygone range where they have what they call 'Serene Bite' maneuvers, plus there is the Spadeadam range up here in the middle of the UK. [Spadeadam electronic warfare training range in Northumberland is the RAF's equivalent of Saylor Creek and Polygone but with less mobility.] We can switch them on and get a report back that tells us the effectiveness of those settings.

Restrictions on using chaff and flares are strictly enforced also, primarily because of environmental considerations – the prospect of fiercely burning pyrotechnics raining down indiscriminately over the countryside is an unpleasant one!

Whatever the tactics, payload and mission 'frag' the F-111's long-ranging capability places it at the forefront of USAFE air power. Training for the night TFR mission is closely supervised. 'It's a very demanding mission,' remarked Capt. George Kelman. 'We joke about it because it's probably the most dangerous thing we do.' It requires a high degree of 'SA' – situation awareness, i.e. knowing what is going on around you; 1Lt. Chris Ross adds:

Down low I've always found if you get low SA and don't know what's going on you feel like you're really zooming. Stuff's just flying by and you can't catch up with the airplane. Down low I think it's more of a mental game than anything else – just keeping ahead of the airplane and knowing what's going to happen.

In the USA pilots can be trained in night TFR by other pilots; in England a newcomer has to fly with an

Below: 'Heartbreaker', F-111E No. 65 (68-055), was the official mount of 55th TFS CO Lt. Col. Bill Savage in the spring of 1987; the present CO is Col. Rob Balph. The blonde is dressed in the 'Fightin' Fifty-Fifth's blue squadron colour and the logo is in red and white. (David Robinson)

Instructor WSO who can tell him exactly what he should be doing. Many of the problems, such as misleading TFR radar returns from sand-hills, snow or heavy rain are best experienced under that kind of supervision. Once the pilot has been checked and cleared by the Operations Officer and Commander he can fly with a regular crewman. 'Stan/Eval' crews constantly check levels of attainment in the squadrons and they in turn are checked in no-notice inspections from above. All air crews have to maintain minimum numbers of TFR sorties, ordnance drops and AAR hook-ups.

On one issue, at least, there is total standardization of response: night 'TF-ing' in murky Europe offers a uniquely exciting experience for those aboard. Dave Skakal notes: 'I've flown intense air battles at "Red Flag" where there are airplanes all over the place, and when you've finished that mission you're really on a high. You get the same feeling from completing a night TFR mission.' Greg Lowrimore thinks it is 'Better than any carnival ride I've ever had!', and George Kelman that it is

Better than a double-E ticket at Disneyland, Your first daytime ride isn't too bad because you still have your eyeball out there telling you everything's OK. Then you go up in the Scottish Highlands restricted area and it's night time. There's no moon and you descend through a cloud deck and now you're underneath the weather. The right-seater's very intent upon his job, so is the pilot. And then, out of the corner of your eye, you'll see a red flash – that's the aircraft's rotating beacon reflecting off a mountain peak that's only about 70ft off your left side. This is about 15ft greater distance than the machine is guaranteed for, so you're doing OK. When you fly the same thing in daytime you say "Holy sh**!" Look how close I was to this thing. It's huge! It's granite! But the hundredth time you do it you're still as exhilarated and scared as the first.

Medium ride is still selected, usually for comfort, on these sorties. Those who get a kick out of negative g will select 'hard' ride which (as George describes with an expression of simulated terror) 'flies you closer and closer – and closer to that hill!' It also sends dust and junk flying around the cockpit and it can be very disorientating at night. It can 'tumble your giros'. Mike Conway, a Lakenheath 'Wizzo', reckoned he might switch to 'hard' ride if he was going into East Germany, but only then. 'Then you wouldn't be worried about your stomach so much. There's other parts of your anatomy that could be in worse shape!' Chris Ross (on his first 'One-Eleven' tour and assigned for a time to F-111E 68-068 'Flak Ducker') recalled a TFR flight at dusk which says it all:

We came up over a hill, out of the cloud, into the light. Looking to the right I could see the tips of peaks sticking out of the cloud. Then next thing you know the airplane's going back down into the darkness, into the cloud and your heart jumps into your throat. You hope it works, you're riding on faith. I'm doing my job on the radar to make sure the "eye" can see out there but there's still that little thing at the back of my mind, going "This could be wrong . . .".

Capt. Greg Lowrimore, in jocular tone, added: 'The right-seater can take off his hood on his scope so the pilot, when he's got a free moment, can look over there and see the scope – you do that because it's not right for just the WSO to be scared!'

The 20th TFW's excellent safety record is ample evidence of its members' skills and stringent training standards. Even so, twelve aircraft and twelve crewmen have been lost, mostly in low-level sorties and ten of them before 1980. Three sustained bird-strikes, four struck the ground in the Highlands and the rest crashed in the sea during range sorties or on other training routes in the UK. However, safety factors continue to improve and the Wing has not lost an aircraft (at the time of writing) since F-111E 68-019 'took a bird' on the Tain range and crashed on the banks of Loch Eye in August 1984. The crew took to their capsule and survived. Despite the intrinsic dangers of realistic training within the boundaries of crowded USAFE, the 20th TFW has a strong claim of 'right of user', and who can question that Upper Heyford's 'swing-wingers', now resident in the UK for some eighteen years, have not become something of a major Anglo-American institution!

# TAB-V Pigs

Keeping modern aircraft in business is a labour-intensive activity. In 1966, just to match the demands of the Vietnam War, the USAF recruited 107,000 new ground crew and Air Training Command's primary Technical Training Centers (TTCs) shifted to a 24-hour six-days-a-week regime. Today those centres continue to produce a stream of motivated technicians, some of whom are destined to become full-time F-111 fixers. Depending on their personal goals and academic qualifications, ground crews opt to specialize in one of four key branches – as avionics, munitions or propulsion specialists with the 'intermediate' level shops or as flight-line 'organizational' jack-of-all-trades crew chiefs or commanders, responsible for overseeing the aircraft's readiness at dispersal.

## Dedicated Crew Chiefs

Crew chiefs go through Sheppard, Keesler, Lowry or Chanute TTCs.* Training them and the other technical specialists to mission-ready status takes about the same two-year period as that required for air crews. As Maj. Dave Stringer, boss of the 20th Aircraft Generation Squadron (AGS) at Upper Heyford, explains, 'In contrast to aircrew training which is highly formalized and mostly done elsewhere, most groundcrew training is accomplished in the field. The Sheppard course is only six weeks long, yet it takes 14–24 months to build a guy into a fully qualified crew chief.' The TTCs have permanently grounded GF-111As among other 'GF' types, all RDT&E or pre-production 'One-Elevens', employed for initial familiarization. These various airframes can be dismembered so that crews become acquainted with the general theory behind the electrical and hydraulic gizzards of flying machines. On-type, F-111 training will then follow at the operational base or under the guidance of a Field Training Detachment (FTD), with FTD 513 at Mountain Home, FTD 526 at Cannon or FTD 210(S) at Plattsburgh. It is a 'hands on' learning process, starting as an assistant crew chief or technician alongside an experienced fixer and consulting the highly detailed technical manuals until such time that the officers and chief NCOs-in-charge in the AGS deem that the novice can be left alone without constant supervision.

Every F-111 has a Dedicated (in both senses) Crew Chief with responsibility for all aspects of his or her charge. SSgt. Ismael Sarraga from the 77th AMU and DCC of F-111E 68-078 'Whispering Death' takes great pride in his aircraft, going beyond his normal responsibilities of keeping the aircraft airworthy and presiding over launches and recoveries personally to handle patchwork over minor skin cracks and to touch up the paintwork. Flyers seldom take to the air in the machine which bears their names on the nosegear doors but DDCs stay with their 'tails' and get to know them thoroughly. On the specifications sheets all F-111s of a given variant are the same (apart from minor variations deep in the structure), but every machine has its own unique 'glitches' and the DCC soon gains familiarity with the idiosyncracies of his own aircraft, largely by spending a good portion of his working day in close proximity to his 'baby'. SSgt. Larry Casteel's wife thought her husband was spending so much time with F-111E 68-040 that she suggested he nickname it 'The Other Woman'! All DCCs constantly kid each other about the jets: 'Your's is a pig!', or 'Mine's better than his'. SSgts. Sarraga and Colson, who both describe the 'One-Eleven' as 'The Cadillac of the Air Force', point out that this friendly rivalry acts as a spur to higher availability rates.

Existing availability figures are classified but it is widely known that keeping the birds in good plumage requires a lot of love and labour. The USAF considers the F-111 as 'complex' and in 1980 the F-111F, the model usually used as the statistical yardstick, required an average of 74.7 MMH/FH, including 9.2 maintenance 'events' per sortie; by comparison, the F-4E Phantom required only 38 MMH/FH, and that for an aircraft which often consumes many manhours in indirect maintenance (for example, every time the F-4's radio needs to be fixed the rear ejection seat has to be extracted). Many F-111 ground crews previously worked on F-4s and they welcome the 'Aardvark's superior accessibility. As GD proudly announced at the 'One-Eleven's introduction, 95 per cent of the areas needing regular attention can be reached from ground level and 94 per cent of the 323 precision-machined access panels are interchangeable. Maj. Dave Stringer believes that the F-111 'was built with maintenance in mind. You will go crazy on a Phantom taking things out to try to get to the thing you need to fix!' The accessibility and built-in test features of the porcine 'swing-winger' make it a popular jet with its ground crews and one well-suited to 'surge operations' of two or more launches per day.

Introduced in 1981, ICT (Integrated Combat Turn-around) is a method of generating sorties in the shortest time possible by fusing all the refuelling, re-arming and

---

*Chanute TTC in Illinois is to be deactivated in 1990 and its ground school activities transferred to Sheppard TTC in Texas, Keesler TTC in Mississippi and Lowry TTC in Colorado.

TAB-V PIGS   119

**Left, top: DCC SSgt. Ismael Sarraga from the 77th AMU, 20th AGS, next to his personal charge, F-111E No. 88 (68-078), nicknamed 'Whispering Death'. (Authors)**

**Left, bottom: 'Miss Liberty', F-111F No. 78 (72-1448), bearing the badges of the 'Statue of Liberty Wing's component squadrons, is pushed back into her TAB-V for undercover ICT treatment. (Authors)**

**Above: 'Miss Liberty' about to be connected to a pressure refuelling umbilical while an armourer loads cartridges into the BRUs ready for the bombs. (Authors)**

inspection tasks into one simultaneous operation. The technique was demonstrated to the authors at Lakenheath during a rehearsal for a competitive 'Lodeo' event. The 48th TFW commander's jet 'Miss Liberty' (F-111F 72-1448) rambled back from a morning sortie to position itself outside its TAB-V, then shut down. Immediately, crew chiefs conducted a brake check and started 'safing' the aircraft with red-tagged safety pins. As the tow tractor's bar was attached to the nosegear to push 'Miss Liberty' back into the shelter, a tyre check was completed together with examination for possible external airframe damage. The aircraft was then rolled back, in this instance at rather dramatic speed with its wings swept (pre- and post-flight inspection duties require that the wings be extended, but during rapid turnarounds much of this can be done just prior to

launch, at the 'last chance' pad, where the air crews can flex the flaps and spoilers). Once the aircraft had been placed under cover the huge R9 gas truck reversed in and its hose was connected to the single-point socket beneath the left fuselage national insignia. 'Hot' refuelling – i.e. with the engines on – is not possible as the F-111's tank venting system would spray kerosene into the proximity of the hot exhausts, causing the tail empennage to erupt in flames. A full load of around 3,600 US gallons of fuel was pumped onboard while the armourers readied the two BRUs for their burdens, loading ejector cartridges to kick the bombs free over the target. Then it was all down to the key man in the operation, the 'jammer' driver. Properly called the MJ-1 munitions loading vehicle, his nimble 1960s-vintage bomb-lifter is still the quickest means of getting the bombs on the BRUs. At speed, a great deal of skill is required. The Mk. 82 AIRs were lifted individually from sliding rails on the pre-positioned bomb trailer, and were then swivelled into line with the 'jammer's forward dash. The little vehicle chugged rapidly to offer its bomb to the F-111 and the weapon was snapped into place without much pushing and shoving (the larger Mk. 84 category stores, which hang straight on to the pivot-pylons, can be uploaded with even greater vitesse). While loading progressed, rapid checks were made on the aircraft's engines and other systems via the large hinged quick-release panels. The aircraft was latched

TAB-V PIGS  121

secure, bombed up, refuelled and cleared to roll within eighteen minutes of arrival!

**Tweak and strip**

On-base maintenance is organized similarly at all tactical 'One-Eleven' locations.* At Upper Heyford for example Maj. Dave Stringer's 20th AGS and Lt. Col. Richard Bereit's 520th AGS ready the jets for flight and launch them, operating from small huts nestling close to the TAB-Vs. They in turn are supported by incoming and outgoing munitions, fuel, engines, parts and spares from Maj. Everhart's 20th Component Repair Squadron (CRS) and Maj. Corley's 20th Equipment Maintenance Squadron (EMS), conglomerated shop-level maintenance units composed of a number of 'branches' which operate from centrally located buildings painted in tasteful cream and brown – the aesthetic preference of a high-ranking USAFE official. These squadrons embrace the vital Rapid Aircraft Maintenance (RAM, or battle-damage repair) branch and War Readiness Spares Kit (WRSK) branch (maintaining a stock of some 5,300 different parts), both of whom aim to keep the Wing combat-ready and to sustain that capability in the event of war. Other functional units, including the 20th Transportation, Supply and Civil Engineering squadrons, alongside the hospital and physiological support, ensure that things run smoothly and that air and ground crews and flight-gear are healthy. A host of other units meet the daily needs of the whole American community in the overseas home-from-home enclave.

These on-base 'organization' and 'intermediate' units

**Above:** An MJ-1 munitions loader – known to ground crews as the 'jammer' – about to bear the burden of a Mk. 82 AIR 'Ballute'. The 'jammer' safely negotiated a racetrack between the prepositioned bomb trolley and underwing BRUs with considerable speed, thanks to the skilled ground crews practising for a 'loadeo' event. (Authors)

**Right, top:** Hinged panels removed from a 77th TFS F-111E to show off the hot end of a P&W TF30-P-103 powerplant. Note also the tail skid, which retracts along with the landing gear. (Authors)

**Right, bottom:** Barbecue time! A TF30-P-103 in fifth stage afterburner on 'Heyford's test rig. Water is sprayed at 500 gallons a minute on to a steel deflector but the whole assembly still becomes white hot. Fuel consumption at that moment equals 37,750 US gallons an hour. All engines have their 'hot' sections inspected at 750hr intervals. (Authors)

are in turn supported by a string of major Air Force Logistics Command (AFLC) depots: Tinker AFB's Oklahoma ALC handles spares, major strips and repairs for the TF30s, Warner-Robins ALC in Georgia and San Antonio ALC in Texas the aircraft's avionics and

*SAC continue to employ their unique Wing-level hierarchy composed of Avionics, Munitions and Field Maintenance Squadrons, the AMS, MMS and FMS respectively. The pre-Combat Orientated Maintenance Organization system, used before 1979, featured a similar set-up to that of SAC but it was later decided to change the flight-line Organization Maintenance Squadron into an Aircraft Generation Squadron, split up into Air Maintenance Units one for each flying squadron.

TAB-V PIGS   123

**Above: Oven-ready 'Aardvark'? An F-111D with protective foil wrapping awaits fuel tank deseal and reseal treatment at SMALC, California. (R. Holman, BAe)**

electronic support equipment. The airframes, too, are regularly given depot treatment on a TCTO basis and this is why they show little sign of up to twenty years of active service. 'Wizzo' Mike Conway pointed out that GDFW's 10,000hr fatigue estimate was possible because 'The F-111 doesn't take a beating like the other airframes do. We can do 6g [up to 7.33g, in theory] but generally we don't. In the F-4 we used to go out and *try* to break the airplane, and *they* seem to last for ever!' Both aircraft have the built-in beef of naval origins, of course.

Airframe refurbishment takes place at one of three locations qualified to perform Programmed Depot Maintenance (PDM). Sacramento ALC (SMALC) at McClellan AFB, California, is the worldwide *matériel* manager for the series and provides PDM for all Ravens and Stateside F-111s; British Aerospace (BAe) Filton, Bristol, England, serves as a rehabilitation depot for USAFE's F-111E/Fs, stripped of classified equipment prior to dispatch; while Australian models receive their major tear-downs under the aegis of the RAAF's own No. 3 Aircraft Depot. All aircraft fall due for PDM every 48 months, this frequency being dictated by the need to replace the crew capsule ejection pyrotechnics, and as capsule demate/remate is a potentially explosive process it makes sense to perform other major internal work at the same time. A full PDM ranges from 13,000

to 21,000 man-hours, depending on the model, taking an average of four and a half months to complete, a cycle of 110 days from roll-in to roll-out – shortly to be increased.*

One of the most demanding tasks is fuel tank deseal/reseal. The degeneration of the original sealing compound in the fuselage and wet wings necessitates total or partial renewal on a regular basis to avoid hazardous fuel leaks during operations. At BAe, aircraft first have their tanks vented to purge them of high-volatility JP-4 fumes and then flushed with denser, high flashpoint JP-5. After the complex array of transfer pipes and gauges has been removed the tanks undergo a visual 'Dash 6' inspection, to decide whether a complete reseal or a 'pick and patch' repair is needed. Aircraft earmarked for the full reseal then leave the tank-venting hangar and enter the adjacent, purpose-built two-bay building with their wings detached. Highly trained volunteers work inside the fuselage tanks with 6,000psi water lances which emit a hot diluted detergent solution, to cut away the polysulphide rubber sealant. The rubber is pre-softened with a substance called SR-51, consisting mainly of petroleum but containing powerful chemicals such as dimethyl acetemide and phenyl mercaptan. The latter is the most pungent substance known to man: it can be detected at 0.2 parts per billion and extremely low concentrations cause uncontrollable

---

*PDM man-hours average 21,000 for the EF-111A, 20,000 for the FB-111A, 19,000 for the F-111A, 18,500 for the F-111D, 16,000 for the F-111E and 13,000 for the F-111F.

vomiting. All air leaving the building passes through large 'scrubbers', with standby tanks of sodium hyperchlorate at hand to neutralize any spills. Working inside the F-111s' tanks was described as a 'bloody revolting activity' because of the heat, stench and confinement. Most men can cope with only about 20 minutes of lancing, despite breathing apparatus and highly elaborate protective wear. There are potential dangers too: a water lance, despite its low mass flow and three-trigger safety operation, is so fine that it can easily trim off part of a limb. In the event of injury an emergency kit is at hand comprising massive two-handed cutters so that a section of the F-111's flank can be sliced out to gain access to the hapless worker. Fortunately the desealing process has been in use at SMALC for ten years with no major injuries; Filton's safety record is also unblemished.

Wings, meanwhile, have their upper skins removed. These one-piece sculptured panels form the roof of the 'wet' wing. Sealant is removed using a hand-held lance or the faster Thorn/EMI Workmaster robot. Once cleaned up, magnetic fluorite rubber tests are then performed to check for fatigue. Passed fit, the wing is recoated in zinc chromate primer and all 1,900 fasteners are reinstalled in an orchestrated panic, within 20 minutes, before the sealer sets.

At the end of PDM the aircraft's mass of carefully stock-coded parts such as inlet spikes, flaps and seats are restored to their rightful place, engines are bolted in and the jet is run through a sophisticated systems test process. Cleared for the next stage, the aircraft has its paintwork touched up and a Functional Flight Check (FCF) takes place, with a skilled AFLC crew at the controls. They take the machine through the entire flight envelope before signing for it and returning it to its operating unit, hopefully in one piece, without the paintwork charred and peeled by the work-out. Incidents do occur now and again though: much to the frustration of SMALC, on 27 January 1982 an FCF team abandoned 68-110, a newly reworked, pristine F-111D, which flopped into the ground near Woodlin, California.

### Staying viable

Shop- and depot-level maintenance procedures have remained fairly standard since the 'One-Eleven's début, with a few exceptions: avionics test equipment is being modernized under a major AIS-R (Avionics Intermediate Shop Replacement) effort. Westinghouse, San Antonio ALC and Bendix have developed a streamlined

Below: F-111E No. 12, 68-002 (known at BAe as 'B****
Two') propped up on jacks, displaying the 'at ease' position
of the main landing gear. This design was the result of the
location of the intakes and the original requirement for
STOL, rough-field performance; in fact, the heavy FOD-
eating characteristics of the 'Aardvark' necessitate pristine
runways. (Authors)

TAB-V PIGS   125

package of 106 benches to replace the 324 currently in service. The large mainframe-type test stations tackle the whole gamut of electronic 'black boxes' and sensors and the new arrangements will enable the bases' avionics technicians to cope with a large number of repairs *in situ*, without the need to send shop replaceable units back to the avionics depots. This important behind-the-scenes update is related to the enormous $1.4 billion Avionics Modernization Program (AMP) which aims to reconfigure the F-111 fleet with a common, more reliable bank of electronic systems. The trustworthy but rather tired Mk. II and Mk. IIB systems' hardware has always caused maintenance problems and could do with a facelift. Col. Rick Matteis, who headed the pioneering FB-111A phase of the AMP effort, which kicked off on paper at the ASD in May 1984, explains that he had to stress this aspect. 'It was easier to get reliability money than it was to get capability money.

The major thrust was to improve the radars and computers', and off-the-shelf equipment was sought wherever possible. GDFW are taking care of the 'Bullet Bombers', their 500hr flight-test programme now over, while Grumman are handling the equally complex analogue-to-digital rework effort and have two F-111As (66-011 and 67-050) on strength to support the development work. The final, 'Pacer Strike' F-111D phase, at present in competition, is to follow. The significance of AMP cannot be over-emphasized: in terms of 'main differences', the post-AMP fleet will be distinguishable mainly by their engines and wing-spans, facilitating the reorganization and cross-breeding of operations; until now each different mark has required its own base and unique, costly support and logistics network. Along with radar and computer updates – including a new USAF-standard Gould Combined Altitude Radar Altimeter (CARA), Texas Instruments TFR revision, INS and weapons panel modifications and enhanced GE AN/APG-67 ARS – wiring bundles ('sausages') have been fabricated in anticipation of Rockwell International's exotic command, control, communications and navigation systems: the Joint Tactical Information Distribution System (JTIDS) and Global Positioning Satellite (GPS Navstar), which will 'pull' the F-111 back into the 'netted' command and control system for greater efficiency yet at the same time provide an added element of autonomy via Navstar, which will be able to update the aircraft's inertial platform with precise co-ordinates – accurate to within 16m – in a matter of seconds. 'Wizzos' will have access to a plethora of facts and will be able to update their computers with present position, target co-ordinates and details of the enemy threat at the push of a few buttons, to be displayed as coloured artificial graphics on the new multifunction display laid over the sharpened radar imagery. Australia is opting at present for a domestic version of AMP but may turn to the United States if the home-grown version proves to be too expensive. The varied AMP and interface kits, manufactured by GDFW and Grumman, are being gradually introduced to the fleet during scheduled PDM, adding some 4,600 man-hours to each rework cycle. SMALC's AMP conversion line is in

progress, having commenced with the FB-111A variant in December 1986; the final American aircraft is scheduled to be completed in 1993 and the RAAF's by 1995.

An avionics update of this magnitude would be worthless unless the airframes are maintained in good order, so in addition to routine PDM and AMP the aircraft are being subjected to a continuing Structural Integrity Program (SIP). These tests have been a feature of the 'One-Eleven's life since the tail and wing-box failures early in the type's career. By March 1970 GDFW and the US Air Force has devised and constructed cold-test facilities in Texas and California, and this essential work is carried on to this day at SMALC under the III-SIP Speedline, consuming an average of 4,500–5,100 man-hours per machine. In September 1986, to cut transatlantic fuel bills, a further cold-test facility came into use at BAe Filton, constructed at the company's own expense during a bitter winter; each F-111 attracts a fee as it passes through this and other stages of PDM.

The 'victim' aircraft is wheeled in, its main gear following two channels; its nude, tailless stabilizer spigots are then clamped into two beefy U-shaped brackets and its undercarriage members are locked to an underfloor fixture. The wings are connected by their pylon attachment sockets to a pair of massive swinging arms weighing 70 tons, able to duplicate the F-111's various sweep settings. In all, the suffering 'Aardvark' is

**Below: Batteries of 'man cooler' fans stand ready to circulate the freezing gaseous nitrogen as F-111E No. 88, 68-078, is fastened to the 'rack' at BAe preparatory to SIP III torture. Wing-flexing rams can be seen under the starboard wing whose 'glove' section is at an atypical angle. The nose gear is attached to stanchions in the trough. (BAe Filton)**

clamped at seventeen points. Up to 7,000 gallons of liquid nitrogen is then vaporized in the sealed chamber, soaking the airframe down to –40°C over the course of five hours. Torture then commences. Loads equivalent to the most severe that the jet is likely to encounter in operations are measured by accelerometers at seven locations, including three in the critical WCTB: bending movements, applied by immense hydraulic jacks, are more likely to reveal incipient metal fatigue cracks at such low temperatures – and 'bending' is the word. At the forward-sweep position the tips can rise 44in and move down 20in, a total travel of over five feet! Jack loads are programmed by computer and BAe's results are cross-checked with SMALC.

So far only two structural failures have occurred at BAe, one of which was in cold-proofing. F-111E 68-043

**Below: The Fort Worth cold chamber in action: the triple exposure shows the degree of wing-flexing exerted during the tests. With the wings fully forward the tips travel 64in as they are flexed using forces equivalent to +7.33g and –3g. (General Dynamics)**

was found to have cracks in its WCTB during a visual inspection prior to being placed in the 'rack' and the minute flaws, barely visible to the naked eye, were deemed sufficient to necessitate the replacement of the entire box. Such items are not acquired with ease these days and must be salvaged from the dwindling number of redundant airframes. A replacement WCTB was brought over from SMALC and dropped into place using a massive overhead support beam. F-111E 68-001, 'The Stump Jumper', was the aircraft which suffered the cold-test failure. In June 1988 its right stabilizer spigot, an 8in diameter steel pivot shaft, snapped off. Mr. Keith Fudge, Senior Test Controller, heard a 'mighty crash' as the fracture occurred. Afterwards it was clear that other fatigue cracks had been latent in the area but had been disguised by structure. The possible consequences of such a failure in flight are probably sufficient to justify the entire cost of the BAe programme. There were a few hard questions from across the 'pond' about the 'breakage' of an aircraft in the British factory but the taped data verified that the correct procedures had been followed. Aircraft '001 received a refurbished tail frame

in a major surgical graft, completed in March 1989, and had the distinction of being the 250th F-111 're-lifed' by BAe.

As the 1990s approach, new technology is making waves. As part of the USAF's non-destructive Durability and Damage Tolerance Assessment initiative, SMALC have just introduced a series of brand new inspection processes which are cheaper, quicker and more effective than cold-proofing and tedious visual examinations. A smart, robotically operated $30 million facility performs instant health checks on structure, probing for fatigue and honeycomb bond integrity (including pyrotechnic

**Right: A 27th TFW F-111D exposes its taileron spigot for critical examination. Fatigue cracking in this area has been one of the F-111's life-long problems. To the left can be seen the rectangular slots for the AN/ALE-28 CMDS chaff/flare dispenser. (R. Holman, BAe)**

**Below: Looking like a four-eared 'Aardvark', this F-111 has everything swung open as it undergoes diagnosis at SMALC. (USAF)**

TAB-V PIGS   129

Above: FB-111A No. 8, 68-7194, was severely damaged in February 1976 following a hard landing and ensuing fire. Shipped to GDFW two years later, it became the subject of the first of thirteen very successful restorations. A total of 150 employees, of the 1,000 still committed to F-111 Program Support, worked directly on the rebuilds; no fewer than 30,000 people were engaged with the F-111 in the programme's heyday. (General Dynamics)

checks), using neutron radiographic, ultrasonic and x-ray devices which can isolate those components requiring immediate replacement or refurbishment. Sacramento, the 'Vark' logistician's paradise, also performs a good deal of serious repair work, but the real resurrections take place at Fort Worth, where there have been some remarkable resuscitations.

## Aardvark Hospital
On 2 August 1982 F-111A 67-101 was 'TF-ing' over south-western Montana when it swallowed a large bird. The right engine disintegrated, shredding its fan blades through the aft fuel tanks and causing the aircraft to

shake and vibrate violently. When the red engine fire and bleed air duct cockpit warning lamps flashed their danger signals Maj. Patton and his 'Wizzo' 1Lt. Singale witch's worst fears were confirmed. No one would have chastised them had they decided to abandon ship and drift back to earth in the capsule but the crew elected to nurse the crippled 'Aardvark' back to the nearest field to attempt a recovery. By the time the jet was lined up on approach at Idaho Falls Airport the fire had eaten its way through the tanks and fuselage skin and had knocked out the hydraulics. Using emergency systems to lower the landing gear and flaps, Maj. Patton placed the aircraft down skilfully on to the tarmac. The damage sustained by the airframe and systems was so severe that the two flyers were forced to leave their smouldering F-111 on the runway. It was later towed away somewhat ignominiously like a broken-down old car. That was the story related to GDFW Restoration Office's Joseph B Brown Jr., who commented that 'The damage seemed hopelessly extensive'. Five years earlier an incident of this magnitude would have caused the battered airframe to be stricken from the inventory, to be coated in spraylat plastic and left to rot in the Davis-Monthan desert 'boneyard' amidst the scrub and spiders, there to be butchered for its remaining usable spares. Remarkably however, by August 1985 the 'Alpha' was back in service with the 'Gunfighters' at Mountain Home, as good as new.

The roots of the Restoration Office go back to February 1976 when FB-111A 67-7194 was involved in a landing accident during appalling visibility. Its main gear collapsed and ignited a fire which caused severe structural damage before fire-fighting vehicles could dowse the flames. The wreckage was placed in storage at SMALC while the USAF scratched its head in despair; despite the F-111's excellent overall safety record the production line had just been terminated and this 'national treasure' was being eroded as aircraft were written off in training accidents. Following a detailed appraisal of the hulk, SMALC and GDFW came up with the obvious solution: repair the machine and return it

to service. General Dynamics was the natural choice: the repair was considered too complex for either SMALC or the specially trained USAF RAM teams. A contract was signed on 17 July 1978 and thus began one of GDFW's most spectacular mating procedures.

Shipped to Fort Worth, 67-7194 had begun its restoration by 1 September. A C-5A Galaxy brought in the mortal remains of FB-111A 67-160 from Davis Monthan AFB's Aerospace Maintenance and Regeneration Center (AMARC), where it had been stored following development testing, to provide the spares for the revamp effort.* The burnt strategic bomber shed its

---

*Four grounded ex-RDT&E and pre-production F-111As – 63-9779, 65-5706, 65-5709 and 65-5710 – are at GDFW in support of the restoration effort. Additional inactive F-111As include 63-9768 'City of Graham' (CC), 63-9770, 63-9772 'City of Frederick' (LN), 63-9773 and 63-9775 'City of Vernon' (UH), all at Sheppard TTC, Texas; 63-9767 at Chanute TTC, Illinois; and 66-012 at Lowry TTC, Colorado. Gate guardians and static display F-111As comprise 63-9776 at Mountain Home, 63-9766 at Fox Field, 65-5702 at FAA-Atlantic City and 63-9771 at Cannon, while Griffiss AFB, New York, has 63-9782 on strength for tests with Rome Air Development Center. An additional seven F-111As are in storage at AMARC (63-9777, -0781 and -9783 and 65-5704, -5705, -5707 and -5708).

Below: FB-111A No. 8's damaged airframe stripped for inspection at GDFW, revealing its charred WCTB. Restoration of this aircraft proved 'to be the catalyst for a very successful program', say GDFW. (General Dynamics)

TAB-V PIGS   131

wings and was severed just aft of its weapons bay, making room for the rear end of '160, which was duly spliced in place, refitted with a replacement, residual Australian WCTB. The rework was extensive: new intake assemblies and ducting were fashioned, while the entire aircraft had to be brought up to the latest specifications, requiring numerous TCTOs and TOs to be incorporated to catch up with lost time. Final assembly, a new paint job and systems checks proceeded through to December 1980, when SMALC flight acceptance crew Lt. Col. Drittler and Capt. Teague test-flew and signed for the machine. Handed over to SAC's 380th BW(M) on 18 September 1980, the revitalized, composite aircraft was at the time of writing still going strong at Plattsburgh with the nickname 'Virgin Abroad' painted on its fuselage.

**Below: The restoration of FB-111A No. 8 in progress: it was severed aft of the cockpit to make room for the rear end of No. 2, 67-160, which was spliced in place and both aircraft, No. 8 dismembered, are in view in this photograph. No. 8 was returned to service in September 1980 and now, nicknamed 'Virgin Abroad', flies with the 380th BW(M) at Plattsburgh AFB, New York, Four F-111As and FB-111A No. 2 served as 'spare parts lockers' for the restoration effort. (General Dynamics)**

Impressed with the results, the USAF investigated the possibility of having further seriously damaged 'articles' repaired. Several aircraft had been relegated to 'spare-parts locker' status at AMARC and would readily lend themselves to rework. As GDFW put it, the initial FB-111A rebuild 'proved to be the catalyst for a very successful program'. In all, 150 employees (of the 1,000 still committed to F-111 Program Support) would become involved over the ensuing years as follow-on contracts were issued to restore 'Aardvarks' back to full, operationally ready C1 ('Code One') status. 'It's amazing. The aircraft come in as real "basket cases" and fly out as good as new. Some have been completed for less than $1 million; if new, they would probably cost $45 million each.' By March 1984 some 2,740 flying hours had been recaptured through the 'plane hospital's efforts, at an average unit cost of a mere $4 million over a 21-month rebuild cycle. More ambitious reworks followed, bringing extensively cannibalized hulks languishing at AMARC back to C1 status. Joseph R. Brown Jr. notes: 'Because no two aircraft are alike, each restoration is unique. Several restorations have been completed by reusing major components from production, pre-production or test airframes'.

Other aircraft have required special engineering

talents. One special example is F-111E 68-082. On 25 March that year a stall warning light flashed up on the cockpit dashboard during take-off from RAF Fairford, England. The pilot immediately aborted and in the ensuing hard landing the jet overshot the runway at 90kts, collapsing the nose gear and smashing its nose and weapons bay doors. Pre-production F-111A 65-5706 was taken out of mothballs and its well-preserved nose was retrofitted on to the damaged F-111E. The reborn aircraft was handed back to USAFE in September 1982 and later acquired the appropriate nickname 'Phoenix'. In total, two FB-111As, no fewer than six F-111Ds and three F-111Es have been refurbished, but Joe Brown went on to point out that the rework effort has ground to a halt following the last redelivery in November 1988. Ten years have elapsed since the Restoration Office was established and most of

the potential rebuilds have been accomplished. 'It now appears that the Restoration Program will close at thirteen aircraft. Unfortunately we are not restoring the pre-production F-111As.' There were plans to rebuild six such aircraft; at the time of writing seven grounded RDT&E and pre-production F-111As were inert at AMARC, while a further dozen examples, in various states of disrepair, were on hand at the TTCs or serving as gate guardians, providing a sufficient pool of major subassemblies to create a half-dozen 'new' 'One-Elevens'. 'While interest in restoring those aircraft to the F-111E configuration was very strong at one point, the "budget crunch" seems to have taken its toll.' Work continues on related efforts. Twenty-six wings from early test aircraft are being remanufactured as spares and it is possible that the 'plane hospital' will be restarted on a piecemeal basis should further F-111s became damaged in the line of duty. Joe Brown points out that 'It's totally unpredictable'.

### Project Warrior

One rather obvious aspect of the F-111's character which has remained fairly constant is its external appearance. The RDT&E and early pre-production jets flew in the 'Navy' scheme of light Gull Gray with white

Below: 'My Lucky Blonde', F-111E No. 30, 68-020, assigned to the 20th TFW CO Brig. Gen. Dale V. Thompson in 1986, receives a paint touch-up in BAe Filton's ASPF (Aircraft Strip and Paint Facility). All 'Aardvarks' get a thorough strip and repaint once every eight years; in between they make do with 'touch-up' work at SMALC, BAe and the bases. RAAF aircraft going through No. 3 Aircraft Depot receive more frequent decorative treatment. (BAe Filton)

undersides and control surfaces. Combat dress for Vietnam introduced TO 1-1-4 from May 1967, comprising two-tone green plus tan, with black undersurfaces, and the majority of F-111s wear that same scheme to this day, albeit that a revised camouflage *pattern* was introduced following the 'Alpha' (which retained its original design for some time – a useful identification feature if codes are not visible).

The FB-111A had a different scheme from the outset, to denote its SAC ownership. Its three-tone green hues with white 'anti-flash' undersides became its hallmark, identical colours to those worn by B-52s of the era. This scheme continued in use for sixteen years, until the FB-111As entered a complete strip and repaint programme, using on-base facilities in New York and New Hampshire, to emerge from the 'paint barns' in a sombre dark grey and green lustreless finish.

Ravens have always had their own 'medium altitude' scheme composed of 'Teenage' fighter 'Ghost Grays', and in mid-1988 it was announced that the entire tactical F-111 fleet would also switch to two-tone grey paint over a two-year period. A large new 'strip and paint' facility was constructed at BAe Filton in anticipation of a repaint programme, and it may yet have F-111s to decorate at some stage, while SMALC's comptrollers have gone almost mad with the variety of colours they must continue to stock!

Repainting is not a cheap business. A nose-to-tail repaint takes 880 man-hours and is reserved for alternate PDMs, in other words it takes place once every eight years. In between, the aircraft must make do with a cosmetic surface coat or touch-up, much of this resting with the SMALC and BAe spray shops and the seemingly indefatigable DCCs, who go to inordinate lengths to keep their 'tails' looking good. 1Lt. Lesley Rossillon, from the 77th AMU, says she is having her F-111Es sequenced through RAF Kemble to receive the new grey scheme. For the immediate future, most tactical 'One-Elevens' must preserve their Vietnam colours long after most of their contemporaries have renounced them in favour of 'European 1' or ghost 'Hill Gray' (popularly known as 'Egyptian 1'). Air crews still find the old scheme adequate even though, as Capt. Greg Lowrimore pointed out, the 'brown doesn't match too well with the bog and green over here'.

The F-111 has never been guilty of flamboyance and this perhaps has encouraged DCCs to imbue a little individuality into its appearance. It has been the nose art and aircraft nicknames which have subtly provided character. This practice seems to have begun on a modest scale with the 366th TFW in 1978. Four of its

F-111As carried names for the SAC 'Giant Voice' bomb competition – 67-079 'Bionic Annie', 67-088 'Streak Bean', 67-090 'Three Times a Lady' and 67-108 'Rionto Choice'. The 366th TFW also fielded the most dazzling Bicentennial F-111Fs, matched only in part by the 20th TFW. In May 1982 names began to catch on again. Upper Heyford's aircraft began to adopt artwork; perhaps they were a reaction to the toning-down process which appeared at this time. At first the names appeared discreetly on nosewheel doors but the idea was obviously good for morale and it grew. Several aircraft started to emerge from their TAB-Vs with more accentuated artwork until in June 1987 the whole thing became official and assumed the title 'Project Warrior – initiative for aircraft nose art'.

Each 20th TFW squadron was invited to submit a list of names and designs. The directive from CinC USAFE stated that

> Each unit is authorized to display World War II commemorative nose art on assigned aircraft. Units should research their history. If none is available, units may design their own or select art from another unit which had a similar mission. Only replicas or tasteful art should be sought.

In practice all of these sources were employed and some imaginative suggestions emerged. For example, the 55th AMU came up with 'California Cutie II' (an Eighth Air Force B-29), the 79th AMU leaned towards recent Wing history with examples such as 'Hat Trick' (for Brad Insley's '033), and 'Strange Music' (inspired partly by '072's hatred of 'Victor Alert' duties when it would

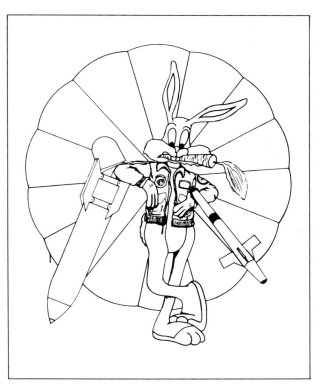

TAB-V PIGS    135

Above: F-111E No. 12, 68-002, alias 'Imperial Wizard', from the 79th TFS 'Tigers'. The nose art, applied to both sides of the aircraft, is finished in golden yellow and brown, pink, red, green and blue. (Authors)

Left: 'Free Bird', F-111E No. 16 (68-006), seems to have derived its name from Rebel Rock in the southern States. (M. J. Francombe)

habitually dump fuel and drop its hook on take-off!), while the 77th TFS cooked up a good range of names and colourful paintings drawing on the poker hand and red colour in the squadron insignia. Not all designs were applied or retained for long, yet they certainly brightened up the base. The blue splash of 'Whispering Death' (a traditional F-111 sobriquet), the Disneyesque 'Mad Bomber' and humorous 'Flak Ducker' were eye-catching at quite a distance. Of Upper Heyford's squadrons, the 42nd ECS approached the problem with the most precision: their neat dossier of designs was approved and applied *en bloc*.

The CinC USAFE directive had included the proviso that all art should be removed if an emergency arose and toned down for exercises. Sadly, this happened all too quickly, though not for those reasons. General Kirk took hold of the helm in USAFE and issued a directive in the spring of 1988 to the effect that only commanders' aircraft should retain nose art. Within a few weeks most of the paintings were erased. There was a feeling at Third Air Force HQ, Mildenhall, England, that things had gone a little too far and that some of the artwork was not good public relations material. A rash of gaudy F-16s with bright tails and well-endowed ladies on their noses may also have influenced the tone-down. This opinion was shared to some extent on the bases in England, where one tech. sergeant told the authors that

he felt that some of the paintings were 'really amateurish, almost embarrassing' and wished they could have been smaller and more tasteful like the recent FB-111A examples he knew so well during his FTD training. None of the SAC art has quite the impact of Upper Heyford's 'A Knight to Remember' or the superbly painted 'Imperial Wizard' – but those, at least, have avoided official disapproval so far.

The other F-111 Wings have eschewed such decorative distractions, but one cannot help thinking that it is hard to keep a good habit down and that this dazzling epoch will soon be resurrected.

TAB-V PIGS   137

# Cosmic Aardvarks

The biggest concentration of open-air 'One-Elevens' is to be found basking on the High Plains of eastern New Mexico, near the Texas panhandle, at Cannon AFB: including an average of six aircraft in for depot work at any one time, the base boasts no fewer than 72 F-111Ds, all squatting on their fat tyres, wings spread-eagled, soaking up the sun.

Named in honour of Gen. John K. Cannon, Second World War commander of all Allied Air Forces in the Mediterranean theatre, Cannon AFB is one of the 'Aardvark' crews' favourite bases. The nearby town Clovis offers few great attractions but the near-constant sunshine, the cool nights and the open terrain, not to mention the opportunity to use plenty of live ammunition in relatively unrestricted airspace – a feature of both TAC 'One-Eleven' bases – all add up to the right image for the 'Earthpig' drivers and maintainers. It is a tightly knit community of some 3,800 military and 400 civilian personnel dotted over a 25,663-acre site.

Cannon, in some respects, has claims to a stronger F-111 tradition than Nellis. It is closer to Fort Worth, and its Melrose range was specially adapted for the 'Aardvark' from 1968 as the base geared up for its new, albeit much delayed machines. In the interim, pending delivery of its own 'swing-wingers', the resident 27th

TFW soldiered on with the F-100 'Hun' and provided ground-school training for the 'Harvest Reaper' crews and flying training for their follow-on 'Echo' colleagues using 29 F-111Es and ten 'Alphas', and was even nominated as home for the ill-fated RF-111D model. There were a lot of chops and changes before the dust finally settled, the last of the temporarily assigned F-111Es departed for England in July 1971 (to be followed a year later by the last F-100, destined for the Air National Guard) and the 27th TFW, with its three component squadrons of F-111Ds as they are known today, came into being. After a long and traumatic prenatal work-up, finally, on 1 November 1971, the first 'Delta' arrived, piloted by the Wing CO Col. C. E. Francis.*

Ostensibly similar to the Triple Plow II F-111E, apart from its beefed-up, FB-type landing gear which overcame strut crack problems experienced during 'Linebacker' operations, the F-111D is in fact a very different

**Below: F-111D No. 60 (68-144), from the 522nd TFS 'Fireballs', on approach to RAF Boscombe Down, England, during the Wing's inaugural 'Coronet Hammer' NATO deployment in May 1980. Eighteen 'Deltas' took part and flew 282 training sorties over two weeks. (Robin A. Walker)**

**27th TFW (12th AF, TAC) (F-111D)**
**Cannon AFB, New Mexico**

| Squadron | Colour | Nickname | Code To mid-1972 | From mid-1972 | Notes |
|---|---|---|---|---|---|
| 481st TFS | Green | – | CA | CC | Activated with F-111D Dec. 1972; disbanded Aug. 1973. Re-activated Jan. 1976 as F-111D RTU, replacing 4427th TFRS; disbanded Jan. 1980. No longer active. |
| 522nd TFS | Red | Fireballs | CC | CC | Equipped with F-111D starting May 1972. IOC as first combat-ready F-111D sqn. Nov. 1972. |
| 523rd TFS | Blue | Crusaders | – | CC | Reassigned to Cannon Aug. 1973, replacing 481st TFS. Still operational as deployable unit. |
| 524th TFTS | Gold | Hounds | CD | CC | Converted to F-111D mid-1972; took over from 481st TFS as F-111D RTU 1 Jan. 1980. Still operational as F-111D RTU. |
| 4427th TFRS | Purple | | CE | CC | Activated as F-111D RTU Oct. 1971. Disbanded Jan. 1976. No longer active. |

**Note:** The 'CB' tail-code was used by the 90th TFS, 3rd TFW, flying A-37s from Bien Hoa and was never used on F-111s. F-111A/Es were flown by the 481st, 522nd and 524th TFSs following initial F-111E deliveries to Cannon in October 1969. The F-111Es were subsequently reassigned to USAFE and the 27th TFW started to re-equip with F-111Ds from November 1971.

aircraft indeed. Pilots and 'Wizzos' who fly the 'Delta' point to the Cannon 'CC' tail code on the fin of the aircraft and claim with some pride that it stands for 'Cosmic'; the motto of the 27th TFW is, appropriately, 'Intelligent Strength'.

**Flying by TV**

The F-111D was intended as the next USAF model off the line following the F-111A but development hiccups connected with its 'cosmic' but rather complex Rockwell Autonetics Mk. II avionics precipitated the cancellation of the similarly equipped British TF/F-111K derivative, while the production line at GDFW leapfrogged from the F-111C to the 'Echo' model. In the words of one commander, 'We were a tad too ambitious'. Final assembly of the bulk of the 96 'Deltas' eventually produced did not take place until 1972, yet, despite these upsets, by 28 February 1973, when the last of the breed arrived on Cannon's runway, the newly reequipped 27th TFW was slowly but surely counting down towards combat-ready 'Code One' status.† By May 1975 the Wing was able to initiate TAC's 'Silver Bullet' weapons meet, a special session for F-111s, and two years on it began to participate in SAC's 'Giant Voice' competitions – one of the harshest tests of readiness.

It was the initial delays resulting from the Mk. II BNS development effort which gave rise to the less complex Mk. IIB avionics packages fitted to the FB-111A and F-111F, simplified versions of the F-111D, whose cockpits share more in common with the analogue models. Nevertheless all three digital types share a core bank of IBM/GD AN/AYK-6 digital general-purpose computers plus a Rockwell AN/AJN-16 INS, able to store just under one thousand waypoints fed in via a tape to fly the jet in a completely 'hands-off' manner – not that any self-respecting TACAIR 'One-Eleven' pilot or WSO would fold his arms and go to sleep!

The commonality between the digital F-111s ends abruptly if one dismisses the central computer complex,

for the F-111D uses a brand new first-generation 'glass' cockpit built around the Norden AN/AVA-9 Integrated Display Set, wired up to a new suite of Rockwell AN/APQ-130 ARS, twin Sperry AN/APQ-128 TFRs and Marconi AN/APN-189 doppler radar.‡ The brains of the Norden AN/AVA-9 package is the inconspicuous 58lb signal transfer unit (STU), tucked away in the nose of the F-111D. Informed by a myriad multipin electrical umbilicals, this black box converts raw, slow-scan sensor data from the ARS and TFR radars into synthetic TV format imagery for continuous display on the two primary cockpit instruments: the pilot's 7in vertical situation display (VSD) and WSO's bigger, 11in multisensor display (MSD), both large 'green monitor' CRT tubes. For the pilot, the primary viewing mode is 'Flight Situation' – a graphic equivalent of the traditional ADI instrument – providing roll, dive and climb, plus height and heading indications and cues; and, for the 'Wizzo', radar. The aircraft shares much in common with the F-111B in this respect, using digitally driven television displays instead of needles and dials but with the system optimized for ground-mapping and air-to-ground weapons delivery. Both primary displays are interactive. Maj. Dick Brown, just embarking on his second session in the F-111D at Cannon and second only to Brad Insley in the all-time high-hours league, notes:

The big thing about the D model is that you can work from both sides. For instance, if you wanted to use the radar and

*F-111D No. 6, 68-090.
†Mk. II project difficulties forced GDFW to switch production to the F-111E which, in turn, resulted in a reduction of F-111D orders from 315 to 96. Cancellation of the F-111B, and FB-111A cut-backs, diverted 22 B and 36 FB assemblies to the F-111D assembly line. The cancellation of the RAF order for 46 F-111Ks and 4 TF-111K trainers as two of the aircraft were approaching completion (67-149 and -150, which were handed over to the USAF as YF-111As for ground trials and later scrapped for spares) resulted in the diversion of the remainder of the F/TF-111K airframes to FB-111A production. Owing to the niggling development problems and contractual changes many F-111s started life at GDFW as one model but emerged from the plant as a completely different type!
‡Doppler is explained in 'Warsaw Pact Central Heating' (Part 2).

Above: Its tan and green well matched to the desert and bush, F-111D No. 3, 68-087, displays its 26° VG lock-out. The 'CE' tail-code belongs to the defunct 4427th TFRS, 27th TFW, whose fin-stripe was an unusual colour – purple. (Alan Howarth)

Below: Armed with 1,000-pounder 'slick' bombs preparatory to a 'Red Flag' sortie in December 1980, a 27th TFW F-111D nestles in among a flight line of Cannon's 'Cosmic Aardvarks'. In the background are F-111As from the 366th TFW 'Gunfighters'. (Frank B. Mormillo)

bomb from the left seat the pilot can do that; you could put the attack radar display in front of you and the WSO could put the attitude indicator in front of him and fly from the right-hand seat.

All but the Raven have two sticks. VSD and MSD display options, selectable at the twist of a grey knob, include attack radar, flight indicator and TFR (in PPI sector-sweep in three range scales, at 5, 10 or 15 miles ground map, as a back-up to the attack radar, something all F-111 TFRs can perform; or, at a fixed range scale,

in E-scan mode, providing terrain avoidance monitor). Also available are 'real-time' Aided Visual Element TV-sensor and Weapons TV mode, for use with imagery generated by, say, a GBU-15 electro-optical glide bomb.*

The Rockwell Autonetics AN/APQ-130 attack radar set, too, works in a different manner from the GE types installed in the other 'One-Elevens': in addition to PPI sweep, the dish offers an 'HRGM' mode providing selective ±30° azimuth and ±45° elevation 'patch' and 'strip' mapping. The radar works effectively at long range even at very low grazing angles, down in the weeds, to furnish a quality ground map and extremely accurate slant-range to target. 'Normal' and sharpened, 'Expanded' display options are available, the latter for the bomb run. Dick Brown: 'It's quite sophisticated. It has selectable 1-, 2- or 4-bar scan and you can work from 2½ to 200 nautical miles' range'. Eight range scales are available in all. Image crispness is said to be 'excellent', making waypoint, target and offset identification relatively easy, with prominent and reliable terrain returns. Image 'Freeze' capability can place a radar scan on hold, to provide a measure of 'stealth', while radar ground 'Beacon' interrogation and moving target detector (MTD), both providing easy-to-identify 'blips', are built in. All radar controls with the exception of the tracking handle are positioned around the MSD, which also includes the regular handy plug-in film cassette. In the F-111D the system is able to photograph any of the modes being presented, not just radar, set to shoot frames ranging from 1 second to 2 minutes apart, with a manual shutter option. A vertical tape counter displays the percentage of film remaining, in 25 per cent increments.

The 'Cosmic' instruments extend to the Norden heads-up displays (HUDs) which jut out at the top of the dashboard. Unusually there are two such units, one each for the pilot and 'Wizzo'. Also driven using data from the STU, these displays provide high-resolution collimated optical green symbols on the cropped combining glass for true 'blind' (but typically visually aided) heads-up weapons delivery. According to Dick Brown, in place of the old ODS ring sight and command bar used by the less sophisticated 'Earthpigs', the 'Delta's display 'is a lot like the latest HUDs. It has cursors that move onto the different points, and a velocity vector [where you are heading] indicator', for chin-up steering. All the pilot has to do is follow the pointers and 'pickle' the bomb load. Again, the HUD system shares much in common with that installed in the defunct F-111B, all of it way ahead of its time. Full manual depression capability is available as back-up for a 'canned' visual bomb delivery at set airspeed, dive angle and weapons-release height etc. should the automatic systems start to malfunction. The 'MILS' depression knob is located on the side of the HUD boxes.

Other notable cockpit variations exist. A unique facet of the 'office' is the Astronautics Corp. AN/AYN-3 horizontal situation display (HSD) which dominates the middle of the forward console where other 'Aardvarks' have their TFR scope. The pilot has a conventional but miniature compass-like horizontal situation indicator under his VSD but the AN/AYN-3 goes one better, providing much more detailed aircraft heading, position and track, denoted by a black pointer and electric green track cursor and aircraft cross symbols

*See 'The "Can Do" Squadron' in 'Statue De Libya Raiders' (Part 3).

Below: F-111D No. 5, 68-089, basks in the noonday sun with its avionics bay open and its engines removed. This aircraft has been assigned to the 6512th Test Squadron, Systems Command, at Edwards AFFTC, California, for most of its life. Photographed here in December 1976, it remains on the AFFTC roster of six 'Aardvarks', one of which is flown by NASA Dryden (see Appendix VI). (Frank B. Mormillo)

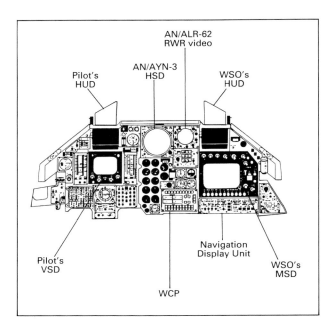

Above: F-111D dashboard Norden AN/AVA-9 Integrated Display Set. Slow-scan sensor data from the TFRs and ARS is processed by the Signal Transfer Unit and displayed on the vertical situation display, multisensor display and two heads-up-displays. The horizontal situation display furnishes heading and ground track over a projected map display, the navigation display unit provides LED digital co-ordinates, the RWR video alphanumeric shows threat symbology and the weapons control panel is used to select ordnance and stations. The nuclear select panel is to the right of the MSD and NDU. (Norden)

generated by the INS and STU, all superimposed on a projected moving-map display. Cross-reference can thus be made from VSD or MSD to the HSD for easy navigation 'in the weather'.

The other major variation in the F-111D is the WCP, generically similar to the right-hand console-mounted Mk. IIB weapons panels but located on the dashboard in a smaller, more compact layout. Maj. Dick Brown:

The system holds the ballistics for all the different types of weapons – we call it a 'protected memory'. If you have a special weapon and it's not in the 'protected memory' then you just load it in with the tape-load for the mission and it loads into the weapons control computer. All you have to do is say 'this' weapon is located on 'these' stations, say, a pivot-pylon [and select fuses, interval and release mode and give a quick stab at the appropriate buttons which light up to confirm selection]. You just push the buttons and it gives you automatic ballistics for everything – CCIP, toss bombs, loft bombs – pretty fancy. For additional ballistics there are cassettes which plug in and you just change the legend.

Dick Brown produced a small yellow screwdriver from his flight-suit pocket: 'You need this in a $50 million airplane to change the legend!' Manual ballistics are always inserted as back-up as the 'Cosmic' Mk. II system remains somewhat temperamental. The general

button-pushing procedures are similar to those used in the FB-111A or F-111F:

It's the same theory; it's like driving a different automobile or having a different stereo. It does the same thing, you just push different buttons; but, like a remote control on television, it takes you a short while to learn it, and then it's easy.

The F-111D was from the outset designed with a vastly superior air-to-air capability, made possible by the more sophisticated attack radar which features clutter processing (getting rid of unwanted background returns) and target acquisition in synthetically displayed B-scan mode, radar data processed into pure graphics which furnishes relative airborne target position. Capt. Brad Insley describes it as a 'pie-shaped picture turned into a square-shaped picture'. Maj. Jim Rotramel, 'Earthpig' flyer and noted photographer, explains that

B-scan is used mainly for tanker rendezvous. While a PPI presentation gives you a 'picture' of the ground in front of you, a B-scan spreads the vertex across the bottom of the scope. This artificial display facilitates intercepts, which require holding the 'target' at a fixed angle from your aircraft. For instance, if you want to hold the tanker at a 26° offset to the left of your aircraft using a B-scan presentation, you put him at the desired offset angle and maneuver your aircraft to keep him tracking straight down the scope (since the vertex is spread out across the bottom of the scope, different angles are represented by vertical lines, not angled lines as in a PPI presentation).

Originally, having acquired enemy in the sweep, the F-111D was to have had the capability of 'painting' the quarry at an offset- or off-axis angle with its radar to guide Ku-band semi-active radar-homing Raytheon AIM-7G-1 Sparrow III missiles to target, at ranges of up to 60 miles at altitude. Successfully test-bench-developed by 1971, the XAIM-7G prototypes were subsequently shelved as Mk. II avionics costs rose, before operational deliveries of the F-111D commenced.

In common with the PPI mode, the air-to-air B-scan can work in eight range scales from 2½ to 200 miles in wide or narrow scans. It can plot an aerial beacon and it has a manual target-acquisition capability via the radar tracking handle. Maj. Dick Brown describes the F-111D's air-to-air capabilities as potentially superb, and Sparrow III missiles or the latest AIM-120 AMRAAM could be reinstated if the operational requirement ever arose, but that is extremely unlikely – the crews would probably end up spending too much time setting up BVR 'kill boxes' instead of concentrating on their earthborne targets! Short-range Sidewinder heat-seeking missiles and a 20mm 'Gat-pack' are now the norm and carried purely for self-defence.

**Winders and Gats**

The use of the AIM-9 Sidewinder has always been a feature of the 'Aardvark' Fighter Weapons School course but for many years operational F-111s were not assigned the scarce missiles, which were diverted to the air defence 'Zulu Alert' F-4 Phantoms and F-15 Eagles instead. All that changed in May 1983 when Lakenheath's F-111Fs started to tote the slender weapons on newly introduced air combat training sorties, shoulder-mounted on Aero 3A rails on stations 3A or 6A (pivot-pylons 3 and 6). Today the old, uncooled, PbS seeker-equipped AIM-9B makes only an occasional appearance at air shows, having been superseded at an operational level by the Ford Aerospace AIM-9P model with its distinctive wide-chord cranked canards.* This type uses Peltier-effect thermoelectric cooling to provide greater seeker sensitivity, a factor which has permitted the cumbersome F-111 to enter the air combat arena in a limited way: the AIM-9B, and even the later -9E and -9J, could only be locked-on to the prey if pre-manoeuvred into the quarry's six o'clock position to acquire its hot jet exhaust, and thus demanded dogfighter manoeuvrability from the attacker. The AIM-9P's active optical fusing enables the missile to be fired virtually in an all-aspect mode, in a point-and-shoot fashion.

Soon to join the AIM-9P as part of the AMP modernization effort are the latest all-aspect, off-axis-launch-capable Raytheon slender-chord 'Lima' and 'Mike' models, which use Navy-style gas cryogenics instead of electrical cooling (although USAF AIM-9L/Ms employ internal argon gas bottles instead of nitrogen in the rails, keeping the launch equipment simple). The AIM-9L/M versions have demonstrated a consistent Pk (kill probability) of over 90 per cent in all weathers, providing an excellent self-defence capability. Training rounds are carried usually. These are inert, blue missiles with live seekers which can be flown captively for lock-on practice. With Sidewinder selected and the radar caged at boresight (or tracking at an offset in B-scan, to provide steering cues too), the pilot manoeuvres to hold the enemy within AIM-9 lock-on parameters. A 'growl' on the headset will confirm that the missile has acquired the target, after which the weapon can be let loose for the kill.

All F-111 types with the exception of the RAAF and F-111F versions may use the GE 20mm 'Gat-pack' also, though they are now standard mission equipment on the F-111Ds only. Lt. Col. Dave Skakal points out that the packs are available from storage for use in the F-111A/E models for self-defence if needed, but that the weapons bay is more often than not required for other purposes – clip-in fuel tanks or nuclear weapons. Crews are unanimous that the latest Sidewinders make the 'Gat' somewhat superfluous. Lt. Col. Tom G. Runge reckons he would 'rather have an AIM-9L'. Tony Sobol is more explicit:

> You have to look at the cost and value of going around with a multi-million-dollar airplane strafing the roads – you gotta be sh****** me! The gun's a short-range weapon and it's pretty obvious that the F-111 is not much for turnin' and burnin'. The missile is a much better weapon, so we use the missile to make them respect our nose instead of a gun.

Lt. Col. Dave Skakal, a former F-4E pilot, explains that

*The AIM-9E Peltier-effect Sidewinder replaced the AIM-9B and was followed by the cranked-canard-equipped AIM-9J by late 1972. The -9J was later modified and redesignated -9N and was superseded by the -9P model. The N and P models are virtually identical, as are the L and M. The missing letters in the sequence are US Navy variants. The B/L/M types only have been used by both services.

**Below: 'Slick', low-drag bombs dominate the camera frame as 27th TFW F-111Ds are readied for a 'Red Flag' mission from Nellis TFWC, Nevada. (Frank B. Mormillo)**

## F-111 TRAINING – ANALOGUE AND DIGITAL

### Basic Course – B Course (F-111A-BOOPI/WI and F-111D-OOPC/WC)

This is for students with no previous fighter experience who have completed UPT or UNT and also FLIT. The course lasts for five months and covers 280hrs of classroom academics, 16 simulator missions and 30 sorties (about 80 flying hours). Upon completion, air crews are assigned to squadrons where they receive a two-month local area 'check out' and become mission-ready.

| | |
|---|---|
| Pilot Track 1 | First assignment UPT graduates. |
| Pilot Track 2 | T-37/T-38 instructor pilots with no fighter experience. |
| WSO | First assignment UNT graduates and WSOs with no fighter experience. |
| All | 100 training days (19 ground, 81 flying). |

### Transition Course – TX Course (F-111A-TXOPI/WI and F-111D-TXOPC/WC)

This is for air crews with experience in fighters. The course lasts three months and covers 195hrs of classroom academics, 16 simulator missions and 20 sorties (about 54 flying hours). Upon completion, air crews are assigned to mission-ready squadrons.

| | |
|---|---|
| Pilot Track 1 | 300hrs in fighter/attack aircraft and current within 42 months; or 500hrs in fighter-attack aircraft and current within 5 years; or 1,000hrs in fighter/attack aircraft and current within 8 years; or an experienced F-111 pilot, non-current in the F-111 between 5 and 8 years. 67 training days (19 ground, 48 flying). |
| WSO Track 1 | As for pilot. |
| Pilot Track 2 | Experienced F-111 pilot, non-current in the F-111 over 18 months and not more than 5 years (EF-111A pilots must have completed a mission-ready tour in the F-111 or another air-to-ground fighter to qualify for this Track, unless the assignment is back to the EF-111A). |
| WSO Track 2 | As for pilot. |
| Pilot Track 3 | 200hrs or 1 year of operational experience in the F-111, non-current for not more than 18 months. 16 training days (5 ground, 11 flying). |
| WSO Track 3 | As for pilot. |

### Instructor Course – I Course (F-111A-IOOPI/WI and F-111D-IOOPC/WC)

This course is designed to provide qualified instructor pilots and WSOs. Each pilot must be two-ship lead-qualified, and all students must be experienced in the F-111 with 500hrs or more of flying time. The course lasts one month and covers 65 classroom academic hours, 4 simulator missions and 10 sorties (approx. 26 flying hours). Graduates are qualified to instruct all phases of F-111 training. 30 training days (10 ground, 20 flying).

If a Soviet pilot knows that the F-111 doesn't carry any forward-firing ordnance and he recognizes you as an F-111 and has the speed to catch you, he may decide to do that. But if he has any doubt in his mind, or he knows we do have that capability, he's going to stand off from you a bit more, regard you as more of a threat; and definitely if you point your nose at him and he knows you have that capability, whether you have that missile on or not, he's going to honour you.

Capt. George Kelman, also drawing on his previous experience in Phantoms, agreed:

If an F-4 turned and looked like he was going to gun-shoot you everybody backed off until they got a close look and then said 'Oh, that was a [gunless] RF-4C or F-4G'. It made you give up enough way so now he can get away whether he has a gun or not. One day his nose is going to light up and it's going to be a real guy – say an F-111D – with a real gun, so you can't take that chance.

The same philosophy applies to the modern point-and-shoot Sidewinder missiles.

### 'We have the mobility'

In much the same fashion that flyers destined for Upper Heyford usually go first to Mountain Home, so the majority of crews assigned to combat-ready units at Cannon or Lakenheath go to the 27th TFW for F-111 training. Performing the 'digital RTU' function are the 524th TFTS 'Hounds'. People brand new to the Air Force's flying community come from the 449th TTW's FLIT or Fighter Lead-in Training programme at nearby Holloman AFB, New Mexico, where the pilots have undergone 26 sorties embracing transition, formation flying (classic 'finger-four' and pair work), traditional fighter manoeuvres (old-fashioned barrel-rolls etc.) and basic low-level flying and ground attack (strafing and bombing) in Northrop AT-38Bs equipped with SUU-20 dispensers and 7.62mm gunpods. WSOs go through a shorter course: the idea is to get the new flyers prepared for an operational assignment, and all the day-to-day back-up administrative work and officer bravado that goes with it, over a period of 2–6 weeks.* At Cannon the 'Hounds' put their F-111D students through three phases – 180hrs academics, 50hrs simulator time and 80hrs flying. Academics provides an introduction to aircraft systems, emergency procedures, weapons, electronic warfare and offensive/defensive tactics.

Following each phase [say Cannon] the student practices in the simulator what he was taught in the classroom. The simulator reduces the aircrews' training costs since it costs more than fifteen times as much to fly an actual F-111D than it does the simulator. The heart of our program is the Flight Simulator Facility which went into operation on 26 October 1971. The facility is staffed by eighteen highly trained maintenance personnel from Simiflight Simulation Division whose specialties include computer programming, computer modeling and digital computer repair. They work around the clock (three shifts per day) Monday through Friday and weekends if required, to provide up to 14 hours of aircrew training per day.

The building houses two F-111D flight simulators which were purchased from Singer Simulator Products Division. Simulator number one was modified in 1982 by the addition of a digital image generator visual system which greatly enhances the realism of training by providing the aircrews with a three-dimensional multicolor presentation of the actual terrain.

Both simulators provide exact replicas of an actual F-111D aircraft cockpit and all instruments. Controls and lights etc. function as they do in the actual aircraft. As a result aircrews can establish the habit patterns and procedural knowledge required for flight before they even get to the actual aircraft. In addition, instructors have at their disposal a control console with which they can create in-flight situations which force the aircrews into decision-making under stress (i.e. emergencies, combat situations etc.), freeze the entire problem, discuss aircrews' strengths and weaknesses and then 'press on' with the mission. This increases the aircrews' confidence and ability to deal with stressful situations.

Above: In regulation toned-down national insignia but bearing the colourful unit badges of the 27th TFW, F-111D No. 47 (68-131) roars into the desert sky armed with eight Mk. 82 low-drag bombs. (Frank B. Mormillo)

Until the visual modifications were completed aircrews flying the simulator had to rely solely on cockpit instruments to fly; they couldn't look 'outside'. Now aircrews have a very realistic 'outside' provided by a three-screen visual simulator. They can look outside and see taxiways, buildings, terrain features etc. With the proper maps, charts and pictures our modelers can provide aircrews with a dynamic, realistic 'outside' anywhere in the world – or some other plane, if required!

Although the radar landmass sytem is old (late 1960s technology) it deserves mention because of the ingenuity that went into its design (given the technical limitations of the day). At the heart of the system is a series of photographic transparencies, three feet on a side, each of which represents an area about one-half as large as the United States. To give some idea of the size reduction involved, a piece of dust on the transparency would show up as a large mountain! The photographic transparencies are made from multicolored hand-painted representations. Still, the photographic transparencies are so accurate they show details as small as rivers and higher-power transmission lines. The simulator radars actually transmit a light beam which passes through the multicolored photographic transparency and into light-sensitive devices that decode the color combinations and translate them into signals which provide very realistic cockpit radar presentations for aircrew use.

Although we can simulate the real world on instruments, flight controls and visual repesentations we cannot simulate the real world physiologically ('G' forces, for example) or psychologically (fear, for example) for the aircrews – they must get into a *real* aircraft.

Once a student has mastered the required skill levels in the 'sim' he progresses to the flying stage. Missions are divided into four phases. Initial transition covers basic handling. This is followed by the 'Strike Day' and 'Strike Night' phases covering low-level TFR and 'level' and 'angular' weapons delivery procedures. Ground attack, the final phase, expands on these procedures and introduces the students to tactical formation, terrain-masking and the more dynamic tactical weapons delivery modes available. Apart from being conducted in a drier climate, the five-month-long course is identical to that run by the 389th TFTS 'Thunderbolts' at Mountain Home, with sparsely populated countryside over which to work, but with the emphasis placed on the Mk. II avionics and switchology. Navigation takes the students on routes over the four corner States, with

medium-altitude AAR hook-ups and low-level bombing on their own special range – Melrose, 24 miles west, deeper into the Llano Estacado. Melrose is orientated north–south, with 'entry' points at both ends, and comprises an assortment of targets ranging from a circular weapons 'dartboard' to 'ammunition storage bunkers', a 'truck convoy', 'runways', 'taxiways', 'mobile missile launchers and radars' and a strafing range. 'Cleared hot' (an OK from the Range Control Officer), trainees can pound the place to bits with practice bombs.

Capsule egress is an important, unique feature of the F-111 induction process. The novices are strapped in a capsule bobbing about in the swimming pool and can play with the bilge pump and learn how to get out and dog-paddle in heavy flying gear to the 'shore'. Dry and confident, upon graduation crews may be posted to the 'Aardvark University' in England to convert to the F-111F; equally likely, they will switch to one of Cannon's two resident operational squadrons and wear the patch of either the 522nd TFS 'Fireballs' or the 523rd TFS 'Crusaders'.

Both 'Red' and 'Blue' squadrons have a worldwide commitment in times of crisis and regularly put their mobility to the test during off-base excursions, both to Stateside venues such as 'Red Flag' and SAC's 'Bomb Comp' and on longer-legged trips overseas. Capt. Greg Lowrimore, IWSO, who cut his 'Aardvark' baby molars at Cannon some years ago, pointed out that the SAC bombing competition sorties often last a gruelling 6–7hrs apiece with no AAR support. This requires the weapons bays to be fitted with purpose-built fuel tanks, providing an extra 585 US gallons of vital 'go juice':

---

*Prior to FLIT, pilots have completed an Undergraduate Pilot Training (UPT) course, averaging 80hrs on Cessna T-37s and 108.8hrs on supersonic Northrop T-38As at one of six ATC bases located in Arizona, Mississippi, Oklahoma or Texas. WSOs have gone through Undergraduate Navigator Training (UNT) with the 323rd FTW at Mather AFB, California, where they fly an average of 25hrs on T-37s and 124hrs on Boeing T-43 navigation trainers.

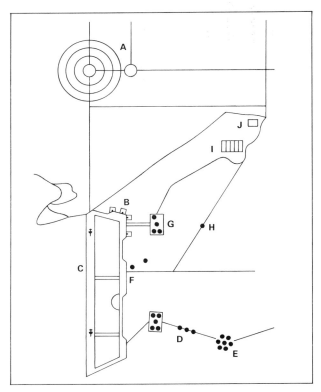

Above: The Melrose Range. A. Special and conventional weapons range. B. Aircraft in parking areas. C. Main runway with several aircraft. D. Convoy of trucks. E. Six fixed missile launchers and radar site. F. Radar approach control building. G. Fuel storage targets. H. Mobile missile launchers and radar. I. Practice strafing targets. J. Main range tower.

There are two of them that sit side by side and hook up on the same MAU-12 mountings that are underneath the pivot-pylons. This is a useful facility, but the problem is that we use the bay for other things so it's constantly a matter of taking them out and putting them back in. It normally takes about a day to put them in, hook them up and check them.

The external 600 US gallon capacity drop tanks compromise stores carriage and have the drawback of greater drag but they can be fitted to any of the wing pivot-pylons, typically in symmetrical pairs on stations 3, 4, 5 and 6 (the tactical maintenance manuals prohibit simultaneous fully mobile tankage on the inboard fully mobile pylons and fixed, seldom-used outboard pylons), and jettisoned or replenished in-flight. They have the advantage that they 'can just be slapped up and checked out in about 15–30 minutes'.

Aircraft usually deploy on short hops with empty BRUs on the wings to facilitate rapid turnaround but for further-reaching flights the racks can easily be ferried by the great ensemble of C-141 Starlifters and C-5 Galaxies supporting the outbound party, permitting the bombers to carry twin internal and external strap-on tankage to the tune of some 1,785 US gallons, equating to an extra 35 per cent of fuel. This enormous capacity has enabled the 522nd TFS 'Fireballs' to tour exotic places like Egypt for 'Bright Star' or Elmendorf (Alaska) for 'Brim Frost' manoeuvres with relatively little tanker support, providing the backbone air strike element of the US Central Command (formerly known as the Rapid Deployment Joint Task Force) to whom they owe a major commitment.

The transoceanic hops started in September 1978 when eight 'Fireballs' deployed to Gardermoen in Norway under 'Coronet Kingfisher' to support the NATO exercise 'Northern Wedding'. The 27th TFW has since opened up a series of regular trips to Europe and

Asia. In May 1980 the 'Fireballs' inaugurated a series of triennial movements to RAF Boscombe Down, England, with 18 F-111Ds as 'Coronet Hammer'. September 1983's 'Coronet Archer' brought eight 'Fireballs', and the September 1986 'Coronet Comanche' manœuvre brought a dozen of their number back to grey, rainy England in company with six Ravens from the 'Gunfighters': ' "Coronet Comanche", supported by KC-10 Extender aerial refuellers, was the first ever deployment and redeployment with no ground or air aborts'. Oriental outings started in 1979 when the 'Hounds' – then a deployable, operational unit as opposed to an RTU – traversed 18,000 miles and two continents to spend four weeks at RAAF Amberley and three weeks at Sachon AB, South Korea. The 'Coronet Beacon' deployment has now become a regular biennial feature for the 523rd TFS 'Crusaders', who have returned every other year since March 1981 to Sachon AB to provide extra firepower for PACAF's major 'Team Spirit' exercises.

This mobility is in sharp contrast to the 1970s when the complex F-111Ds were averaging a meagre 34.4 per cent mission-capable rate, with the highest mean-flight-hour-between-failure rate in the USAF with one component malfunctioning, on average, every 12 minutes! Keeping the 'Cosmic' birds airborne was described as something of an epic and one prompted perhaps by an ulterior motive. Several senior F-111 flyers told the authors that the avionics in the D model were intended as prototypes for the B-1, and that the intent was to wring out the bugs – and there were plenty – in the avionics of the D so that these systems could be available, when required, for the B-1. The shortage of spares did not help. Pressured by the 'hawks' in Washington for continued aircraft procurement, the Carter Administration tended, as a result, to skimp on

logistics budgets, creating service-wide spares shortfalls in the mid to late 1970s; the policy to give SAC and USAFE 'One-Elevens' top priority further compounded Cannon's problems (by comparison, for example, the F-111Fs were achieving a mission-ready rate of 63.1 per cent on a day-to-day basis at that time). Despite the spares crisis the 27th TFW's maintenance people worked extremely hard and were able to generate a highly respectable 0.43 sorties per aircraft per day, rising to two per aircraft per day in October 1978 during the Wing's 'Bold Eagle – Surge Delta 78' mass launch and deployment to Homestead AFB in Florida – part of the 'Black Flag' project initiated by TAC Commander General Dixon, who put his units on periodic wartime footings. The 'Surge Delta' event was the first occasion a full strength squadron of two dozen F-111Ds was deployed. By this time all aircraft had been through PDM once and had had new fuel tank sealant installed; a defect during the manufacture of many F-111Ds caused them to leak profusely in the early years. As for the avionics, Norden introduced an STU update in 1979 and an MSD/VSD update in 1984, substantially aiding reliability as well as capability; Norden claim that AN/AVA-9 MTBF is now 270hrs. The AMP and AIS-R efforts will further reduce 'down times'.

Below: Inflating their survival vests, a pair of novices at Cannon undergo 'capsule egress' training. The module is a genuine, expended example, stripped of its valuables by the maintenance division. (27th TFW)

Overleaf: The 'flagship' of 'Intelligent Strength' – a GDFW rebuilt example, F-111D No. 43 (68-127) – over the high-plains homedrome with a GBU-10/B LGB installed. The fin-top colours, from front to rear, are red (522nd TFS 'Fireballs'), blue (523rd TFS 'Crusaders') and yellow (524th TFTS 'Hounds'). (27th TFW)

These moves have given the F-111Ds a new lease of life, and plans to stretch and convert the aircraft, along with the FB-111As, to FB-111B/C standard have long since been discarded. Proposals for the so-called 'un-reliable' F-111Ds to be retired have been similarly quashed.* The successful 'Coronet' deployments have demonstrated that the 'mature' F-111D is extremely reliable, and the Air Force still considers the type the most advanced aircraft in the tactical inventory. The importance of the F-111D is also underlined by the fact that six previously stricken 'basket cases' have been restored back to full operational status by GDFW and that no fewer than eight examples serve on the highly demanding flight-test roster in California: three with AFSC's 6512th Test Squadron at Edwards, performing, *inter alia*, as avionics test-beds and chase and support aircraft to the B-1B effort; two with AFLC's SMALC Engineering Flight Test organization, working with the Depot Center there as TO modification trials platforms; and three with Detachment 3 of the 57th Fighter Weapons Wing, also at McClellan, whose job it is to perform pre-service entry trials of new weapons systems.†

## Patchmen
Cannon's own F-111Ds are drawn upon for another important training effort – the Fighter Weapons School. Run by Detachment 2 of the 57th FWW, which has no aircraft of its own but which flies some 700 sorties a

**Above: Banking over Lake Mead in the desert near Las Vegas, F-111D No. 2, 68-086, from the 431st Test and Evaluation Squadron, shows off its svelte lines and Vietnam-era camoulage paint scheme, still the standard decor for the tactical interdictor variants, including the RAAF's F/RF-111Cs. Apart from its black and yellow chequered fin stripe, 'WA' tail code and TAC and 431st TES badges, the aircraft wears only pivot-pylons and Aero 3A Sidewinder missile launch rails. (USAF photo by Ken Hackman, via Robert F. Dorr)**

**Left: This skeletal view of F-111D No. 32, 68-116, displays a stripped-down airframe plumbed to the chemical desealant plant at SMALC, California. The trailing ends of the 'speed bumps' house receivers and transmitters for the Sanders AN/ALQ-94 deceptive electronic countermeasures system. (R. Holman, BAe)**

year, allocated 'Deltas' on a daily basis as needed by the 524th AMU 'Hounds',

> The course teaches already experienced aircrews advanced academic and flying training in F-111 aircraft systems, weapons delivery and defensive tactics, weaponeering and tactical employment concepts. The mission of the FWS is to train FWS graduates who possess the knowledge and skills necessary to support the operational Wings by providing them with the most qualified instructors possible. Therefore we strive to use the newest weapons and technology available. By staying on the cutting edge of technology and tactics, graduates leave fully prepared for the challenges of tomorrow.

The people assigned to FWS report to the commandant of FWS, which is part of the 57th FWW, assigned to the Tactical Fighter Weapons Center at Nellis. The active Air Force has only one FWS located at Nellis, consisting of six divisions – the F-111 Division detached to Cannon, the A-10, F-15, F-16 and Air Weapons Controller Divisions, and an academic department. Each F-111 Wing in the US and Europe submits its best flyers as nominees for FWS to Headquarters Manning Personnel Center and the most qualified are selected by a formal selection board. Each nominee must have a minimum of two years' tactical fighter experience, have a minimum of 300hrs' F-111 flying time and be an instructor in the F-111.

'Top Gun' devotees will immediately appreciate what it is all about – in the case of the F-111 FWS, an air-to-surface 'Aardvark doctorate' or PhD in 'Earthpigology': after completing the course each FWS graduate can receive 9–12hrs of credit towards a masters degree. F-111 FWS is a highly select 'club': to date only 190 air crew have graduated and the annual requirement is for a mere eighteen men, initiated in groups of half a dozen (three pilots and three WSOs) during three 12-week sessions each year. This small size adds to the clique ethos, and graduates wear their FWS and unit patches with pride; their highly-decorated flight suits lend them the nickname the 'Patchmen'.

---

*In 1979 the US Government's five-year Defense Plan recommended withdrawing the entire F-111D Wing by the end of FY81; it also deleted the Phase II offensive avionics package from its budget that year.
†The closeness, in flying time to Nellis, means that the 431st TES can be more conveniently located at McClellan. The Edwards test force also operates one A model and one E; SMALC's engineering force an FB-111A; and Det 3, 431st Test and Evaluation Squadron, 57th FWW, three F-111Fs.

## TRIALS 'AARDVARKS'

| Unit/Command | Location | Aircraft | Serial | Code | Fin stripe |
|---|---|---|---|---|---|
| Det. 3, 4485th TS, TAWC, TAC, USAF | Mountain Home AFB, Idaho | EF-111A A-9<br>EF-111A A-34 | 66-013<br>67-048 | OT | Black/white chequers |
| Det. 3, 57th FWW, 431st TES, TFWC, TAC, USAF | McClellan AFB, California | F-111D No. 2<br>F-111D No. 4<br>F-111D No. 34<br>F-111F No. 39<br>F-111F No. 104<br>F-111F No. 105 | 68-086<br>68-088<br>68-118<br>70-2400<br>74-0186<br>74-0187 | WA | Black/yellow chequers |
| SMALC Engineering Flight Test, AFLC, USAF | McClellan AFB, California | FB-111A No. 1<br>F-111D No. 38<br>F-111D No. 91 | 67-159<br>68-122<br>68-175 | – | AFLC logos |
| 3246th TW, ADTC, AFSC, USAF | Eglin AFB, Florida | F-111E No. 4<br>F-111E No. 10<br>F-111E No. 68 | 67-118<br>67-124<br>68-058 | AD | White with red diamonds |
| 6512th TS, AFFTC, AFSC, USAF | Edwards AFB, California | F-111A No. 13*<br>F-111A No. 71<br>F-111D No. 1<br>F-111D No. 3<br>F-111D No. 5<br>F-111E No. 1 | 63-9778<br>66-053<br>68-085<br>68-087<br>68-089<br>68-089 | ED | Dark blue with white Xs |
| ARDU, RAAF | RAAF Edinburgh, South Australia | F-111C No. 8 | A8-132 | – | ARDU badge |

*Assigned to NASA Dryden, at Edwards AFFTC

The F-111 FWS was formed originally at Nellis, then shifted to Mountain Home as Det 2 in July 1977 as part of Operation 'Ready Switch'; ten years later, on 15 May 1988, the 'Patchmen' upped and shifted to Cannon. Det 2 commander Lt. Col. Richard Brenner wanted his outfit to switch to the F-111D as this would allow the school to encompass digital systems and also to take advantage of the type's superior air-to-air capability and dual-control qualities, making it the ideal 'advanced trainer'.

FWS is a very structured graduate-level program that uses the building block (simple-to-complex) approach in all of its academic and flying training. This ensures that each student is prepared as much as possible for each event flown. The F-111 syllabus contains 290hrs of academics covering defensive tactics, conventional and nuclear weapons delivery, manual and computer weapons delivery, ECM, enemy defenses, precision weapons, avionics, tactics, instructor pilot and WSO training – the whole thing! Flying training consists of 23 sorties covering aircraft handling characteristics, ground and air defensive maneuvering, day and night tactical employment, live and inert munitions drops and composite force training with the full spectrum of both USAF and US Navy TACAIR.

It has been likened to a non-stop WTD backed up with intensive classroom study. When at Mountain Home the 'Patchmen' would 'steal' a few F-111As and conduct an exclusive 'mini Red Flag' in company with the other FWS Divisions, to make things that much more demanding during the climactic Mission Employment Phase of the course. The recent move to Cannon has brought a few changes to the syllabus yet the net product is the same: graduates percolate back into the combat-ready F-111 community to keep the Wing up to date with the latest ideas.

At the Wing and Squadron levels the FWS graduate is the commanders' adviser on weapons and tactics matters. In other words FWS provides F-111 commanders with instructors who are experts in the full array of weapons certified for use on the F-111.

This, in part, is what has kept the 'swing-winger' at the forefront of tactical air power for twenty-one years and which, in all likelihood, will keep it there for the next twenty-one. Flying is a dynamic profession in more than the obvious sense of the word and the aircraft are only as good as the men who fly them.

# Statue De Libya Raiders

Lakenheath's transition to the F-111 was a much smoother, quicker affair than Cannon's. 'Creek Realign' was one of a series of 'Ready Switch' operations within the USAF in the 1970s which caused whole tactical Wings to exchange equipment virtually overnight. It began with the November 1976 announcement that Lakenheath, in Suffolk, England, was to receive the 'Foxtrot', at that time assigned to the 366th TFW 'Gunfighters' at Mountain Home AFB in Idaho.

Four F-111Fs had already visited Upper Heyford in November 1975 but the shift of a whole Wing to the UK underlined the importance of the F-111's role in the notional European 'front line'. The 48th TFW ('Statue of Liberty Wing') Phantoms at Lakenheath stood down from 'Victor Alert', ceasing all flying by 28 February 1977. On 10 March Col. J. W. Kittinger, Deputy CO of the 48th, led 24 Phantoms off 'The Heath's runway. By 22 April the last F-4D had departed to its new owners, the 474th TFW at Nellis; they, in turn, relinquished the F-111As whose service and combat initiation they had pioneered, passing them to the 366th TFW at Mountain Home, thereby completing the triangle.

While the departing F-4s smartly tucked up their gear and sped west most of their flight-line crews remained at Lakenheath for 'hands-on' retraining on the new 'swing-winger'. Three F-111Fs led by Maj. Messerli arrived on 1 March 1977 and all withdrew to the large maintenance hangar;* for a time Lakenheath's offensive capability consisted of this trio and an ex French Air Force F-100D! 'Creek Swing', the F-111F section of 'Creek Realign', began on 1 June when 70-397 arrived for the official handover ceremony to the 494th TFS 'Panthers'. It was one of four flights of four aircraft which arrived after a 4,900-mile, 10hr 20min journey, supported by three in-flight refuellings over South Dakota and the eastern seaboard of the United States. Led in by the 48th TFW Vice Commander Col. J. W. Tietge, the F-111Fs arrived with BRUs in place, ready for action! The importance of the occasion was underlined by the presence of Gen. Alexander A. Haig, Supreme Allied Commander in Europe, and the British Defence Minister. The new F-111Fs were declared operational soon after arrival and training flights of 2½hrs, soon extended to 3½hrs, began. Further batches of sixteen aircraft arrived shortly afterwards to equip the

---

*F-111Fs 70-394, -373 and -371.

**Below: In its 366th TFW days at Mountain Home F-111F No. 5, 70-2366, was an obvious billboard for both the decorative recognition of TAC's thirtieth anniversary and the United Sates' Bicentennial in 1976. Squadron and commemorative badges and logos appear on the flank and doors, along with 'stars and bars' trim on the inlet lips, vertical stabilizer and strake leading edge. Assigned to the 'Liberty Wing' the following summer, this aircraft was lost over the North Sea on 21 December 1983, its crew ejecting successfully. (MAP)**

Above: With only a white AN/ALQ-119(V) ECM pod and a 20mm 'Gat' gun installed, F-111F No. 25 (70-2386) returns to Lakenheath in June 1979. This aircraft was still with the unit in late 1988 and was a participant in the Libya operation. (Robin A. Walker)

493rd, 492nd and 495th squadrons, in that order, thereby making the 'Statue of Liberty Wing' the first four-squadron establishment in USAFE. It is that fourth squadron, the 495th TFS 'Aardvark University', which makes the Lakenheath Wing unique.

## Aardvark University

Many of the original F-111F crews transferred from the 366th TFW to Lakenheath in company with their aircraft, providing a core of experienced crews. Other senior posts in the Wing were staffed by officers from Cannon and Nellis and an extra 600 personnel appeared on base to tackle the formidable training programme. Central to this had always been the 495th, the only RTU in USAFE. Phase 2 of the training programme passed from Cannon to the 495th in September 1977. Maj. Les Alderman, the squadron's Assistant Operations Officer in 1986, explains:

Other USAFE units receive aircrews that are already checked out in the aircraft they'll be flying. But because the only F-111Fs in the Air Force are at Lakenheath, aircrews have to be trained to fly them when they arrive on station. Some will have received basic qualification on the A model, but crews are more likely to originate from one of the F-111D courses at Cannon because the digital systems in the D are preparation for the F.

From the pilot's viewpoint, the extra thrust of the TF30-

P-100 engine in the F-111F is a big bonus. Virtually a new engine in the same area of technology as the P&W F100 which pushes the F-15 and F-16, the P-100 offers a massive 8,500lb on top of the total which the F-111D's two TF30-P-109s generate in full afterburner. This can be a real asset in the low-speed regime, for example in a wind-shear situation where a quick pile-on of thrust is needed. Mike Conway, a 48th TFW WSO, feels that the F-111D is rather underpowered, and many would like to see the P-100 engine fitted throughout the fleet as a sideline to the AMP effort. Although not quite as reliable as the earlier models, and far more expensive because of its limited production run, the P-100 gives pilots the extra 'go' required to overcome problems associated with the slow spool-up time of the turbofan.

Crews are brought up to combat readiness in the same 45 working days that Upper Heyford generally specifies. Maj. Dick Brown describes their training schedule:

We teach them to fly in the European environment. Because of the range F-111s have and the different international rules, we teach them UK, Belgian, Dutch, German, French and some Spanish flying rules. We put them through the academics – self-study on local flying procedures, low flying and the ranges. Then there is systems study. The hardest transition on [F-111F] systems study is for the WSO. In the right seat, although the components have the same generic names, the operation's completely different. We fly eight rides and then take a tactical evaluation check. In the midstream they fly with one of the top three officers, myself, and Major Alderman'.

Newcomers are airborne ten days after arrival in the UK and their programme usually involves about four simulator sessions as well. The 'sim' is the best place to learn emergency procedures and basic switchology but the technology now seems a bit simplistic compared with the more recent digital types available and tends to be 'procedural': it is used mainly to practice switches and emergency drills as opposed to flying tactics and so it is in the throes of an update. Lt. Col. Tom G. Runge, 492nd TFS commander, points out that

There is no *set* time in the 'sim'. You probably spend seven or eight times as much time in the airplane as in the 'sim'

**48th TFW (3rd AF, USAFE)**
**RAF Lakenheath, Suffolk, England**

| Squadron | Colour | Nickname | Code | Aircraft |
|----------|--------|----------|------|----------|
| 492nd TFS | Blue | Bolars | | |
| 493rd TFS | Gold | – | LN | F-111F |
| 494th TFS | Red | Panthers | | |
| 495th TFS | Green | Aardvark University | | |

and the short answer is that the 'sim' is under modification, and there there are only two 'sims' and *several* airplanes out there.

SSgt. Dave Malakoff points out that 'It costs $10,000 every time one of those jets is started up'; taking in all the back-up maintenance, logistics and support, flying the F-111F is in the 'big league'. Crews also take up to fourteen F-111F flights in all, though there is Proficiency Advancement for more experienced flyers. In all, 60 areas of proficiency have to be mastered.

Adapting to the crowded skies and poor weather of Europe after initial training in the wider spaces of the USA is quite a problem. Dick Brown:

> There is so much congested airspace due to gliders, microlites and everybody else who has their little foot in the flying system that it is virtually impossible to go more than one minute in air time and not run into something. It's like me, driving on the left side of the road for the first time and trying to go through central London.

Just how difficult the low flyers' task has become was demonstrated in August 1985. The Ministry of Defence were asked by Mr. Richard Livesey, Member of Parliament for Brecon and Radnor, to explain how three F-111s flew *under* a group of six hang-gliders in the Usk Valley. The problems are not confined to the air either. In 1983 the 48th TFW were accused of causing damage amounting to thousands of pounds by overflying houses on the Isle of Benbecula at low altitude. Similar difficulties face all NATO pilots on comparable sorties.

**Below: The aggressive lines of the 'Foxtrot', the most powerful 'One-Eleven' ever built, pushed by P&W TF30-P-100 engines which generate 50,200lb of thrust in afterburner. (Tim Laming)**

Above: Special fin markings and an early appearance of Pave Tack on F-111F No. 56, 70-2417, at the RAF Tactical Bombing Competition in June 1981. The 48th TFW's contingent of six aircraft flew over to gain experience of the event rather than to participate competitively. Visitors to the 1987 IAT will have had a closer look at '417 in 494th TFS markings. (MAP)

Emergency procedures form a big part in the training programme too. For aircraft with hydraulic or landing-gear problems the BAK-12 remains in use at every 'One-Eleven' base, including the depots. All 'Varks' have a 6ft hook regardless of their ancestry, most frequently attached to a loop at the rear end of the TAB-Vs for static engine runs and tail-tows back into the 'barn'; it is used less often for its intended purpose but sometimes to more dramatic effect. On 13 December 1979 F-111F 73-715 lost a main wheel on take-off. The BAK-12 was hastily deployed and the runway foamed. The pilot made a good approach but thought his hook had failed to take the wire, so he applied afterburner for another circuit. In fact the hook was engaged firmly and the F-111 was summarily dragged back from its attempted lift-off, striking the runway with some force. The crew escaped with little more than dazed expressions but '715 had major fuselage damage and a wing bent 2° out of true. Salvaged and repaired at SMALC, it returned to Lakenheath in August 1985.

Because of the specialized character of the F-111F and its local environment most 495th TFS instructors are drawn from the other three squadrons and upgraded with a two-month course. Other air crews with expertise of the FWS are interspersed among the squadrons as well. All instructors, and the 495th itself, are as mission-ready as the combat-ready people. Maj. Dick Brown emphasizes that the 495th is not a training-only outfit like the Stateside RTUs, who are not assigned a 'mobility' responsibility, but 'more like the RAF Opera-tional Conversion Units, with a shadow operational role'. There is a great deal of F-111 experience concen-trated at the 'Aardvark University' – a whole squadron of instructors, described by their commander, Lt. Col. 'Willy P.' Kramer, as the 'cream of the crop'.

The training environment in the USA is not the best preparation for Europe. Most training is conducted in the western and southern USA, with good weather and visibility and very few of the 150ft electricity pylons that bestride the UK. Dick Brown:

> There are places where you can fly lower and faster without the encumbrance of a zillion roads and a million villages. In the UK the minimum altitude is 250ft. That's about 150ft too high for combat, to negate the threats. But there's so much population and its getting tougher.

About one-third of training flights are scheduled for the hours of darkness, mostly in winter to minimize late-night annoyance to the population. Procedural differences are slight compared with daytime flying but it is more frightening at night. A typical sortie would involve about an hour's flight to the range where attacks would be made with practice bombs for up to half an hour. En route to the range low-level practice can be fitted in using TFR and offsets in the usual way. None of this will involve supersonic flying. Lt. Col. Tom G. Runge does not see this as a problem:

> I've been supersonic in the F-111 at 200ft. The only way you can tell that you're supersonic is to look at the airspeed indicator. There's no real payback in terms of supersonic training at low-level; the gas you use doing that, the noise you create – they're all negative.

Afterwards there may be an airborne tanker-call, mainly to 'keep up currency' in in-flight refuelling. On returning to base there is the chance to practise approaches at various fuel loads and wing configurations. The F-111's

**Below: F-111F No. 61, 71-885, roars down the runway at Lakenheath in a shimmer of engine exhaust-generated haze. (Tim Laming)**

clean aerofoil and high lift mean that landings are often marked by a tendency to 'float' down the runway as the dangling main wheels displace two or three feet on compression, spreading to take the weight. At light weights the jet needs driving on to the runway in a no-flare, carrier-style approach. Wing lift is only cancelled when the spoilers pop-up to kill it.

A major element in the 48th TFW's training programme, as in any F-111 Wing, is the development of the cockpit 'partnership'. The side-by-side arrangement has strengths and disadvantages. When one sits in the cockpit its small size in relation to the aircraft is apparent; 'snug' is a word that comes to mind. The space is similar in width to a family car (UK model or US compact) and it is quite easy for both men to survey the entire front-panel complex. Proximity is helpful. Lt. Col. Runge gives the pilot's viewpoint:

I can see things he's doing. A peek is worth a thousand words. I can cross-check. The right-seater is flying with his attack display. He can also see my TFR scope so he doesn't need a repeater of it. Talking about visual look-out for someone trying to intercept you, it's a handicap because when I look right all I see is his smiling face! The right-seater's got to look while I fly.

**Below: F-111F No. 21, 70-2382, flexes its wings and takes to the murky skies over eastern England. (Authors)**

This would also be the case in a turn to the right, and F-111 formation work is rather different from the standard finger-four practised by the USAF, with jets joining-up mainly in twos or threes, in echelon trailing off the lead's right wing. 'In TFR flight all you have to do is just sit there and talk to the WSO to make sure he's not asleep!' WSO Mike Conway, hardly one to fall asleep, sees his function as 'operating the "big eye" that sees the real terrain on the radarscope. If the TFR is lying the WSO can remedy that or say, "I see terrain we should be climbing over right now".' This can be accomplished by comparing returns from the ARS's PPI sweep with the vertical 'ski' pattern of the TFR. If things do not look right the pilot will disconnect the automatic flight control inputs and hand-fly the scissor-winger. During the attack run the WSO can initiate pull-ups verbally (Mike suggests loud screams *in extremis*) if the pilot is not following the usual pull-up bar indications. Tom Runge is adamant about the 'Wizzo's' vital function, despite all the usual jokes that pilots make about their 'flying ballast': 'It's a great piece of kit when it's all working. You could probably sit over there and sleep, but when little things go wrong, that's the *true* test'. Mike Conway shares the view of several navigators when, with experience of other types, he says, 'of any aircraft in the current inventory, it's definitely the WSO's'.

Visibility in the cockpit is obviously rather poor by

Above: Lt. Col. Tom G. 'Grunge' Runge with his F-111F, 'Bolar 1', at the 1988 Lakenheath Open Day. He managed to generate a lot of business for his 'Blue Squadron's undercover hamburger stall on a wet day; the nickname was a present from one of his instructors. (Authors)

'Teenage' fighter standards though the rearward 'blindness' is only a problem in the air-to-air situation. Side-by-side seating really 'comes good' in the night-time all-weather sortie when both crew members can monitor the scopes, check maps and work in a highly intense environment without worrying about what is happening behind them. Several ex F-4 WSOs were in no doubt that they preferred a joint front seat to being buried in the 'pit' of a Phantom with only a wall of instruments to stare at. There have been several occasions when right-seaters have noticed a potential emergency ahead of the pilot, seized the stick and pulled-up out of trouble. This seldom happens in a tandem cockpit. Most WSOs get the chance to fly the aircraft for longer periods too. In the UK the opportunity presents itself on the return journey from the ranges, when the WSO might get in about 300 miles of flying. All WSOs are trained to recover the aircraft from unusual attitudes, for example in the case of pilot disorientation.

It is the subtleties which make for a good cockpit rapport. If the pilot is on the radio and his WSO notices some vital indication on an instrument he can just nudge and point to the dial. A pilot may require a heading while the WSO is intent on his job and he will then get a finger pointing to the compass rather than a long explanation. A head-nod or a thumbs-up will often save reaching for the microphone button if the crew are on 'cold mike'. This teamwork is vital for safety, and there is never any complacency about the hazards of low-level flight. The 'Statue of Liberty Wing' lost fifteen aircraft in the eleven years up to 1988, with four losses in 1982 alone. When set against the hazardous nature

of the mission this loss-rate is regrettable but acceptable. Whereas bird-strikes were a common denominator in the 20th TFW's early losses the 48th had the benefit of the later 'bird proof' windshields from the outset. Five losses happened on landing approaches and three were probably due to TFR failures. True to the 'One-Eleven's usual public image, every loss made news. In fact the crew survival record has been comparatively good. Five crews are known to have perished in crashes, invariably where aircraft hit the sea or ground during low-level flying, but at least fourteen men owe their survival to the capsule, often in difficult ejection conditions. It only failed conspicuously on one occasion. On 29 March 1978 F-111F 73-717 was returning to base during a 'sortie surge' exercise. As it entered the approach pattern over Thetford Forest a couple of miles west of Mundford, there appears to have been a lightning strike. The ejection process was initiated but no parachutes deployed and both 492nd TFS crew members died. A week-long ground order followed in which all capsules were inspected. It was concluded that ejection had been attempted outside the design parameters of speed and altitude. On a similar occasion in February 1987 the crew of F-111F 70-2418 escaped in their capsule, suffering only minor injuries when it struck a clump of trees in the descent. The aircraft, again from the 492nd TFS, seems to have gone out of control, possibly as a result of a mid-air nudge from another 'One-Eleven'. Its wreckage landed close to houses in Newmarket Heath, marking the end of a period of 3 years and 2 months without a training loss.

**Panthers and Bolars**

The F-111F model itself is a digital hybrid, part FB-111A, part F-111D, part utterly unique. The core of the nav/attack package comprises the Mk. IIB avionics system and its familiar bank of AN/AYK-6 computers, GE attack radar set and Rockwell AN/AJN-16 INS, sharing much in common with the SAC model but with the 'protected memory', pre-programmed with fourteen different types of weapons, geared towards the conventional role (with the mission tape, alternative screw-in WCP 'cassettes' and manual ballistics as back-up) as in the F-111D.* The major distinguishing feature of the 'Foxtrot' is its belly-mounted Ford Aerospace AN/AVQ-26 Pave Tack navigation and targeting pod, now the heart of the Lakenheath bombers' mission equipment. This important update, introduced on the F-111F some five years after the last example rolled off the Fort Worth assembly lines and now also installed in the RAAF's F-111Cs, has created yet another right-hand seat 'sub-cult' in the 'One-Eleven' community.

Pave Tack owes its origins to the conflict in South-East Asia. Many of the targets confronted – particularly the more lucrative ones dotted along the Ho Chi Minh

*The F-111F has no doppler or astrocompass and introduced improved radars, the AN/APQ-146 TFR and AN/APQ-144 ARS and the ASG-27 ODS. In common with the other digital aircraft a 'mission tape' is used which can feed in up to 999 waypoints, including up to four offsets for each waypoint or target. 'Penaids' are the same as those used in the F-111A/D/E.

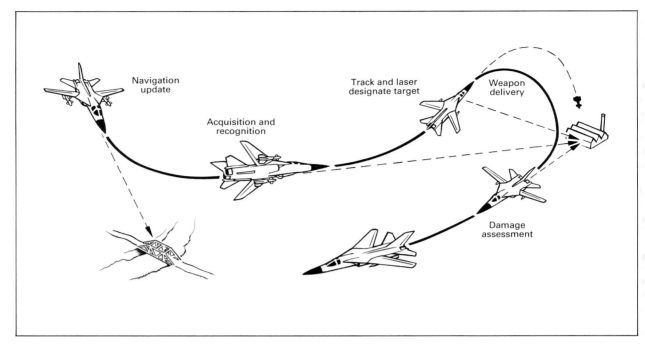

Navigation update

Acquisition and recognition

Track and laser designate target

Weapon delivery

Damage assessment

**Above: The AN/AVQ-26 Pave Tack pod can be used as a navigation and weapons delivery aid. A Pave Tack toss manoeuvre is demonstrated in this mission profile.**

Trail and bottled up in the border chokepoints – were not radar-significant, rendering accurate 'blind' attacks with radar and INS almost impossible. New sensors were required, and took years to perfect. Pending the introduction of the most important, synthetic aperture radars which would offer photo-quality radar ground-map presentations to the WSO, the USAF decided to invest considerable sums of money in a range of electro-optical sensors capable of picking out targets by looking for a hot-on-cold or cold-on-hot contrast. The F-111 was a prime candidate for the upgrade: supplementing radar in this fashion would enable the all-weather 'Aardvark' to be an all-target striker too. The sensor that emerged was the Texas Instruments/USAF common modular forward-looking infra-red (FLIR), otherwise known as the Infrared Detection Set (IDS), packaged by Ford Aerospace into a 1,227lb, 13.5ft-long pod called Pave Tack.

Flight-tested by McClellan's 431st Test and Evaluation Squadron with Maj. Bob Rudiger as Project Officer, the pod entered full production in August 1979 and found its way to Lakenheath, along with Maj. Rudiger as chief instructor, when the first 'Tack Vark', 72-1441, touched down in Suffolk in January 1981. Follow-on conversion of aircraft to Pave Tack standard was accomplished at SMALC at a rate of about two aircraft a month, as and when the F-111s became due for PDM. All the early deliveries went to the Pave Tack pioneers – the 494th TFS 'Panthers', until recently commanded by veteran Tony Sobol, which achieved IOC with the new system on 15 September 1981. By the spring of

1984 the entire 83-strong Lakenheath establishment had been re-equipped with the device.*

Introducing new WSOs to Pave Tack is conducted on a second-tier level long after graduation from the 495th course. Ex 'Aardvark University Professor' Maj. Dick Brown:

> For the pilot it's easy: there's not much to do that's new. As for navigators, they usually have him work for six months before he's upgraded to Pave Tack. The only reason for that is to make him a good radar operator of the radar *first*, because it is an integral part of the Pave Tack mission.

Pave Tack FLIR imagery is so good that WSOs might become complacent if not honed on the ARS first. An explanation of the switchology in an operational context best explains how the 'Tack Vark' goes about its business.

The crew have crossed the FEBA and are 'Auto TF-ing' at 200ft. At the push of the 'extend' button on the Pave Tack control panel located between his knees, the 'Wizzo' deploys and activates the pod. Pave Tack is bolted to a large steel cradle which dominates the modified weapons bay, no longer used for bombs, fuel, the gun or luggage. Within five seconds the drab green pod rotates through 180° on its cradle and swivels down so that it juts out under the fuselage, the zinc sulphide window of the IDS visible in the gimballed metal 'beachball' at the rear end. In front of the WSO are two CRT displays: a nine-inch tube and a six-inch tube, collectively known as the virtual image display (VID), which are able to flash up either direct-view radar or IDS TV-type imagery, the former in wide or narrow

*There are slightly fewer Pave Tack pods available than there are aircraft so the primary users are the 492nd TFS 'Bolars' and 494th TFS 'Panthers' (although all of Lakenheath's squadrons use the system).

'Ground Auto' or 'Ground Vel' sector scans, at different tilt and range scales, and the latter in optional narrow 3° or wide 12° FOVs. Navigation is performed using the 'mission tape' and radar on the primary, hooded VID, but as range to target closes in the WSO will switch the Pave Tack FLIR display over to the larger screen to take advantage of its superior quality imagery. Range? Quizzed on that point, Mike Conway, IWSO, commented: 'That depends on the type of delivery and the bombs being used, how big the target is . . .'; 'Bolars' boss Tom G. Runge cut in with the succinct remark: 'Plus we can't tell you!' Published estimates in the technical press claim it is customary to switch over from radar to Pave Tack at a range of about 4 miles to target. In fact, the system is variable, according to weather and even pollution; smoke from a factory, for example, can really obscure target acquisition.

Placing the VID FLIR crosshairs on target is accomplished initially in an automatic manner. The top of the Pave Tack control panel has a series of trigonally marked, lit buttons which enable the WSO to select and confirm the desired Pave Tack mode in the subdued cockpit lighting: 'Cue', 'Snow Plow', 'Left Acq', 'Fwd Acq', and 'TFR Mon'. With the radar crosshairs falling right on the target and offset(s), confirming that the INS

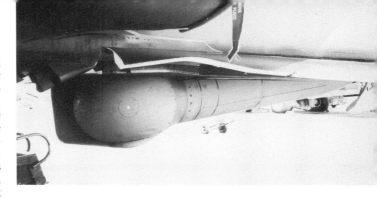

Above: A Ford Aerospace AN/AVQ-26 Pave Tack mounted in F-111F No. 92 (73-0716) of the 495th TFS. Weapons bay doors had to be remodelled to accommodate the cradle and rude-looking pod. This particular aircraft crashed eighteen months after this photograph was taken, near Incirlik AB, Turkey, on 1 November 1982. The crew escaped unscathed. (Robin A. Walker)

is properly aligned, the WSO flashes up the FLIR and presses 'Cue', which will automatically slew the IDS on to the target. If the video crosshairs are slightly off the mark the WSO will grasp his tracking handle, interfaced with the Pave Tack turret motor drive, and slew the sensor about to put the desired image in place. Switching to narrow, expanded image, the WSO holds the target in the VID crosshairs with the tracking handle. As an alternative, if visibility permits, the WSO may elect to use 'Fwd Acq' instead. Pave Tack will be caged at boresight with the pilot's gunsight. Mike Conway:

Below: Banking over the runway at Lakenheath, a 'Statue of Liberty Wing' F-111F reveals its Pave Tack pod, its AN/ALQ-119(V) ECM pod and a quartet of GBU-10 Paveway II LGBs. (USAF)

'The pilot can put his pipper on the target and tell me it's on the target'. Tom Runge: 'All I have to do is to see the target, a factory or whatever, and roll in and put the sight on it. Mike would then see the factory in the Pave Tack display and start tracking.' Either way, Pave Tack now assumes the role of the radar, tracking the target in the attack sequence, and furnishes alphanumeric symbols superimposed on the VID imagery, providing an abbreviation of Pave Tack mode, time to target and time to bombs-off. The radar may perhaps be switched off at this stage: the IDS is a passive sensor whereas radar is not, and may contribute to the 'stealth' approach. According to Mike Conway, 'It's always an option. It has pros and cons. You have to know what your threat is before you get there, otherwise you're going to get "involved" over your target'. Radar, therefore, is considered a necessary back-up. Tom Runge emphasized that bombs-on-target is the bottom line: 'It's like walking through a cold shower to Jennifer

O'Neill. You know you're going to get wet and yo▪ know it's going to be cold but Jennifer O'Neill's at th▪ other side!'

With Pave Tack the F-111F has an autonomous 'Pav▪ Tack Toss' 'smart' and 'quasi-smart' bombing capabilit▪ Boresighted with the FLIR in two little peepholes are ▪ laser transmitter-receiver and a marked target receive▪ to plot the laser spot. With the laser gun activated th▪ WSO can do one of two things to hit the target: 'sparkle▪ the aimpoint to guide laser-homing bombs to the targe▪ a feat which can be accomplished during the 3g pull-o▪ 'toss' and egress, exercised as soon as the LGBs com▪ off the wings; or use laser slant-range data, generated b▪ processing the reflected laser pulses, to help the ba▪ listics system compute the release of unguided 'iron' o▪ cluster bombs, with twice the delivery accuracy o▪ that available from routine radar-ranging.

Laser-ranging may also be used to update the naviga▪ tion computers en route to the target or on the retur▪ legs home. The integrated nav/attack system 'knows▪ where Pave Tack is pointing, so, by feeding in an offset▪ co-ordinates – a prominent terrain or man-made featur▪ to the side of the jet's flight-path readily visible in th▪ FLIR display – and tracking the point in the crosshairs▪ angular sensor geometry and laser-range data can b▪ used to update the inertial platform. Mike Conwa▪ reckons that 'It is a super capability'. Although there ar▪

Below: 'WA'-coded 431st TES F-111F No. 39, 70-2400, on the McClellan AFB flight line with a Pave Tack in its belly and Texas Instruments Mk. 82 GBU-22 Paveway III LLLGB bombs on its pivot-pylons. LGBs, regardless of their size, are always fitted directly to the pivot-pylons. Only the Mk. 84 2,000lb GBU-24 LLLGB has entered operational service. (Texas Instruments)

a number of set 'mission tapes' for training purposes, with 'canned' flight routes, F-111F crews like to deviate from the pre-planned, pre-programmed flight path considerably, to take advantage of any available masking terrain and to avoid anti-air hot-spots that crop up; the ability to 'tap in' new co-ordinates and keep track of the aircraft's progress in geographical and chronological degrees, minutes and seconds makes Pave Tack a vital tool. 'Overflight' may also be used as an update mode. The only problem is that the neodymium YAG laser gun is a fairly powerful device which could cause serious injury to bystanders' eyesight. Mike Conway: 'Unfortunately we're not allowed to "squirt" the laser at all during low-level navigation; we can only use it on the ranges'. Many scientists have expressed concern regarding reflected laser hazards, but the crews at Lakenheath know their business: 'The laser is very specific in where it's aimed so every place we practice with the laser has to be pre-surveyed for any kind of reflectivity whatsoever. In fact we are very limited in where we can use it'. As for the crew, 'We don't need to wear protective goggles'.

Checking on waypoints can be done completely manually, using the tracking handle to steer the IDS about, or semi-automatically, by selecting 'Left Acq', whereby the pod is directed to look 90° abeam; adjustments can then be made by the WSO. Other special modes available include 'TFR Mon' and 'Snow Plow'. TFR monitor points Pave Tack at the aircraft's velocity vector, permitting the 'Wizzo' to look out for and warn the pilot about obstacles which may not readily be picked up by the TFR or ARS scans, such as electrical cables. Dick Brown, in his typical, casual style pointed out that 'I have flown with Tack at 100ft AGL – it's real easy, and after a while it's even boring'. Doubtless the slightly less experienced Lakenheath drivers disagree about the adrenalin factor! 'Snow Plow' provides stabilized tracking at a fixed angle in space, with manual adjustment using the tracking handle, so that the 'Wizzo' can follow, say, a river or a highway, up to the point where a bridge appears in the scope. The options are considerable.

After the sortie a video cassette is down-loaded which has a recording of the VID FLIR imagery. Lt. Col. Tom Runge:

We consider ourselves pretty specialist. Pave Tack's a unique capability and it's a difficult skill to acquire and maintain, so when Mike says we do a lot of Pave Tack we do exactly that. We try to practice as much as possible using

**Below: The right-hand portion of the F-111F cockpit display, after the Pave Tack update. The pilot's side is virtually identical to that in the FB-111A. (General Dynamics)**

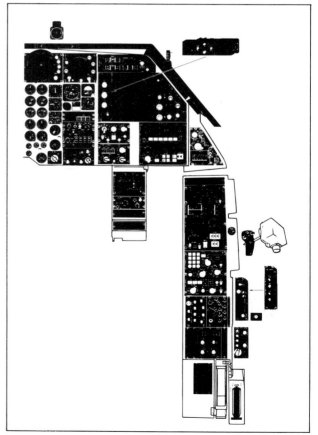

the 'full-up system' for proficiency's sake, and we spend almost as much time looking at the tape after the mission as we do during the mission.

Mike Conway added: 'You see, "Oh, that was the problem. I wondered why it wasn't tracking right", afterwards'. It is an invaluable training aid.

LGBs compatible with Pave Tack include the Texas Instruments Paveway II and Paveway III kits, which are attached to regular D-ring Mk. 82 or Mk. 84 'iron' bombs and loaded up directly on to any or all of the four pivot-pylons, one per station.* The Paveway II modules offered pop-out glide wings and other refinements over the early Vietnam-era Paveway I, for extended range. Paveway III, the new low-level laser-guided bomb (LLLGB), now in stock in Mk. 84-adapted GBU-24 form only, offers substantial gains over the old-generation weapon. Featuring high-aspect-ratio flip-open glide wings, its own miniature mid-course autopilot and a non-gimballed wide-FOV seeker, the LLLGB can be 'tossed' at low level, after which time it flies itself to the assigned target. Laser marking during the terminal phase of the bomb's flight, to guide the GBU-24 right on to a specific aimpoint, may then be performed by the F-111F using only a brief pop-up, by relying on stored co-ordinates to auto 'Cue' Pave Tack, obviating the need for extensive arm-wrestling with the tracking

**Below: A trio of 493rd TFS 'Aardvarks' coming in over the coast from the offshore range. The squadron specializes in the Rockwell GBU-15 glide bomb but the aircraft are carrying SUU-21 dispensers on this occasion. (General Dynamics)**

Above: The latest Texas Instruments GBU-24 Paveway III LLLGB; note the wide-FOV, 'solid' noses which replaced gimballed seeker heads used in the earlier Vietnam-era Paveway I and postwar Paveway II class laser-guided bombs. (Authors)

handle. The laser bomber can thus stay low for the bulk of the delivery, in sharp contrast to operations in Vietnam where pioneering AVQ-9 Paveway and AVQ-10 Pave Knife 'zot' ships orbited near the target for relatively long periods, right in the thick of the AAA and SA-2 SAM defence boxes. Paveway LGB accuracy is legendary: the new LLLGB can be employed off-axis in 'level', 'loft', 'dive' or 'toss' with a first-pass probability of a kill demonstrated during tests to be 3½ times more than Paveway II. The development of autonomous, point-and-lob versions equipped with dual-imaging infra-red ($I^2R$) and millimetre-wave seekers which can be 'handed off' to targets being tracked by Pave Tack are in development at Eglin ADTC as part of the latest Paveway IV effort.

The F models are not the only 'One-Elevens' with a Paveway capability. Capt. Greg Lowrimore points out that RAAF F-111Cs have Pave Tack cradles and pods and the remainder of the F-111 TACAIR community is capable of carrying and dropping LGBs:

Back in the States when Moody [the 347th TFW] had F-4s they carried the Pave Spike daytime laser designator. We could work together, and did so once at 'Red Flag'. We can practice it here in USAFE too, using a ground team such as special forces. Navy SEALs fire a laser from the ground; or we 'buddy' up with Lakenheath as a hunter-killer team with us carrying the weapons and relying on their designator.

The 20th TFW recently went to Garvey Island to drop LGBs, working with SEALs who did the designating using portable packs no more bulky than video cameras. Working on occasion in a CAS mode, primarily with beacons, is only part of the F-111A/C/D/E brief though; Lakenheath's laser-bombers are full-time interdictors, primed to power their way deep behind enemy lines with their laser capability to destroy key installations,

---

*The Mk. 82 Paveway II is known as the GBU-12, the Mk. 84 version as the GBU-10.

**Above: Like all other squadron commanders' aircraft at Lakenheath in 1988, F-111F No. 51 (70-2412) had its serial amended and outlined in its unit's colour – yellow in the case of the 493rd FTS 'Can Do' squadron. (Authors)**

second echelon forces and supply depots. Mike Conway: 'Everybody wants a piece of Pave Tack. Once they know you have the precision munitions capability everybody has a bridge that they want dropped!'

Day-to-day Pave Tack training does not involve the use of LGBs; such practice drops are reserved for WTDs on the grounds of cost. Paveway is one of the less pricy 'smart' bombs on the market but it is still in the big dollars league, about $45,000 for a GBU-10, all-in. Lt. Col. Tom G. Runge:

> We do get the opportunity to drop LGBs on WTDs which are held once or twice a year. We try to get all those guys who are Pave Tack qualified to be able to drop an inert LGB [a working seeker attached to a blue, inert Mk. 82 or Mk. 84]. On the other hand, you can practice all the things that you need to do in the airplane without the laser-guided bomb being on the wing. You can go through all the switches, all the things you need to do without *physically* dropping the bomb.

BDU-33 practice bombs are used instead, which possess similar if not identical ballistic characteristics. Mike Conway:

> Obviously, they don't have the laser seeker so you're not going to get the 'shack' on the target, but it's going to be pretty close; if you go through all the procedures up to getting the bomb off to where it would actually 'see' a marked target you're going to get a close bomb anyway.

Paveway CEPs are measured in feet, not yards, and crews have every confidence in the system.

### The 'Can Do' Squadron
Working in league with the LLLGB is the GBU-15. This Rockwell International bomb is classified as a missile, although it employs no rocket motor: imparting only kinetic energy, a supersonic 'Aardvark' can 'toss' this

2,000-pounder a staggering eight miles! And how accurate is it? Weapons specialist Sgt. Fox confides: 'When we were in Nellis they dropped two from the same aircraft and they were both on target. One was right in an eight-foot hole and the other hit the side and went in'.

Developed from Rockwell International's pioneering electro-optically guided GBU-8 Homing Bomb System (Hobos), which remains an F-111F option in the 'protected memory' at the push of a button, the GBU-15 is a second-generation autonomous 'smart' bomb which uses glide wings, steering vanes and a lock-on 'before or after' launch imaging sensor to steer itself to its assigned target. A 'Vark' can carry up to four GBU-15s, one on each of the pivot-pylons – now the speciality of No. 1 Squadron at RAAF Amberley and Lakenheath's appropriately named 'Bomb in the Ring', 'Can Do' Squadron, the 493rd TFS. Achieving IOC first with the 493rd in 1984, the GBU-15 is supplied as a kit to be plugged on to 2,000lb rounds at short notice, checked out ready for flight by 'GJM' support units. The 493rd TFS air and ground crews, now the sole USAFE users of the weapon, know its capabilities well and exploit them fully. Maj. Dick Brown, also an ex GBU-15 IP with Lakenheath's 'Gold Squadron' ('I've been everywhere in the F-111 except China – and then some!'), emphasizes the special nature of the unit: 'There are a few select crews who do strictly that and that's all they do'. Configured for battle, a GBU-15-toting interdictor also carries a 10ft-long Hughes AN/AXQ-14 data-link pod on the aft ventral hardpoint normally reserved for the external ECM pod, containing a phased, scanned-array antenna to track the weapon despite aircraft manoeuvres, plus a jam-resistant radio transmitter/receiver permitting the 'Wizzo' to communicate with the bomb after weapons release by remote control.* The bomb's seeker generates a TV image of the outside world within its 2.5° FOV, which is in turn relayed via the data link and flashed up on the cockpit VID. To put the bomb smack on target the WSO takes hold of his tracking handle and slews the seeker

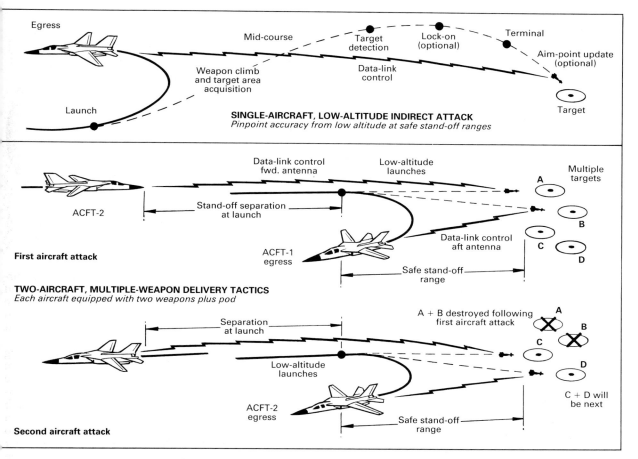

Egress

Mid-course

Target detection

Lock-on (optional)

Terminal

Aim-point update (optional)

Weapon climb and target area acquisition

Data-link control

Launch

Target

**SINGLE-AIRCRAFT, LOW-ALTITUDE INDIRECT ATTACK**
*Pinpoint accuracy from low altitude at safe stand-off ranges*

Data-link control fwd. antenna

Low-altitude launches

Multiple targets

A

ACFT-2

Stand-off separation at launch

B

Data-link control aft antenna

C

D

**First aircraft attack**

ACFT-1 egress

Safe stand-off range

**TWO-AIRCRAFT, MULTIPLE-WEAPON DELIVERY TACTICS**
*Each aircraft equipped with two weapons plus pod*

Separation at launch

A + B destroyed following first aircraft attack

A

B

C

Low-altitude launches

D

ACFT-2 egress

C + D will be next

Safe stand-off range

**Second aircraft attack**

**Above: The GBU-15 glide bomb is a versatile weapon which can be guided or locked on to the target using solo or 'buddy' techniques.**

about until the target image is centred under the TV crosshairs. Using this method he may manually fly the weapon all the way to target or make last-minute lock-on adjustments during the terminal phase of the glide bomb's ballistic flight just prior to impact.

The data-link facility goes beyond the one-aircraft one-bomb mission, permitting another F-111 to share the workload, to enhance survivability. In this mode one aircraft will ingress the target area fast and low, taking advantage of any available masking terrain, to 'toss' its weapon towards the target before breaking away to safety. The 'buddy' bomber, 'at a considerable stand-off distance', then assumes control of the GBU-15 via data link and steers the bomb to the target. The stand-off communication capability varies with the topography and the 'prevailing electronic environment', but tests at Nellis have demonstrated that positive bomb control is possible at ranges of up to an astonishing 45 miles! Mission accomplished, the 'buddy' bombers are free to trade roles and take on a second target, a typical F-111F mission load comprising two GBU-15s apiece for a two-aircraft multiple-weapons delivery effort.

The GBU-15 itself comes in a number of configurations, made possible by its modular design. The GBU-15(V)1/B model employs a daytime DSU-27/B TV seeker and the GBU-15(V)2/B version is fitted with a day- or night-capable WGU-10/B I$^2$R seeker. Both these formats are now operational in 5ft-span, 'wide chord' cruciform wing form and should soon be supplemented by 'short chord' cruciform wing models reminiscent of the old Hobos. According to Rockwell International, the change in wing chord has been made for two reasons:

When the weapon is used with a cluster bomb warhead the long-chord wing extends over the clam-like opening of the dispenser system whereas the short-chord wing does 'not get in the way'. Also the short-chord version does not change the flight profile or performance but is cheaper to produce.†

*If required, bombers equipped with the data-link pod carry their AN/ALQ-131 ECM pod under the weapons bay. Electromagnetic pattern trials were carried out at Rome Air Development Center using a salvaged F-111A mounted on a wooden truss. The outcome of the tests is unknown and it is likely that the simultaneous use of the data-link pod and ECM is prohibited.
†The dispenser munition used in lieu of a Mk. 84 warhead is believed to be the SUU-54 canister.

GBU-15s are, in fact, by far the most expensive conventional bombs carried by the F-111, so the launching of glide weapons fitted with working seekers and precision-engineered wings, just like the Paveway drops, is a costly business, performed only on an occasional basis. Instead, for 'continuation training' purposes, the 493rd TFS launches two F-111Fs equipped with GBU-15s and data-link pods which play the roles 'bomber' and 'bomb' and record the data-linked video imagery on their AN/AXQ-14 mission recorders for post-sortie analysis. To simulate weapons release the 'bomb' breaks formation towards the assigned target with its weapon activated, while the 'Wizzo' in the 'bomber' acquires seeker imagery via data link and provides verbal flying instructions over the radio ('Up a notch, left a notch' and so forth) to manoeuvre the target into the crosshairs. The two crews then switch roles. The aim is to instruct WSOs in the rather complex act of acquiring the target on the display crosshairs at stand-off range and to perfect data-link switchology – something which requires considerable practice in the cloudy northern European skies.

To expand the envelope Rockwell International have since developed a powered version of their glide bomb. Known as the AGM-130, it consists of a rocket canister strapped underneath a short-chord GBU-15, to double the stand-off attack capability to 15nm. Several hiccups were encountered in the initial six-shot engineering development phase when only one missile worked as advertised but Rockwell are pouring their own money into the follow-on eight-shot development, test and evaluation programme which commenced in March 1988, and Eglin ADTC 'One-Elevens' assigned to the

Above: Short-chord GBU-15 glide bombs installed for weapons trials on an Eglin ADTC, 3246th Test Wing F-111E. The wide- and short-chord cruciform wing GBU-15s use identical guidance electronics. (Rockwell International)

Below: The Rockwell GBU-15 stand-off glide bomb can be fitted with either a DSU-27/B TV seeker or a WGU-10/B I²R seeker. The weapon is depicted in these two photographs in its wide-chord cruciform configuration. (Authors)

job are meeting with success. The project may be terminated however, and as an insurance policy the USAF FWEP team is taking a close look at the very similar Israeli Rafael Industries Popeye TV-guided stand-off weapon. Martin Marietta have teamed with Rafael and F-111 Popeye launches are scheduled for late 1988 under a programme designated 'Have Nap'. One or other of the new missiles will give the F-111s that much-needed stand-off punch for the 1990s.*

## North African Bomb Competition

There has only been one occasion since the Vietnam conflict when the F-111 community has been called upon to prove its mettle in combat – although things got very close to that in Korea in 1976. The political background to Operation 'El Dorado Canyon' has been charted effectively elsewhere. Briefly, to the National Security Council in Washington, and eventually to President Reagan, it was the inevitable finale to years of increasing tension and provocation between Colonel Qadafi of Libya and the United States. The Berlin disco bomb of 5 April 1986 was seen as the final challenge to America's patience and to the credibility of a President who had been elected on a pledge to stand up against terrorists. With the loss of 200 Marines in Beirut in 1983 and the TWA hijack in June 1985, followed by the *Achille Lauro* incident in October that year, the public demand for action became overwhelming. After five more American civilians died in the Rome airport massacre in December 1985 influential figures in the National Security Council and the Central Intelligence Agency began to advocate the bombing of Tripoli. Circumstantial evidence appeared to link Qadafi with all the previous outrages. Following the Berlin bomb, which killed an American serviceman and injured 230 other customers, the military option became all too pressing. As Pentagon anti-terrorist specialist Noel Koch put it, 'All the excuses ran out'.

It took well over a week to settle the details of 'El Dorado Canyon'. Punitive action against Qadafi could be generated effectively from the two Navy carriers on station in the Mediterranean. However, the five target areas selected by the planners would have required two separate strike missions by the two overstretched A-6E Intruder squadrons. Only the A-6E TRAM could guarantee the kind of accuracy demanded against targets so close to sensitive civilian areas.† There was another option. In most contingency planning for a large air strike by the Sixth Fleet on its 'home patch', British-based F-111s were already included in the reckoning. Under the terms of the 1951 Anglo-American agreement on the use of bases in the UK, Prime Minister Margaret Thatcher could veto such an effort if she felt there were insufficient justification. It is possible that her direct access to the messages between terrorist elements in East Berlin and Tripoli which apparently led to the disco bombing and which were intercepted at Government Communications HQ at Cheltenham helped to secure her approval of the strike. Suggestions that the 48th TFW was involved because the USAF 'wanted a piece of the action' were said to be 'absolutely untrue' by State Department officials. So were the insinuations that President Reagan wanted the British to demonstrate their loyalty to the USA as an object lesson to other, recalcitrant European nations.

Eventually it was decided that the F-111Fs would be tasked with attacking three targets in the Tripoli area –

---

*Test-launched and also available via the 'protected memory' is the Hughes AGM-65 imaging infra-red-guided air-to-surface missile. This uses the same guidance technology as the GBU-15(V)2/B but has a comparatively small 300lb warhead (on the latest AGM-65G model). The AGM-65 is not deployed at Lakenheath.

†The Target Recognition Attack Multisensor (TRAM) A-6E Intruder possesses a capability very similar to that of the Pave Tack F-111, combining FLIR and laser optics for night-time attack and the precision delivery of weapons.

Right: 494th TFS 'Panthers' F-111F No. 74, 72-1444, commanded by veteran Lt. Col. Tony Sobol, with GBU-10 Paveway II LGBs on its wings. (USAFE)

Below: A Lakenheath line-up of F-111Fs. (Via BAe)

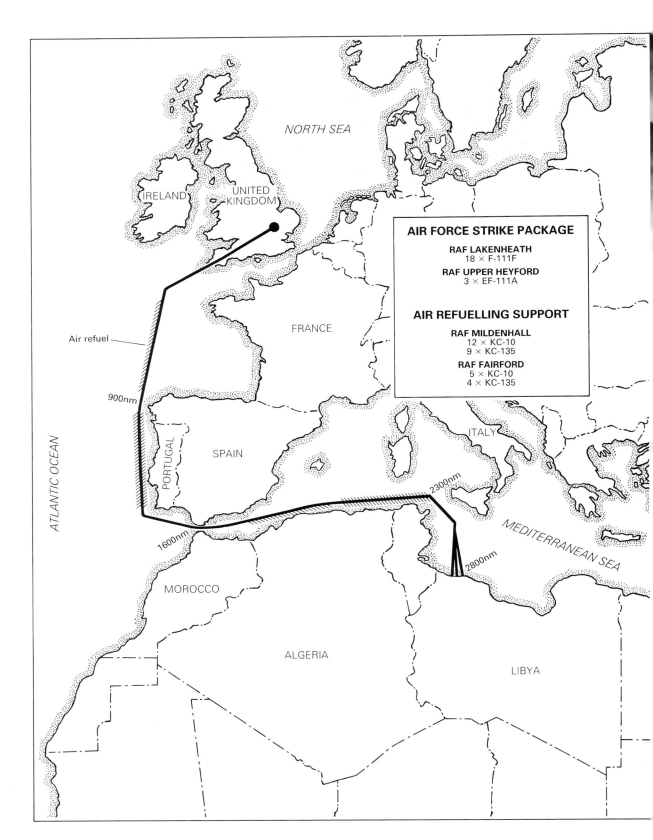

AIR FORCE STRIKE PACKAGE

**RAF LAKENHEATH**
18 × F-111F

**RAF UPPER HEYFORD**
3 × EF-111A

AIR REFUELLING SUPPORT

**RAF MILDENHALL**
12 × KC-10
9 × KC-135

**RAF FAIRFORD**
5 × KC-10
4 × KC-135

NORTH SEA

IRELAND

UNITED KINGDOM

FRANCE

ATLANTIC OCEAN

Air refuel

900nm

PORTUGAL

SPAIN

ITALY

2300nm

MEDITERRANEAN SEA

1600nm

MOROCCO

2800nm

ALGERIA

LIBYA

**Above: An F-111F lays down a string of Mk. 82 'Ballutes'. (USAFE)**

**Left: A map displaying the route and refuelling points used by the F-111F strike package in April 1986.**

the Sidi Bilal training facility, the Azziziyah barracks and Tripoli military airport. The Navy attack squadrons were targeted 350 miles to the east, on Benina air base with its MiG-23 'Flogger' fighters and on Benghazi barracks. All the targets were approved on the assumption that they had direct links with the terrorist activity and the choices all sought to prevent civilian casualties and minimize collateral damage. In all there were thirty contingency targets, though most were of economic rather than military importance. The concerted attack was designed to hit the terrorist training network with a fair element of surprise, saturating the defences. After at least a week of open discussions, delays and 'leaks' Qadafi must have been ready for something fairly close to his tent.

In England the opening movements of the build-up of hardware began. USAFE and the Third Air Force were put on alert and data on the Libyan air defence network, gleaned from a number of sources, were provided by the 'Proud Flame' Joint (service) Electronic Warfare Center (JEWC) at San Antonio, Texas, enabling the Upper Heyford and Lakenheath CNPA divisions to load up the

aircraft's ECM with tailored 'jamming strategies'.* Four KC-10As were transferred from Zaragosa to Fairford on 11 April (it later became clear that the Spanish Government would refuse to allow tankers to operate from Zaragosa in support of a strike). By Sunday 13 April the number of KC-10As in the country had virtually doubled, with two dozen in place at Mildenhall and Fairford along with 30 KC-135s. At the same time elements of the 67th ARRS at Woodbridge sent three of its HH-53C air rescue and recovery helicopters south to Naples, followed by a pair of HC-130N refuellers to support them, as search and rescue (SAR) back-up. It is also likely that two of Alconbury's TR-1A signals recce jets quietly decamped to RAF Akrotiri in support of JEWC. USAFE Headquarters attempted to reassure the public that these irregular phenomena were merely part of a routine 'Salty Nation' exercise. Even the most amateur observer was suspicious of that.

The following day, at 1713 Zulu (or GMT, equivalent to 1213 Eastern Standard Time and 1813 British Summer Time), KC-10A 30080 of the 22nd ARW hauled its vast load of jet fuel off Fairford's runway, followed by six similar aircraft over the following three hours.

---

*JEWC receives constant updates based on data picked up by chance and through communications, electronic and signals intelligence gathered by Electronic Security Command, SAC, other services' intelligence reports, the CIA and the DIA, and then processes the data and catalogues it for use in various contingency operations.

They in turn took along a pair of KC-135s to top up their own reserves, subsequently returning the base with one of the KC-10s. Their task was to support a group of four EF-111As (plus an air-spare) which took off from Upper Heyford. One Raven was to orbit in reserve off the North African coast while the others went to work at 2354Z off the Libyan shoreline, providing spot-noise confusion to the defences in brief bursts. Meanwhile Mildenhall's evening was similarly disturbed by the stately procession of six KC-135 and ten KC-10 tankers off its runway. In scenes almost reminiscent of wartime Eighth Air Force operations they were soon formating with four-ship flights of F-111Fs over the Suffolk airfields; there was thunder over the West Country not long afterwards. The 'Statue of Liberty Wing' was indeed in action, with twenty-four of its aircraft departing Lakenheath in quartets from 1736Z onwards. Any impression that this was just another 'Hammer' mass-launch was soon corrected by the neat clusters of Mk. 82 AIR and GBU-10 bombs on their pylons, each daubed with yellow-for-live bands. All four squadrons were tasked to provide aircraft, with seven from the 492nd TFS, two from the 493rd TFS (plus five air-spares which returned early after the first refuelling), four from the 494th TFS (with an air-spare) and five from the 'Aardvark University'.

The eighteen F-111Fs and their support force headed south after the first refuelling. Ahead of them target co-ordinates had been obtained by a series of SR-71A sorties while the 'Dragon Ladies' from Akrotiri were probably continuing to monitor Libyan air-defence radars and communications from high altitude. For the strike force the trip was to be a long one. In their anxiety to avoid any association with the American approach to anti-terrorism the French, Spanish and Italian Governments closed their airspace to the 48th TFW, resulting in some impromptu changes to the F-111Fs' 'mission tapes'. Instead of a 1,300nm, 6–7hr flight over France they were obliged to take an exhausting 13–14hr, 5,600nm offshore route in a cramped environment leading them through the Straits of Gibraltar. In duration the flight approached the epic spring 1982 solo of Vulcan XM607 in its 15¾hr sortie to bomb Port Stanley runway – and that on top of a long day in which briefings began as early as 2 p.m. The American strike force was after airports too. Some of the bombs were for Tripoli airport, and to make sure that their delivery was not interrupted by the MiGs at Benina the A-6E TRAM Intruders of VA-34 and VA-55 on board the carriers *America* and *Coral Sea* were launched. Their attack, timed to coincide with the highly concentrated TOTs of the F-111 onslaught at midnight Zulu, destroyed at least eight Libyan aircraft. No MiGs got off the ground.

In all there were four silent flight refuellings en route and up to eleven in the entire mission. After the final 'plug' over the Mediterranean the strike elements went to low altitude and divided into two groups. They were protected by a CAP of US Navy Tomcats and Hornets co-ordinated by a Hawkeye, while a backstage fleet of combined-service E-2C, RC-135, E-3A and ERA-3B listening posts monitored the potential threats. The

Above: Two photographs of Pave Tack imagery of the Azziziyah barracks complex in Tripoli as one of a pair of F-111Fs assigned to this part of the target – led by the mission commander – approaches the release point. (US DoD)

42nd ECS Ravens set up their radar-jamming activity offshore (with similarly equipped EA-6Bs doing the same for the Navy to the east). Navy A-6 Intruders, A-7 Corsairs and F/A-18 Hornets destroyed a 'large number' of radars with Shrike and HARM anti-radiation missiles, effectively denying the Libyans much of their tracking capability. As the Intruders started their bomb runs, paralleled by the F-111Fs in the Tripoli area, they reported that 'The cities of Libya were surprisingly easy to spot. The street-lights were all burning.' But the scene quickly became 'thoroughly menacing' as the defences reacted. Vice-Admiral Kelso, Commander of the Sixth Fleet, said, 'I don't think anyone has flown a mission in a denser SAM environment'. Vietnam veterans may have disagreed, but in the Libyan skies the venerable SA-2 was joined by the far more lethal Soviet SA-3, SA-6, SA-8 and French Crotale SAMs, backed up by truckloads of flak.

The American aircraft, still in total radio silence, replied with sixty tons of bombs in all. The two F-111s targeted on the Bab Al Azziziyah barracks each tossed four GBU-10 bombs, causing 'substantial' damage to 'Khaddafi's headquarters and contiguous working spaces', according to Washington. Naturally there was much speculation over the extent to which Qadafi himself was a target. The assassination of a head of state is of course prohibited by the US Constitution in peacetime but there were many in Washington who observed that they would have shed few tears if the Libyan leader had been in his famous tent when the ordnance detonated. The details of the attack are still, understandably, not a topic for public discussion at Lakenheath. However, the authors were assured that a Mk. 84 warhead's 2,000lb shockwave would have been lethal to anyone within 300–400ft of the explosion. Eight GBU-10s landed within that radius from the tent and barracks area. Qadafi presumably spent his night underground. He was not the F-111F's target.

Four 'Foxtrots' put their Mk. 84 bombs on the Sidi Bilal naval training complex (assumed to be an underwater sabotage school) as planned and several small vessels and a building complex were claimed as seriously damaged, though there was less destruction here than at the other target sites. A third group of five F-111Fs each toting twelve Mk. 82 AIRs swung round to the south of the city to hit Tripoli airport. The total size of the strike contingent was reduced to thirteen F-111Fs by five 'systems aborts' in the final stages. This was one mission where the rules said '100 per cent systems capability' and it seems that those five crews were not entirely convinced that their Pave Tack and attack radar acquisitions would be perfect. Civilian casualties and collateral damage were, after all, to be assiduously avoided.

The AIRs raining down on Tripoli airport destroyed two IL-76 'Candids', and in a news release on 8 May the Defense Department said that three other 'Candids' were substantially damaged. These transports were supposedly in use to take terrorist *matériel* around the world to a number of groups. It was also possible that other damaged aircraft were removed from the area before accurate reconnaissance pictures could be obtained to back up the Pave Tack FLIR videotapes.

At some point during the concerted attack F-111F 70-2389 hit trouble. As the 'One-Elevens' passed over the Tripoli area, and for some time afterwards, the Libyan defences blasted the air above the city with everything they could let off, ranging in calibre from AK-47 automatic rifles to huge SAM missiles. It is at least possible that '389 was hit and that its stray bombs went off-target. Washington later admitted that 1–2 per cent of the bombs hit civilian areas and three from a single F-111 hit the French Embassy – an ironic twist! Any other damage was attributed to the Libyan defences. As an F-14 Tomcat pilot noted, they were 'firing missiles straight up into the air and they were coming down on the city'. There is an equally strong possibility that the ill-fated F-111 hit the sea during its low-level egress, or perhaps when evading a missile. There was no radio

**Right: One second to target, with a pair of Il-76 'Candids' in the Pave Tack crosshairs, over Tripoli airport in April 1986; Mk. 82 AIR release; nine black blobs – all 'Ballutes' – mark the descent of the bombs as Pave Tack faces astern; and clouds erupt as bombs go off and the F-111F in question egresses the airport at high speed. (US DoD)**

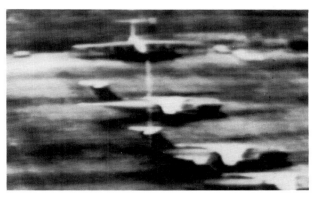

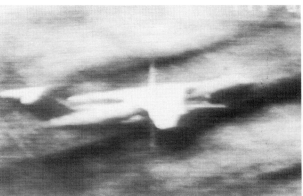

transmission to report 'feet wet' or to register combat damage, and no sign of an attempted ejection. Several pilots reported seeing a 'fireball' off the coast but intense SAR activity revealed nothing. Reporters were told that they would be shown the wreckage of the aircraft, but the bus which was to take them to the site never set off. Later the Libyans produced some hastily painted 'wreckage' with the fictitious serial '423241' daubed on it. The loss of two popular crewmen was a great sadness to all at Lakenheath.

Although world press coverage focused heavily upon the civilian casualties the venture was judged a military success by its planners. Post-strike reconnaissance was rather slow to arrive owing to heavy cloud cover over Tripoli. Unprecedentedly, both SR-71As from Mildenhall were sent together to survey the damage, yet missions had to be flown on three successive days to gather the necessary imagery. When the analysis was complete it could be assumed that Pave Tack had proved itself in action. Apart from the systems aborts, which were probably quite minor, only one aircraft had mechanical problems, spending a night in Spain after an engine warning light appeared indicating a minor compressor problem. Undoubtedly the F-111 was the right tool for a long-range precision attack of this kind;

it is worth recalling that another contingency plan, based on the unavailability of the F-111s for political reasons, called for the use of B-52s operating from the USA.

Back at Lakenheath life soon reverted to routine. Apart from a series of irate phone calls from prominent left-wingers there was less animosity than expected. A memorial service for Maj. Fernando L. Ribas-Dominicci and Capt. Paul F. Lorence, the lost crew of '389, drew many senior USAF personnel to the base on 21 April. The 48th TFW marked its achievements too. The tails of their 'Aardvarks' began to carry the prominent 'North Africa Campaign' stripes as a public reminder of the time they were required to put into practice Ronald Reagan's warning to terrorists: 'You can run but you can't hide'. The tension wound up again when the press deduced that a regular 27th TFW F-111D 'Coronet' deployment to RAF Boscombe Down was a sure sign of 'Round Two' against Libya. One of the oddest aspects of the whole affair was that the 48th TFW were awarded the US Navy Meritorious Unit Commendation in September 1986, some time before being nominated for any Air Force award or the Armed Forces Expeditionary Medal. Navy Secretary John F. Lehman Jr. turned up unannounced and made the presentation in person!

# Into the Twenty-First Century

At the time of writing the US Air Force is contemplating an increase in the F-111 force in Europe with the introduction of sixty ex SAC F-111Gs. After twenty-one years of front-line service it would be more usual for a combat type to be progressively withdrawn from the 'leading edge' rather than see its numbers increase so markedly. With the F-111G boost, 'Aardvarks' would be outnumbered in USAFE only by the omnipresent F-16 – though by less than fifty copies.

The reasons for this continued importance are far from elusive. General Dynamics were not far off the mark when they proclaimed that even after the introduction of the McAir F-15E 'Strike Eagle', now known as the 'dual role fighter', the F-111 will still be the only aircraft capable of striking some 30 per cent of Central European targets. Figures for the Middle East were even more impressive: 70 per cent of potential trouble spots would be beyond the reach of all but the 'Aardvarks'. (This scenario assumes that F-111s would operate from forward bases at Riyadh in Saudi Arabia and Ras Banas in Egypt.) In many respects the 'top of the line' F-111D/F marks can almost match the F-15E: sea-level top speeds are within Mach 0.03 of each other and both

Below: A group of 509th BW(M) FB-111As on deployment from Pease AFB, New Hampshire, jostle for take-off at Lakenheath's runway; to be redesignated F-111Gs, they will soon be a regular sight in England. The GD/McAir A-12 Advanced Tactical Aircraft, a stealth attack design being funded by the Navy, may be adopted by the USAF as an F-111 replacement starting from FY98. The team was awarded a $7.9 million concept study contract in November 1988 to investigate a 'baseline' A-12 suitable for both services. Robert McNamara's old goals might well be realized thirty years on! (Tim Laming)

aircraft have 60,000ft ceilings and maximum speeds, in clean configuration, in the region of Mach 2.4. However, the F-111 can still haul the explosives over many more miles, taking 6,000lb of bombs over a 1,000nm radius whereas a similarly laden Eagle has to turn back at 600nm. Undoubtedly the performance of the F-15E's Hughes APG-70 synthetic aperture radar, 'capable of picking up a 6ft man dressed in tin foil at several miles', and its 1,000k computer capacity exceed anything planned for the F-111, and the Eagle does possess a genuine 'fighter' capability with stand-off and short-range air-to-air missiles and a 'Gat' gun, but range still counts for a lot in high-threat areas.

'Aardvarks' remain viable when set alongside the potential opposition too. Sukhoi's design bureau used many of the innovations of the F-111 in their very capable Su-24 'Fencer'. The NASA outboard pivot 'swing-wing', the side-by-side seating, the TFR (presumed to be automatic) and the rotary gun all appear in an airframe of similar dimensions and configuration. The Su-23 ditched long subsonic cruise in favour of longer dash-speed endurance and more powerful engines and it is unlikely that the Russian aircraft could match the American aircraft's warload and range characteristics. The Soviet fleet of some 770 Fencers, with about 65 Raven-equivalent derivatives, will no doubt continue to 'face' the smaller number of F-111s for some time to come.

'Aardvark' crewmen are adamant that their long-nosed 'swinger' has not been seriously upstaged by the Tornado either. When a Panavia team visited Washington to promote Tornado as an F-111 replacement in the autumn of 1978 there was little real chance of a deal despite contract offsets and the vague possibility of an RAF F-15 Eagle. Quite apart from political considerations, the two types have many differences, even though both types fly a broadly similar mission. An F-111F 'Wizzo' with flying experience in the Tornado GR.1 has remarked that 'their kit in the back seat is incredible, but the range capability and weapons load doesn't compare with F-111. Once they start pushing up past 450kt they start worrying about making it home with enough gas. That's never a concern with us'. To emphasize the size disparity, his pilot chipped in, 'Have you seen a picture of a Tornado with a JP.233 [airfield attack dispenser]? It's tough to tell who's flying who!'

Until significantly better technology is established in service the F-111 is the only true all-weather interdictor on the USAF's tactical inventory. The high price-tag of a replacement makes retention, standardization and long overdue updates of the invaluable F-111 fleet mandatory – the thrust of the AMP and AIS-R efforts. Safety and reliability have steadily improved too, in more subtle ways. Systems and engines can be updated (the TF30-P-103 can be 'kitted' to P-109 standard quite easily) while new maintenance techniques have helped to minimize problems in older airframes and power-plants. For example, JOAP (Joint Oil Analysis Program) gives an instant health-check on a powerplant through a combustion analysis of only a small sample of engine oil after each sortie. Even the problems inherent in the original manufacturing methods have been progressively eradicated. At one stage, in 1973, no fewer than 21 F-111Ds were stored at Cannon AFB awaiting exhaustive but worthwhile deseal/reseal treatment to cure leaking fuel tanks; other marks with defective wing boxes or tail spigots have been 're-lifed' before a catastrophic structural failure occurred. Despite their ungainly tank-like finish, brought upon by age and less devotion to cosmetics, the F-111s are now better than ever before, the maturity and reliability of their systems more than compensating for their advanced years.

In the latter part of the twentieth century we are witnessing how the escalating cost of new technology is delaying or reversing 'planned obsolescence' in defence equipment. The world of aviation has yielded a few examples of designs which are so 'right' and so hard to replace that their service lives far outstrip the original estimates. While it may not quite equal the Boeing B-52's anticipated half-century of service, the long-suffering 'Aardvark' is, unequivocally, among that handful of 'classics'.

# APPENDICES

## APPENDIX I: GLOSSARY OF ABBREVIATIONS AND ACRONYMS

**AAA**     Anti-aircraft artillery.

**AAR**     Air-to-air refuelling.

**AB**     Air Base. Usually where the USAF are a tenant unit on overseas soil.

**ABCCC**     Airborne Command and Control Center. Also known as 'Comfy Levi'.

**AC**     Aircraft Commander.

**ADI**     Attitude director indicator.

**ADTC**     Armament Development Test Center. Eglin AFB, Florida.

**AFB**     Air Force Base. On US-owned or -leased property.

**AFFTC**     Air Force Flight Test Center. Edwards AFB, California.

**AFLC**     Air Force Logistics Command. Responsible for depot-level maintenance, spares and modifications. HQ Wright-Patterson AFB, Ohio.

**AFSC**     Air Force Systems Command. Responsible for the development of aircraft and weapons systems. HQ Andrews AFB, Maryland.

**AGL**     Above ground level. Expressed in feet.

**AIR**     Air Inflatable Retard. High-drag 'Ballute' bomb.

**AIS-R**     Avionics Intermediate Shop – Replacement. Test-benches.

**AMARC**     Aerospace Maintenance and Regeneration Center. Davis-Monthan AFB, Arizona. Also known as the 'Boneyard'.

**AMP**     Avionics Modernization Program.

**AMU**     Aircraft Maintenance Unit. One exists for each USAF tactical squadron, responsible for flight-line readiness of the aircraft.

**ARDU**     Air Research Development Unit. RAAF Edinburgh, South Australia.

**ARS**     Attack radar set.

**ARW**     Aerial Refueling Wing.

**ASD**     Aeronautical Systems Division. AFSC, HQ Wright-Patterson AFB, Ohio.

**Auto TF**     Automatic terrain-following.

**ATC**     Air Training Command. Responsible for training undergraduate air and ground crews. HQ Randolph AFB, Texas.

**AUW**     All-up weight (or gross weight).

**AWACS**     Airborne Warning and Control System. Without command functions, an airborne early warning (AEW) aircraft.

**BAe**     British Aerospace.

**BAI**     Battlefield area interdiction.

**BAK**     Barrier arresting hook-compatible landing aid.

**BCU**     Ballistics computer unit. Used by the F-111A/C/E and RF-111C.

**BIF**     Bomb-in-face. A defensive tactic.

**BMS**     Bombardment Squadron, Medium.

**BNS**     Bomb (Ballistics), Navigation System. Frequently referred to as the nav/attack system.

**BRU**     Bomb Release Unit. Bomb rack, carried on the F-111's pivot-pylons. The modern BRU-3 was introduced to service during the 'Linebacker' era in 1972.

**BuNo**     Bureau of Aeronautics Number. Given to all Navy and Marine Corps aircraft.

**BVR**     Beyond visual range (in air-to-air combat).

**BW(M)**     Bombardment Wing, Medium.

**CAP**     Combat air patrol.

**CAS**     Close air support. Conducted in support of the Army, Marines or Special Forces.

**CBU**     Cluster Bomb Unit. A bomb composed of numerous submunitions.

**CCTS**     Combat Crew Training Squadron. Still used by SAC, the abbreviation was replaced by the designation TFTS in TAC units.

**CMDS**     Countermeasures Dispenser Set. The AN/ALE-28 chaff-flare dispenser.

**CMRS**     Countermeasures Receiving Set. The AN/AAR-34 cryogenic warning receiver.

**CRT**     Cathode ray tube. TV display.

**DAB**     Defense Acquisition Board. Formerly known as the Defense Systems Acquisition Review Council (DSARC).

**DCC**     Dedicated Crew Chief. Every USAF F-111 has one. Navy DCCs are known as Plane Captains.

**DDD**     Detail data (target velocity) display. Used in the F-111B.

**DDI**     Digital display indicator. A multimode systems status and threat display video used in the EF-111A.

**DMZ**     Demilitarized Zone. A buffer zone which separated North and South Vietnam.

**ECM**     Electronic countermeasures. Principally radar-jamming equipment.

**ECP**     Engineering Change Proposals.

**ECRS**     Electronic Combat Range Squadron.

**EMI**     Electromagnetic interference. Generated by a jammer and usually unwanted.

**EST**     Eastern Standard Time.

**EWEP**     Electronic Warfare Evaluation Program.

**EWO**     Electronic Warfare Officer. Of the EF-111A.

**FEBA**     Forward Edge of the Battle Area. The modern term used to describe the battle-front.

**FFAR**     Folding-Fin Aerial Rocket. Used for air-to-ground strikes.

**FLIR**     Forward-looking infra-red (sensor).

**FLIT**     Fighter Lead-In Training. Also known as LIFT and given to all USAF pilot and navigator graduates prior to an operational assignment.

**FOV**     Field of view (of a sensor or seeker).

**Frag**     Fragmentary order (target assignment).

**FTD**     Field Training Detachment. For F-111 fixers.

**FTW**     Flying Training Wing.

**FWEP**     Foreign Weapons Evaluation Program.

| | | | | |
|---|---|---|---|---|
| **FWIC** | Fighter Weapons Instructor Course. At present held at Cannon AFB, New Mexico. | | various radars. The F-111 is at the bottom of the vertex or 'V'. | |
| **FWS** | Fighter Weapons School *or* Fighter Weapons (development) Squadron. | **RAF** | Royal Air Force. | |
| **FWW** | Fighter Weapons Wing. Responsible for developing tactics and training and the initial operational testing of new hardware. | **RAAF** | Royal Australian Air Force. | |
| | | **RAN** | Royal Australian Navy. | |
| | | **RDT&E** | Research, Development, Test and Evaluation. | |
| **GC** | Gigacycle (GHz). | **RHAWS** | Radar homing and warning system. A passive detector. | |
| **GDFW** | General Dynamics, Fort Worth Division (Texas). | **RNZAF** | Royal New Zealand Air Force. | |
| **GE** | General Electric. | **RSP** | Radarscope photography. | |
| **HARM** | High-speed Anti-Radiation Missile. The AGM-88A/B. | **RTAB** | Royal Thai Air Base. Also referred to as RTAFB. | |
| **HSD/I** | Horizontal situation display/indicator. | **RTU** | Replacement Training Unit. A CCTS or TFTS. | |
| **IADS** | Integrated Air Defence System. | **RWR** | Radar warning receiver. The modern term for RHAWS. | |
| **IDS** | Integrated Display Set (F-111D cockpit displays) *or* Infra-red Detection Set (F-111C/F Pave Tack sensor). | **SAC** | Strategic Air Command. The full-time nuclear forces of the USAF. HQ Offutt AFB, Nebraska. | |
| | | **SAM** | Surface-to-air missile. | |
| **IFR** | Instrument Flight Rules. Flying by instruments because of night or bad weather. | **SAR** | Search and rescue *or* synthetic aperture radar. | |
| | | **SEA** | South-East Asia. Embracing Vietnam, Thailand, Cambodia and Laos. | |
| **I²R** | Imaging infra-red (seeker or sensor). | **SIP** | Structural Integrity Program. | |
| **INF** | Intermediate Nuclear Forces (Treaty). | **SLAR** | Sideways-looking airborne (reconnaissance-mapping) radar. | |
| **INS** | Inertial navigation set/system. | | | |
| **IOC** | Initial Operational Capability. | **SMALC** | Sacramento Air Logistics Center. At McClellan AFB, California. The worldwide *matériel* manager for the F-111 and the PDM centre for most USAF F-111s. | |
| **IP** | Instructor Pilot. | | | |
| **IRSTS** | Infra-red search and track sensor. Used to detect enemy aircraft. | | | |
| **IWSO** | Instructor Weapons Systems Officer. | **SPS** | Self-Protection System (AN/ALQ-137 ECM of the EF-111A). | |
| **JSS** | Jamming Subsystem. The Eaton AIL AN/ALQ-99E used in the EF-111A. | **SRAM** | Short-Range Attack Missile. The Boeing AGM-69A. | |
| **JTIDS** | Joint Tactical Information Distribution System. | **SRU** | Shop replaceable unit. A subcomponent of an LRU which can be taken out for shop- or depot-level repairs. | |
| **LADD** | Low-Angle Drogue (retard) Delivery. | | | |
| **LARA** | Low-Altitude Radar Altimeter. | **STU** | Signal transfer unit. Used in the F-111D. | |
| **LCOS** | See ODS. | **SVN** | South Vietnam. | |
| **LGB** | Laser-guided bomb. F-111s use 'Paveway' LGBs. | **SW** | Strike Wing (RAAF). | |
| **LRU** | Line replaceable unit. A 'black box' which can be unplugged for servicing. | **TAB-V** | Theater Air Base – Vulnerability. A hardened aircraft shelter. | |
| **MAU-12** | Cartridge-activated bomb racks built into the F-111's weapons bay and pivot-pylons which use 'D-ring' attachments. | **TAC** | Tactical Air Command. The theatre forces of the USAF based in the USA. | |
| | | **TAC-AIR** | Tactical air power. | |
| **MC** | Megacycle (MHz). | **TAWC** | Tactical Air Warfare Center. Co-located with the ADTC at Eglin AFB, Florida. TAWC is part of TAC; the ADTC is part of AFSC. | |
| **MCAS** | Marine Corps Air Station. | | | |
| **MCO** | Mission (or Missile) Control Officer. The right-seater in the F-111B. | | | |
| | | **TCTO** | Time Compliance Technical Order. | |
| **MMH/FH** | Maintenance man-hours (required) per flight-hour. | **TDY** | Temporary Duty (assignment). | |
| **MSD** | Multisensor display. Used by the F-111D. | **TES** | Test and Evaluation Squadron. | |
| **MTBF** | Mean time between failures (of aircraft systems). | **TFR** | Terrain-following radar. Used by all F-111s except the defunct F-111B. | |
| **MUTES** | Multiple Threat Emitter Simulators. | | | |
| **NAS** | Naval Air Station. | **TFRS** | Tactical Fighter-Reconnaissance Squadron. | |
| **NATO** | North Atlantic Treaty Organization. | **TFS** | Tactical Fighter Squadron. | |
| **NCU/INS** | Navigation computer unit/inertial navigation set. Used by the F-111A/C/E, EF-111A and RF-111C. | **TFTS** | Tactical Fighter Training Squadron. | |
| | | **TFW** | Tactical Fighter Wing. Usually 70–80 aircraft, split into three or four TFSs, or two or three TFSs and a TFTS. | |
| **NDU** | Navigation display unit. The dashboard console navigation displays and controls of the FB-111A and F-111F. | | | |
| | | **TFWC** | Tactical Fighter Weapons Center. At Nellis AFB, Nevada. Home of the 'Red Flag' and 'Green Flag' wargames. | |
| **NKP** | Nakhon Phanom (Thailand). | | | |
| **NVN** | North Vietnam. | | | |
| **OAP** | Offset aiming point. | **TFX/-N** | Tactical Fighter Experimental/-Navy. The original designation of the F-111. | |
| **ODS** | Optical Display Sight. Also known as the Lead-Computing Optical Sight (LCOS). | | | |
| | | **TJS** | Tactical Jamming System. Used in the EF-111A and comprising the JSS, SPS and TTWS. | |
| **ORI** | Operational Readiness Inspection. | | | |
| **PACAF** | Pacific Air Forces. The USAF forces stationed in the Orient and Hawaii. HQ Hickam AFB, Hawaii. | **TLP** | Tactical Leadership Program. | |
| | | **TO** | Technical Order. One requiring a certain modification. | |
| **P&W** | Pratt & Whitney. | | | |
| **PDM** | Programmed Depot Maintenance. | **TID** | Tactical Information Display. Used in the F-111B. | |
| **Pk** | Probability of a kill (of an air-to-air missile or gun). | **TS** | Test Squadron. | |
| **POL** | Petroleum, Oil, Lubricants (storage areas). | | | |
| **PPI** | Plan position indicator. A 'god's eye view' of events; the 'pie-slice' sector-scan of the F-111's | | | |

| | |
|---|---|
| **TTC** | Technical Training Center. |
| **TTW** | Tactical Training Wing. |
| **TTWS** | Terminal Threat Warning System. The AN/ALR-62 RWR used in the EF-111A. |
| **USAF** | United States Air Force. |
| **USAFE** | United States Air Forces Europe. USAF theatre forces forward-based in Europe. |
| **USMC** | United States Marine Corps. |
| **USN** | United States Navy. |
| **VFR** | Visual Flight Rules. Good weather. |
| **VG** | Variable-geometry (wing). 'Swing-wing'. |
| **V/HUD** | Vertical display indicator and heads-up-display (of the F-111B). |
| **VDI** | See V/HUD. |
| **VID** | Virtual image display. Pave Tack FLIR display in the F-111F. |
| **VSD** | Vertical situation display. Used in the F-111D. |
| **V/STOL** | Vertical/Short Take-off and landing. |
| **WARPAC** | Warsaw Pact. |
| **WCP** | Weapons control panel. |
| **WCTB** | Wing carry-through box. Supports the VG wing. |
| **WTD** | Weapons Training Deployment. Periodic training with full-sized inert or live conventional ordnance. |
| **WSO** | Weapons Systems Officer (or 'Wizzo'). The right-hand seater of the USAF tactical strike F-111s, known as navigators in the F/RF-111C and FB-111A and EWOs in the case of the EF-111A. |

# APPENDIX II: F-111 GENERAL ARRANGEMENT

## *F-111E/FB-111A*

(General Dynamics drawings)

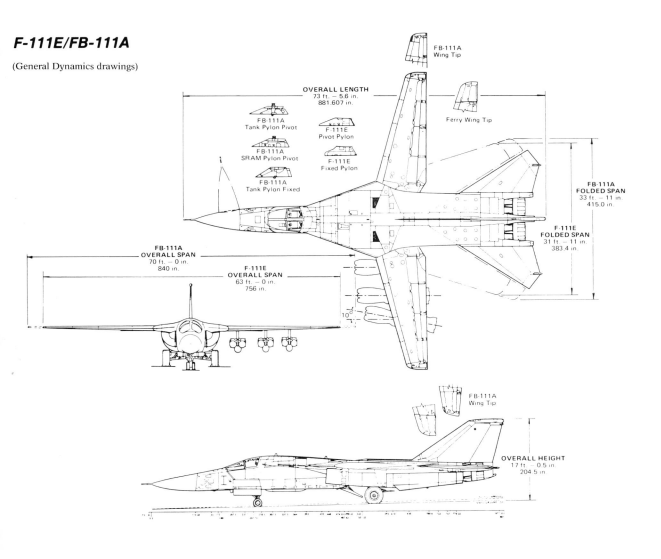

# APPENDIX III: F-111 PRODUCTION

| Contract | Lot No. | Airframe nos. | Qty. produced | Serial nos. | Nos. active* | Remarks |
|---|---|---|---|---|---|---|
| **F-111A** | | | | | | |
| 8260 | 1 | 1–4 | 4 | 63-9766 to -9769 | 0 | |
| | 2 | 5–7 | 3 | 63-9770 to -9772 | 0 | RDT&E aircraft |
| | 3 | 8–11 | 4 | 63-9773 to -9776 | 0 | |
| | 4 | 12–18 | 7 | 63-9777 to -9783 | 1 | |
| | 5 | 19–25 | 7 | 65-5701 to -5707 | 0 | |
| | 6 | 26–36 | 11 | 65-5708 to -5710 | 0 | Pre-production aircraft |
| | | | | 66-011 to -012 | 0 | |
| | | | | 66-013 to -018 | 5 | To EF-111A: 66-013 to -016, -018 to -021, -023, -027, -028, -030, -031, -033, -035 to -039, -041, -044, -046 to -049 (25 aircraft) |
| | 7 | 37–50 | 14 | 66-019 to -032 | 8 | |
| 13403 | 8 | 51–67 | 17 | 66-033 to -049 | 12 | |
| | 9 | 68-84 | 17 | 66-050 to -058 | 13 | To EF111A: 66-050, -051, -055 to -057, 67-032 to -035, -037 to -039 (12 aircraft) |
| | | | | 67-032 to -039 | | |
| | 10 | 85–102 | 18 | 67-040 to -057 | 10 | To EF-111A: 67-041, -042, -044, -048, -052 (5 aircraft) |
| | 11 | 103–121 | 19 | 67-058 to -076 | 12 | |
| | 12 | 122–159 | 38 | 67-077 to -114 | 30 | Inc. 4 RAAF 'C' |
| | | | 159 | | 91 | |
| **F-111C** | | | | | | |
| 13403 (contd.) | 10 | 1–12 | 12 | A8-125 to -136 | 9 | Inc. 4 RF-111C |
| | 11 | 13–24 | 12 | A8-137 to -148 | 9 | |
| | | | 24 | | 18 | |
| **FB-111A** | | | | | | |
| | 8 | 1 | 1 | 67-159 | 1 | |
| | 10 | 2 | 1 | 67-160 | 0 | |
| | 12 | 3–7 | 5 | 67-161 to -163 | 5 | |
| | | | | 67-7192 to -7193 | | |
| 13403 (contd.) | 13 | 8–22 | 15 | 67-7194 to -7196 | 14 | |
| | | | | 68-239 to -250 | | |
| | 14 | 23–34 | 12 | 68-251 to -262 | 10 | |
| | 15 | 35–53 | 19 | 68-263 to -281 | 14 | |
| | 16 | 54–76 | 23 | 68-282 to -292 | 18 | |
| | | | | 69-6503 to -6513 | | |
| | | | 76 | | 62 | |
| **F-111E** | | | | | | |
| | 13 | 1–31 | 31 | 67-115 to -124 | 8 | |
| 13403 (contd.) | | | | 68-001 to -021 | 16 | |
| | 14 | 32–65 | 34 | 68-022 to -055 | 31 | |
| | 15 | 66–94 | 29 | 68-056 to -084 | 25 | |
| | | | 94 | | 80 | |
| **F-111D** | | | | | | |
| | 13 | 1–2 | 2 | 68-085 to -086 | 2 | |
| | 14 | 3–8 | 6 | 68-087 to -092 | 6 | |
| | 15 | 9 | 1 | 68-092 | 0 | |
| 13403 (contd.) | 16 | 10–35 | 26 | 68-093 to -119 | 20 | |
| | 17 | 36–77 | 42 | 68-120 to -161 | 36 | |
| | 18 | 78–89 | 12 | 68-162 to -173 | 9 | |
| | 19 | – | 0 | – | | |
| | 20 | 90–96 | 7 | 68-174 to -180 | 7 | |
| | | | 96 | | 80 | |
| **F-111F** | | | | | | |
| 13403 (contd.) | 18 | 1–16 | 16 | 70-2362 to -2377 | 12 | |
| | 19 | 17–43 | 27 | 70-2378 to -2404 | 22 | |
| | 20 | 44–58 | 15 | 70-2405 to -2419 | 12 | |
| 1130A | 21 | 59–70 | 12 | 71-883 to -894 | 12 | |
| 1130B | 22 | 71–82 | 12 | 72-1441 to -1452 | 10 | |
| 0630 | 23 | 83–94 | 12 | 73-0707 to -0718 | 7 | |
| 0369 | 24 | 95–106 | 12 | 74-0177 to -0188 | 10 | |
| | | | 106 | | 85 | |

*Figures correct to December 1988.

# APPENDIX IV: F-111 MAIN DIFFERENCES

| Item | F-111A | EF-111A | F-111B | F-111C | F-111D | F-111E | F-111F | FB-111A |
|---|---|---|---|---|---|---|---|---|
| Length | 73ft 6in | 74ft 0in | 66ft 9in | 73ft 6in | 73ft 6in | 73ft 6in | 73ft 6in | 73ft 6in |
| Height | 17ft 0½in | 20ft 0in | 15ft 9in | 17ft 0½in | 17ft 0½in | 17ft 0½in | 17ft 0½in | 17ft 0½in |
| Span @ 16° | 63ft 0in | 63ft 0in | 70ft 0in | 70ft 0in | 63ft 0in | 63ft 0in | 63ft 0in | 70ft 0in |
| Span @ 72.5° | 31ft 11in | 31ft 11in | 33ft 11in | 33ft 11in | 31ft 11in | 31ft 11in | 31ft 11in | 33ft 11in |
| Gross weight (normal) | 91,300lb | 88,950lb | 79,002lb | 114,300lb | 100,000lb | 91,300lb | 100,000lb | 114,300lb |
| Engines (TF30 × 2) | P-3/-103 | P-109 | P-12 | P-3 | P-9/-109 | P-3/-103 | P-100 | P-7/-107 |
| Maximum thrust (each) | 18,500lb | 20,840lb | 20,250lb | 18,500lb | 20,840lb | 18,500lb | 25,100lb | 20,350lb |
| Triple Plow Inlets | TP I | TP I | TP I | TP II | TP II | TP II | TP II | TP II |
| Mission avionics and special ordnance | Mk. I | Mk. I/TJS | Phoenix | Mk. I | Mk. II | Mk. I | Mk. IIB | Mk. IIB |
| Attack radar set* | APQ-113 | APQ-160 | AWG-9 | APQ-113 | APQ-130 | APQ-113 | APQ-144 | APQ-114 |
| Doppler radar | – | – | – | – | APN-189 | – | – | APN-185 |
| Terrain-following radar | APQ-110 | APQ-110 | – | APQ-110 | APQ-128 | APQ-110 | APQ-146 | APQ-134 |
| Inertial navigation and ballistics system | Mk. I; AJQ-20A, BCU | Mk I; AJQ-20A, BCU | LN INS, CP741 | Mk. I; AJQ-20A, BCU | Mk. II; AJN-16, AYK-6 | Mk. I; AJQ-20A, BCU | Mk. IIB; AJN-16, AYK-6 | Mk. IIB; AJN-16, AYK-6 |
| Special equipment | – | ALQ-99E, JSS | IRSTS, V/HUD displays | AVQ-26, Pave Tack | AVA-9 displays | – | AVQ-26 Pave Tack | ASQ-119 Astrocompass |
| Special weapons | B61 | – | AIM-54 Phoenix | AGM-84 Harpoon, AGM-88 HARM, GBU-15, Paveway laser | B61 | B61 | B61, GBU-15, Paveway laser | B61, AGM-69 SRAM |
| Self-protect jammer | ALQ-94 | ALQ-137 | – | ALQ-94 | ALQ-94 | ALQ-94 | ALQ-94 | ALQ-137 |
| Radar warning receiver | ALR-62 | ALR-62 | – | ALR-62 | ALR-62 | ALR-62 | ALR-62 | ALR-62 |
| Countermeasures receiver | AAR-34 | – | – | AAR-34 | AAR-34 | AAR-34 | AAR-34 | AAR-34 |
| Countermeasures dispenser† | ALE-28 | ALE-28 | ALE-29 | ALE-28 | ALE-28 | ALE-28 | ALE-28 | ALE-28 |
| Strap-on ECM | ALQ-131 | – | – | – | ALQ-131 | ALQ-131 | ALQ-131 | – |
| Conversions | 1 to FB-111A; 1 to RF-111A; 4 as F-111C; 42 to EF-111A; 1 to NASA | – | – | 4 to RF-111C | – | – | – | 60 to F-111G |
| Nos. built | 159 | 42 | 7 | 24 | 96 | 94 | 106 | 76 |
| RDT&E and pre-production | 30 | (2) | 7 | – | – | – | – | 2 |

*Due to be replaced with the AN/APG-67 during AMP. †Due to be replaced with the AN/ALE-40 during AMP.

# APPENDIX V: PAVE MOVER

Today's 'netted' Allied military command, control and communications system relies on a sound knowledge of the whereabouts of the enemy so that forces may be directed to counter the opposition with maximum effectiveness – what is sometimes called the 'Force Multiplying Effect'. As a major ingredient in this evolving concept the US Air Force and US Army are to field a dual-manned aircraft known as the Joint Surveillance Target-Attack Radar System (J-STARS), capable of loitering in friendly airspace for extended periods and probing beyond the FEBA with high-resolution synthetic-aperture radar to map second-echelon enemy ground forces. This 'real-time' data will be processed and in turn relayed to Army missile batteries and Air Force strike aircraft over secure JTIDS terminals, enabling them to 'call up' the latest target positions for pinpoint attacks. J-STARS will also be capable of guiding aircraft and certain 'smart' weapons to target.

J-STARS, still under development, is the culmination of years of tests of what were originally separate projects under the US Army 'Assault Breaker' and USAF 'Pave Mover' efforts. The concepts were later merged to their mutual advantage, under the guidance of the US Defense Advanced Research Projects Agency (DARPA). To fulfil their side of the bargain the Air Force modified a pair of F-111s as 'Pave Mover' radar trials aircraft and were subsequently flown in a head-to-head fly-off between 1981 and 1983 over White Sands Missile Range in New Mexico: the Grumman/Norden Tactical Air Weapons Delivery System (TAWDS) X-band phased-array system was installed in a Raven-like ventral canoe riveted to an F-111A bailed from the AFFTC's 6512th TS, while Hughes Radars developed a large cigar-shaped pod to house their very similar radar, slung under an F-111E on loan from the Eglin-based 3246th TW. In a series of sorties both aircraft were successful in vectoring ARN-101 F-4E Phantoms in a 'hands-off' bomb run to target, without the need for the attack aircraft to 'pop up' into the thick of 'enemy' air defences prior to each bomb pass, and in guiding Martin Marietta T-16 surface-to-surface missiles to target. Weapons delivery accuracies of up to 9ft against moving targets were demonstrated! Grumman/Norden won the production contract for the follow-on J-STARS, which is to be deployed operationally in the early 1990s on board a

new Boeing E-8A. Now suitably 'de-modified', the two 'Pave Mover Aardvarks' are back in service with their respective AFSC parent units at Edwards and Eglin. No longer destined to be the radar platform for J-STARS, the AMP-modified F-111 fleet will nevertheless make great use of the information generated by the system.

**Above: An eager test-flight crew prepare to board the Grumman/Norden TAWDS or 'Pave Mover' test-bed F-111A No. 71, 66-053. Note the large white radome reminiscent of the Raven's 'canoe'. No other externally visible modifications were made, apart from a bold 'Pave Mover' badge splashed on the fin. (Grumman Corporation)**

## APPENDIX VI: NASA's 'AARDVARK'

Since its inception America's space agency NASA (National Aeronautics and Space Administration) – and its predecessor NACA, the National Advisory Committee for Aeronautics – has been intimately involved with the US Air Force in joint efforts aimed at pushing the boundaries of aerospace technology. It was largely through these efforts that the VG wing became a reality, making the F-111 possible.

In 1973 F-111A No. 13 (63-9778) was bailed to NASA's Dryden Flight Research Center, co-located with the USAF Edwards AFFTC in California, for a joint programme designed to explore fuel-efficient transonic cruise through the use of a supercritical wing. The prettily painted F-111A was adapted with a new, smooth laminar-flow wing, thicker in chord and shorter in span and later fitted with 'gloves' at mid-span, which would verify this concept. It was never intended for application to operational F-111s, being limited to wingsweep angles of 10° to 58°, but the facts have been filed away in a safe place for reference purposes.

In a more recent effort, NASA and Boeing modified the jet into a Mission Adaptive Wing (MAW) configuration, which relinquished the traditional control surfaces in favour of a brand new variable-camber wing which used internal jacks to alter the flexible fibreglass skin of the aerofoil to the optimum desired shape for different roles and requirements, as directed

by a digital flight control computer. Traditional flaps and slats can be used only for take-off and landing; the MAW could be used throughout the entire flight envelope. Part of the ASD's Advanced Fighter Technology Integration (AFTI) effort, the MAW test-bed was active at Dryden between October 1985 and December 1988 and demonstrated several gains in performance under both automatic and manual control: Cruise Camber Control (CCC) mode offered maximum speed; Maneuver Camber Control (MCC) provided an improved lift-to-drag ratio to enable existing high-g manoeuvres to be performed in a 25 per cent sharper turning radius, without encountering stall problems; and the Maneuver Load Control (MLC) and Maneuver Enhancement/Gust Alleviation modes, also available at the push of a button on the dashboard MAW control panel, which kept the machine rock-steady in gusty conditions such as mountain turbulence, reducing buffet and wing fatigue, to provide an exceptionally smooth ride. This 'One wing for all speeds and conditions', as MAW was described, is a sound concept with a practical application to future military fighters and bombers.

Still assigned officially to the Edwards AFFTC, NASA's 'swing-winger' will be tinkering with new technology for several years yet as new modifications are authorized.

Above: The NASA F-111A, 63-9778, made its first flight with the Boeing MAW on 18 October 1985, concluding the programme over 50 sorties later in December 1988. The machine employed a smooth-skinned wing devoid of traditional flaps and slats and demonstrated many gains in turning performance, cruise efficiency, reduced bending moments and improved stability. The decor is overall gloss white with pale grey patches and dark grey and black stripes on the wings. The nose and anti-dazzle area are black, with red, black and yellow logos. (USAF)

Below: F-111 adaptation to Mission Adaptive Wing (MAW) configuration. (BMAC)

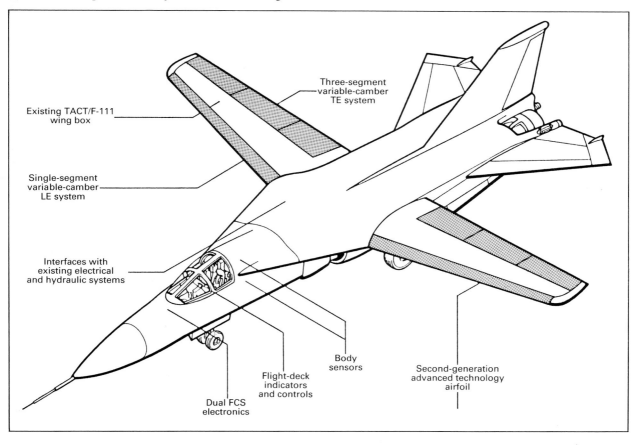

Existing TACT/F-111 wing box

Single-segment variable-camber LE system

Interfaces with existing electrical and hydraulic systems

Three-segment variable-camber TE system

Dual FCS electronics

Flight-deck indicators and controls

Body sensors

Second-generation advanced technology airfoil

# APPENDIX VII: F-111 NOSE ARTWORK

## 20th TFW, 1987–88[*]

| Serial no. | Name | Remarks |
|---|---|---|
| **55th TFS/AMU (F-111E)** | | |
| 68-005 | Born in the USA | |
| 68-006 | Free Bird | |
| 68-026 | Hawkeye | |
| 68-035 | Shamrock Kid | |
| 68-055 | Heartbreaker | Commander's aircraft. |
| 68-065 | Galleon | |
| 67-121 | Night Stalker | |
| | | |
| **77th TFS/AMU (F-111E)** | | |
| 68-001 | The Stump Jumper | Ex B-17. |
| 68-031 | – | Tail-codes outlined in red. |
| 68-047 | 'Til We Meet Again | Ex P-38 of 77th, James Morris (7.3 kills). |
| 68-049 | The Grim Reaper | Ex B-17. |
| 68-059 | The Mad Bomber | Ex B-24. |
| 68-061 | Big Dealer | Ex B-24. |
| 68-068 | The Flak Ducker | Ex B-24, 448th BG, 8th AF. |
| 68-069 | The Wild Hare | Ex B-17. |
| 68-077 | Red Lady II | Commander's aircraft; was 'June Nite', ex P-51D of 20th FG top-scorer Ernest C. Fiebelkorn (9.5 kills). 'Red Lady' used on P-51 flown by father of 20th TFW pilot? |
| 68-978 | Whispering Death | |
| | | |
| **79th TFS/AMU (F-111E)** | | |
| 68-002 | Imperial Wizard | |
| 68-013 | Excalibur | |
| 68-020 | My Lucky Blonde | Ex 20th FG P-51D? |
| 68-022 | Thundercat | |
| 68-023 | Aces High | |
| 68-030 | Top Cat | |
| 68-033 | Hat Trick | |
| 68-040 | The Other Woman | |
| 68-052 | On Guard | |
| 68-062 | Land Shark | |
| 68-063 | A Knight To Remember | |
| 68-072 | Bad Medicine | |
| 68-073 | | Yellow triangle. |
| 68-079 | Tiger Lil | |
| 68-080 | Strange Brew | |
| 68-082 | The Phoenix | |
| 68-083 | Prometheus II | |
| 67-120 | The Chief | Wing Commander's aircraft. |
| 67-122 | Rowdy Rebel | |
| 67-123 | The Bold One | |
| | | |
| **42nd ECS (EF-111A)** | | |
| 66-030 | Mild And Bitter Homebrew | Was 'Sparky's Devil'. Ex B-26B of 322 BG. |
| 66-033 | Excalibur | Was 'Grim Reaper'. Ex B-17F of 91 BG, 8th AF. |
| 66-037 | The Prowler | |
| 66-039 | The Sorcerer's Apprentice | |
| 66-041 | Thumper | Ex B-29. |
| 66-055 | Boomerang | Ex B-24D of 328 BS, 8th AF. |
| 66-056 | Babyjam | Was 'War Eagle'. |
| 66-057 | Special Delivery | Ex B-29 of 73 BW. |
| 67-032 | Black Sheep | Was 'Thunderbird'. |
| 67-034 | Let 'Em Eat Crow | Commander's aircraft. |
| 67-035 | Ye Olde Crow | Was 'Phoenix'. Ex P-51D of 363 FS, 357 FG, 8th AF. |
| 67-041 | Knight Jammer | |
| 67-052 | Cherry Bomb | Ex EB-66 of 42 TEWS, 355 TFW, Korat RTAB, 1972. |

## 380th BW(M), 1988 (all FB-111A)

| Serial no. | Name |
|---|---|
| 67-161 | Liquidator |
| 67-162 | Nocturnal Mission |
| 67-7192 | Moonlight Maid |
| 67-7192 | Slightly Dangerous |
| 67-7194 | Virgin Abroad |
| 68-239 | Rough Night |
| 68-240 | Atomic Blonde |
| 68-241 | Undecided |
| 68-243 | Jungle Queen |
| 68-244 | Lucky Strike |
| 68-245 | Ready Teddy |
| 68-246 | Royal Flush |
| 68-248 | Free For All |
| 68-249 | Gus's Bus |
| 68-250 | Silver Lady |
| 68-251 | Shy-Chi Baby |
| 68-252 | Six Bits |
| 68-254 | Pappy's Passion |
| 68-256 | The Screamer |
| 68-257 | Maid in the USA |
| 68-258 | Hell's Belle |
| 68-259 | Gypsy |
| 68-260 | SNAFU |
| 68-262 | Lady Luck |
| 68-264 | Jazebelle |
| 68-265 | Net Results |
| 68-267 | Pom Pom Express |
| 68-269 | Sad Sack |
| 68-271 | On De-Fence |
| 68-277 | Double Trouble |
| 68-278 | A Wing and Ten Prayers |
| 68-282 | Old Ironsides |
| 68-286 | Miss Giving |
| 68-289 | Queen Hi |
| 68-291 | Shady Lady |
| 68-292 | Liberty Belle |

## 509th BW(M), 1988 (all FB-111A)

| Serial no. | Name |
|---|---|
| 67-7193 | Tiger 'Lil |
| 67-7195 | Dave's Dream |
| 67-7196 | Sea Coast Cruncher |
| 68-0269 | Fireball Express |
| 68-0272 | The Wild Hare |
| 68-0276 | Gruesome Goose |
| 68-0284 | Next Objective |
| 68-0287 | Liberator II |
| 68-6508 | Strange Cargo |
| 69-6509 | Spirit of the Seacoast |
| 69-6514 | Double Trouble |

[*]No direct Second World War connections. 'Hawkeye' was named after the Iowa State football team, the pilot and crew chief at the time being Iowans.

# APPENDIX VIII: F-111 REBUILDS

**FB-111A No. 8 (67-7194, 'Virgin Abroad')** *12 months*
Stricken in a hard landing in February 1976 which resulted in extensive fire damage to the aft airframe, the aircraft was rebuilt using the rear end of FB-111A No. 2 (67-160), which was spliced in place. Work started on 1 September 1978 and the bomber was returned to the 380th BW in September 1980.

**F-111A No. 124 (67-079)** *12 months*
An in-flight hydraulic fire in the aft right-hand corner of the main gear well on 21 January 1981 caused significant damage to the right nacelle and nearby systems components. Rework at Fort Worth, including the incorporation of eighteen TCTOs, started on 4 June that year and the aircraft was returned to service at Mountain Home AFB, Idaho, on 29 May 1982 following FCF checkout by SMALC test-crew Capt. Leslie and Capt. Harman.

**F-111E No. 92 (68-082, 'The Phoenix')** *17 months*
On 25 March 1981 the aircraft was involved in an aborted take-off from RAF Fairford, England. A hard landing ensued, collapsing the nose gear and smashing the forward fuselage, the weapons bay doors and the floor of the F-1 fuel tank. It was delivered to Fort Worth on 12 June 1981 and repaired using the nose from pre-production F-111A No. 24 (65-5706). FCFs were completed on 20 September 1982 with Lt. Col. Stokes and Lt. Col. Johnson at the controls. The aircraft was returned to the 20th TFW in USAFE on 1 October.

**F-111D No. 52 (68-136)** *23 months*
On 9 September 1979 the left powerplant second-stage blades failed, resulting in an in-flight fire which damaged the left-hand nacelle, engine and speed-bump. After the machine landed the fire spread and destroyed the right empennage, flaps, wing seal and engine bay doors. The aircraft was placed in storage at Davis-Monthan AFB, Arizona, but delivered to Fort Worth on flat-bed trucks on 21 June 1981. Repairs and FCFs were completed by 27 May 1982, when Maj. Sienicki and Capt. Harman signed for the aircraft. It was returned to service with the 27th TFW at Cannon AFB, New Mexico.

**F-111E No. 4 (67-118)** *11 months*
In June 1981 this aircraft was parked on the hardstand at Eglin AFB, Florida. A high-pressure bottle for the capsule impact attenuation bag exploded, damaging the crew module aft bulkhead and the F-1 fuel tank forward bulkhead. The aircraft was delivered to Fort Worth by C-5 on 10 August 1981. Following repairs two FCFs were flown on 29 June and 1 July 1982 by Lt. Col. Drittler and Lt. Col. Johnson and the aircraft was subsequently handed back to the 3246th Test Wing at Eglin AFB.

**FB-111A No. 31 (68-259, 'Gypsy')** *16 months*
While 68-259 was on the ramp at Nellis AFB, Nevada, during a 'Red Flag' deployment a BDU-38 was inadvertently activated, punching through the aft right portion of the weapons bay and into the main landing gear bulkhead. Repair work began at Fort Worth on 30 September 1981 and included 20 TCTOs. Two FCFs were flown by SMALC crewmen Maj. Ted Sienicki and Capt. Steve Harman, and then Capt. Leslie and Lt. Col. Johnson, during January 1983. On 4 February 1983 the aircraft was returned to SAC service. It now flies with the 380th BW at Plattsburgh AFB, New York, bearing the nose art 'Gypsy'.

**F-111D No. 64 (58-148)** *19 months*
On 17 January 1979 an engine fire, resulting from the failure of a ninth-stage engine seal in the left powerplant, caused damage to the left nacelle and doors, the aft fuselage centrebody and tank bulkhead, and the left speed bump of this aircraft. On 5 May 1982 GDFW were contracted to perform repairs. The aircraft arrived on a flat-bed trailer, having been heavily 'cannibalized' over the years, and required 74 TCTOs in addition to the skin repairs to bring it up to standard. On 9 December 1983 Lt. Col. Drittler and Capt. Harman flew an FCF, clearing the aircraft to return to service with the 27th TFW at Cannon AFB, New Mexico.

**F-111D No. 43 (68-127, Commander's aircraft)** *27 months*
On 7 July 1981 electrical and hydraulic lines, chafing in the main wheel well, started a fire which damaged both inlets and the right wing. The main gear subsequently collapsed, causing further damage to the left intake duct. On 31 March GDFW got the go-ahead to repair the machine. The aircraft was returned to Cannon AFB, New Mexico, on 6 July following three FCFs flown by SMALC crewmen Maj. Bowman and Capt. McCall. It now serves as the 27th TFW 'flagship'.

**F-111A No. 146 (67-101)** *12 months*
On 2 August 1982 this aircraft ingested a large bird, causing engine failure and a major in-flight fire. In August 1985, following repairs which included 70 TCTOs and the use of some 4,200 specially fabricated parts and replacement line items, the aircraft was sent back to the 366th TFW at Mountain Home AFB.

**F-111D No. 17 (68-101)** *23 months*
A fire in the liquid oxygen converter severely damaged the airframe. The aircraft arrived at Fort Worth in January 1984 and was patched up and flown back to the 27th TFW at Cannon AFB in December 1986.

**F-111D No. 90 (68-174)** *39 months*
In May 1976 this aircraft suffered an engine fan blade failure which resulted in a major fuel tank fire. The aircraft was subsequently stored at the Davis-Monthan 'boneyard' for eight years, during which time it was heavily 'cannibalized' for spares. It arrived at Fort Worth in July 1984 for rework, which required 12,600 parts and no fewer than 229 TCTOs to bring it back up to C1 status. It was returned to the 27th TFW in November 1987 following FCF clearance with Maj. Via at the controls and has the distinction of having the lowest number of flight hours of any F-111 aircraft on the TAC inventory.

**F-111D No. 11 (68-095)**
In April 1976 the aircraft suffered a main wheel-well fire and had to conduct a wheels-up landing. It was stored at Davis-Monthan AFB until June 1984, when it was transferred to Fort Worth for restoration work. It was due to be handed back to the 27th TFW in September 1988.

**F-111E No. 60 (68-050)**
A liquid oxygen bottle exploded while the aircraft was on the ramp at RAF Upper Heyford, causing extensive damage. Flown to GDFW in a C-5 in October 1986, the aircraft was scheduled for redelivery to the 20th TFW by November 1988.

# INDEX

Detham, Col. 'Ike', 23, 27, 28, 29, 32
Dispensers: SUU-20, -21, 106, 144; *see also* Bombs (cluster)
Dixon, Gen. Robert J., 147
Donnell, Ralph, 46–7
Dotson, Sgt., 114
Drittler, Lt. Col., 132

**E**
E-2A/C Hawkeye, 47n, 51–2, 174
E-3A Sentry, 97, 100, 108
EA-6B Prowler, 85, 89, 100, 174
Eaton AIL, 85–6, 101
EB-66C/E Destroyer, 31, 41, 85, 89, 93, 99
Electrical diagnostic systems, 93, 98–9, 116, 125–6, 166, 178
'El Dorado Canyon', Operation, 169, 173–6
Electronic warfare systems: general, 27, 41, 52, 67–71, 85–103, 116–117, 173, 174; ALE-28, -40 chaff/flare dispensers, 27, 33, 68–9; ALR-23, AAR-34 cryogenic receivers, 27, 33, 68–70; ALR-31, -39, -41, -62 plus APS-107, -109 radar warning receivers, 27, 33, 42, 68–9, 77, 89, 104, 116; ALR-37 RASTAS, 71; ALQ-94, -137 internal deception jammers, 27, 41, 68–9, 89; ALQ-87 noise jamming pod, 27, 35, 41, 94; ALQ-119, -131 noise and deception jamming pods, 116–117, 168n; ALQ-99E jamming subsystem, 85–6, 88–9, 93–101, 103; communications jamming, 100; *see also* 'Wild Weasels'
Evans, Sgt. Walt, 166
Everest, Gen. Frank, 15
Everhart, Maj. Wilbert, 122
Exercises, *see* Competitions

**F**
F-4 Phantom II, 12, 23, 35, 37, 38, 41, 44, 73, 75, 79, 82, 89, 94, 103, 108, 110, 119, 124, 142, 143, 144, 153, 159, 183; *see also* RF-4C/E
F-5C/E Freedom Fighter/Tiger II, 41, 100, 109
F6D Missileer, 12
F-8 Crusader, 12
F-14 Tomcat, 15, 47n, 56, 111–112, 174, 175
F-15 Eagle, 78, 79, 82, 110, 111, 142, 154, 177–8
F-16 Fighting Falcon, 78, 95, 100, 108, 110, 111, 154, 177
F/A-18 Hornet, 82, 111, 174
F-84 Thunderstreak, 104
F-100D/F Super Sabre, 104, 138, 153
F-102 Delta Dagger, 41
F-105 Thunderchief, 11, 29, 33, 41, 42
F-111 marks: F-111A, 12–15, 17, 21–45, 46, 57, 73, 79, 83, 85, 88, 93, 94, 104, 105, 119, 126, 130–1, 138, 143, 152, 153; EF-111A, 85–103, 107, 110, 174; FB-111A, 57–72, 126, 131–2, 135, 137, 139, 150, 159; RF-111A, 79; F-111B, 12, 17, 20, 46–56; F-111C, 33, 73–9, 83–4, 85, 159, 165; RF-111C, 79–83; F-111D, 125, 126, 138–152, 154, 159, 176, 177; F-

111E, 33, 71, 99, 100, 104–18, 119, 128, 133, 135–6, 138, 143; F-111F, 71, 94, 107, 119, 121, 126, 139, 143, 145, 153–76, 177; F-111G, 72, 77
F-117 Nighthawk, 101
Fedder, Jerry, 40
Fighter Weapons School, 107, 113, 150-2, 156
FLIT training, 105, 144
Ford, 31-2, 75, 143, 159
Formation flying, 28, 38, 158
Francis, Col. C. E., 138
Fudge, Keith, 128
Fuel tanks, 124-5, 146, 147, 178
Functional check flights, 93, 125, 187
Funnell, Wg. Cdr./Air Marshal Ray, 75, 83

**G**
'Gatling' gun (M61A1), 21, 28, 31, 41, 81, 104, 143–4
General Dynamics, 7, 12-14, 15, 20, 31, 33–4, 46, 55, 59–60, 71, 73, 79, 80, 85, 94, 101, 103, 119, 126–7, 130–3, 139, 150, 159, 187
Gerschied, Tom, 23
Glass, Lt. Steve, 40
Goodman, J. R., 79
Gorton, John, 73
Graham, Dennis, 30, 31–2, 40
Ground crews, 27, 28, 37, 43–4, 55, 61, 71, 73, 80, 81, 83, 89, 96, 98–9, 101, 103, 112, 114–22, 125–6, 135–7, 147, 173, 178
Grumman, 12, 46–7, 55–6, 85–6, 89, 93, 98, 103, 126–7

**H**
Haig, Gen. Alexander A., 153
'Hands off' flying, *see* Autopilot
'Harvest Reaper', *see* Vietnam ('Combat Lancer')
Hellier, Col. Richard G., 98
Heyde, Maj. Thomas, 89
Ho Chi Minh Trail, 31, 35, 37–8, 159–60
Hodges, Joe, 31
Holland, Les, 43
Holloway, Gen. Bruce K., 57
Hughes, 47, 47n, 56, 166

**I**
Inertial navigation systems: alignment and updating, 24–5, 29, 62, 65, 161, 162–3; read-outs, 24, 59, 62; stored co-ordinates, 24, 61, 62, 65, 139, 159n; *see also* Offset aiming points
Insley, Capt. Brad, 7–8, 36, 38, 41, 43, 44, 140
Intakes: compressor stalls, 13–15; foreign object damage, 37

**J**
JEWC, 173
Johnson, Lyndon B., 31n
Johnson, Dick, 13, 73
Jordan, Lt. Col., Jon, 35, 36, 38, 42, 44

**K**
KC-10A Extender, 81, 173, 174
KC-97 Stratocruiser, 16
KC-135 Stratotanker/GLOB: 62, 81, 97, 173, 174; RC-135 Ferret

69, 100, 174; EC-135 Looking Glass, 64
Kemble, Flt. Lt. Andy, 80
Kelman, Capt. George, 18, 76, 110–12, 115–18, 144
Kelso, Vice-Admiral, 174
Kirk, Gen., 137
Kittinger, Col. J. W., 153
Kramer, Lt. Col. 'Willy P.', 156

**L**
Laing, Don, 20
Laird, Melvin, 57
Landing, 56, 131, 157–8
Laos, operations over, 29–30, 31, 35, 36–8, 159–60
Lehman, John E., 176
Lemlein, Al, 46
LeMay, Gen. Curtis E., 57
Leo, Sqn. Ldr. Kevin, 80
Libya, operations over, 8, 100, 108, 169–76
'Linebacker I/II', *see* Vietnam War
Livesay, Meade, 47
Livesey, Richard, 155
Lorence, Capt. Paul F., 176
Losses and write-offs: combat, 7, 30–1, 35–6, 38–41, 175–6; development, 41, 56; training, 33, 83, 118, 159; functional check flight, 58, 125
Lowrimore, Capt. Greg, 20, 108, 112, 113, 118, 145, 165

**M**
McConnell, Price, 38
McCann, Hank, 30
McNamara, Robert S., 12, 23, 31–2, 46, 57
Maintenance manhours, 89, 119, 124, 127, 135, 147, 187
Malakoff, Sgt. Dave, 155
Marquardt, Sandy, 31
Marrett, George, 56
Martin, Col. Eugene, 35
Matcezun, Al, 33
Matteis, Col. Rick, 19, 20, 23–4, 25, 27, 28–32, 33, 88, 89, 99, 126
Maul, Col. Paul W., 66
*Mayaguez* incident, 44
Meeboer, Lt. Col. Richard M., 95
Messerli, Maj., 153
MiGs, confrontations with, 28, 41; counter-tactics for, 111–12, 143–4
Miller, Sqn. Ldr. John, 75
Mirage III, 78, 79
Mirrors, 111
Mission planning, 29, 38, 61, 80–2, 96, 112, 169, 173
Moore, Col. Winston E., 57
Murph, Ben, 31, 33
Myrann, R. E., 94

**N**
NASA, 15, 184
Nelson, Col. William R., 35, 43
Nicknames, origins of, 33, 38, 47
Nitze, Paul H., 46
Nixon, Richard M., 38
Norris, John, 55
Nose art, 9, 135–7, 186
Nuclear bombs and bombing, *see* Bombing manoeuvres, Bombs
Nunnamaker, Roger, 28

**O**
O'Neill, Lt. Gen. John, 55
Offset aiming points, 25, 37, 38, 43, 61, 65, 113, 161; *see also* Cameras
Osterloh, Maj. Robert, 93
Overhauls, 33–4, 89, 119, 122–30, 135, 160, 178

**P**
P-3 Orion, 79, 83
P-38 Lightning, 104
P-51 Mustang, 104
Palmgren, Lt. Col. Ed, 28, 30
Patton, Col. William D., 106, 130
Pave Tack AN/AVQ-26: origins and development of, 75–6, 159–60; training with, 160–6; combat use, 174–5
'Peace Lamb', 75
Perry, Glen, 38
Pickering, Lt. Col. H. Tom, 93, 94
Pivot-pylons, 15, 47, 55n, 61, 121, 146, 164
Prahl, V., 57
Pratt & Whitney powerplants: general, 12–15, 50, 53, 83, 112, 121, 122, 130, 154, 156, 183, 187; TF30-P-1, 13-14, 22, 47; TF30-P-3/103, 14, 23, 31, 73, 103, 112, 178; TF30-P-7/107, 14, 57, 62; TF30-P-9/109, 14, 103, 154, 178; TF30-P-12, 56; TF30-P-100, 14, 154
Pull-ups, *see* Bombing manoeuvres, Radars (terrain following systems)

**Q**
Qadafi, Col. M., 169, 174

**R**
RA-5C Vigilante, 47
Ranges: Bardenas Reales (Zaragosa), 108–9; 'Campsite', 93; Garvey Island, 165; Melrose, 138, 145; Otterburn, 108; Polygone, 100, 117; Saylor Creek, 97–8, 105–6; Spadeadam, 117; Tain, 107; Tonopah, 89; White Sands, 66, 183; *see also* Bases
Radars: attack, 24–5, 36, 47, 51–3, 61, 80, 95, 126, 139–41, 142, 159–61, 178; reconnaissance, 79, 80; moving target capability, 141, 183; terrain-following systems, 18–20, 23–4, 30, 33, 36, 38–41, 43, 59, 64–5, 81, 93, 97, 100, 111, 112, 113, 117–18, 126, 130, 141, 155, 157–9, 160, 163, 183; artificial displays, 47–55, 126–7, 139–42; beacons and reflectors, 37, 108, 141
Raven, *see* F-111 marks (EF-111A)
'Ready Switch', 94–5, 152, 153
Reagan, Ronald, 71, 169, 176
Repairs, 34, 38, 66, 127–33, 156, 187
Ribas-Dominicci, Maj. Fernando, 176
Rich, Lt. Col. Donald, 89
Rollins, Cdr. R. F., 85
Rossillon, 1Lt. Lesley, 135
Rossman, Ed, 13, 14
Rotramel, Maj. Jim, 142